PELICAN BOOKS
A 180
MORE COMMON WILD FLOWERS
BY JOHN HUTCHINSON

MORE COMMON
WILD FLOWERS

BY JOHN HUTCHINSON

WITH 228 ILLUSTRATIONS

PUBLISHED BY
PENGUIN BOOKS
WEST DRAYTON · MIDDLESEX

First published 1948

Made and printed in Great Britain for Penguin Books, Limited,
by C. Nicholls & Company Ltd., London, Manchester, Reading

INTRODUCTION

THE cordial reception given to *Common Wild Flowers* (Pelican Book, A 153, 1945 and 1946) has encouraged the author to prepare a second volume on a similar plan. Like the first book, it has been written expressly for those who have little or no knowledge of botany, and who want to learn the names and a little about the common wild flowers of the countryside. It is intended to stimulate rather than satisfy, and, judging by the letters received by the author, the first book seems to have achieved this object for quite a number of people, young, middle-aged, and elderly.

As remarked in the first book, no doubt the majority of those who use this second volume will be content to match the wild flowers they find with the drawings. Even they, with only this

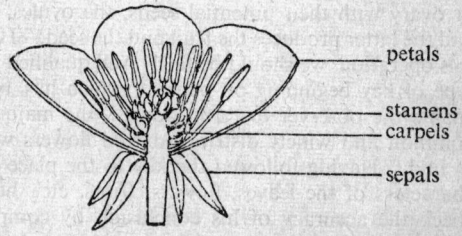

practice, should soon " get their eye in " for characters such as leaf-shape, arrangement of different kinds of flowers, and various types of fruits, and thus subconsciously acquire a little knowledge of botany.

On the other hand, it is hoped that many will see more than the pretty posy and look a little further into the structure of the flowers. This is an interesting and fascinating study which will soon bring its own reward in a more extended knowledge of plants, and perhaps lead on to the use of the many excellent *Floras* and other books, a selection of which is given on page xi. With this object in view, therefore, particular attention has been paid to the illustration of dissections of important parts of the flowers, fruits, and seeds, such as may be seen with the aid of a penknife and hand-lens. These usually exhibit the important characters of the genus and family. In the general sketch of the plant, perspective has as a rule been neglected in order to show clearly the shapes of leaves and other features which are often of great importance for recognising the species.

To use the book intelligently, however, and not merely search mechanically through the drawings for the plants we wish to name, it will be necessary to learn something about the structure of a simple kind of flower, in order to use the key on page xi. For this purpose we cannot do better than pull to pieces the flower of a common buttercup as illustrated on p. v. The five outermost green parts are the sepals (collectively called the *calyx*), the five yellow organs are, of course, the *petals* (forming the *corolla*) with a nectary at the base; then we come to the numerous stamens, consisting of a stalk (*filament*) and pollen-carrier (*anther*), and finally a number of small green parts in the middle and arranged in a spiral, the *carpels*. These, in the buttercup, are free from one another, but in most other flowers they are united together to form a single *ovary*. The stamens with their pollen represent the male element of the flower, and the carpels or ovary with their potential seeds, the ovules, the female part, and the latter produces the fruit and the seed. Having performed this operation, we should be fairly well qualified to use the simple type of key beginning on page xi, which has been provided to enable the observer to "run down" the majority of the really common and widely distributed wild flowers which he is likely to find. Having followed the key to the place indicated by the characters of the leaves, flowers, fruits, etc., he will be able to check the accuracy of his conclusion by comparing the figure and description given on the page indicated. If these do not quite tally, then he may be sure that he has found another plant, which may or may not belong to the same genus. And in order to find out its name it would be necessary to consult one of the *Floras* listed on p. x.

HOW TO USE THE KEY

To put the beginner into the way of using the key, one of the common Buttercups such as shown in fig. 261 may be given a trial. As it is a herb with net-veined leaves and with 5 sepals and 5 petals, it is obviously a *Dicotyledon*, and belongs to part I of the key on p. xi. In that part, as it is neither a tree nor a shrub, it does not agree with line 1, but fits 1a (p. xiii). The flowers are not in heads, so it does not fit line 19, but agrees with line 19a (p. xvi). The flowers are not in umbels, so we pass on from line 43 to line 43a (p. xvii). As the leaves are mostly radical and not opposite, it agrees with line 52, there are more than 2 free carpels (line 53), the leaves are without stipules (line 54), it leaves only the choice between *Trollius* and *Ranunculus*, and fits the description of the latter, and should be compared with figures 258–265.

After a little practice the beginner will probably soon begin to recognise related plants or *families* of flowering plants. In the case of the Rose family, for example, called *Rosaceae* after the genus *Rosa*, it will be observed (figures 203–211) that the female part or ovary of the flower is usually described as being composed of free carpels, which when ripe contain the seeds. The fact that the carpels are free from one another, associated with other features, is therefore one, but only one, of the spotting characters by which the Rose family may be recognised.

Again, it will be very noticeable on looking over figures 324–345 that the apparently single flower is in reality an aggregation of flowers into a head or capitulum. And with a few exceptions it will be found that most plants with a similar head of flowers belong to the Daisy family, *Compositae*, and we soon learn to recognise that family, especially if we have also seen that the anthers are joined together around the style.

Some flowers are hardly recognisable as such because they are very small and have no petals. These are often crowded together into a catkin, which, like the head of the *Compositae*, is a particular kind of *inflorescence*. Most people know at least one kind of inflorescence, a *spike*, which suggests at once a stiff, dense collection of flowers.

The notes accompanying the drawings are confined to a short, general, and very simple description of the usual form of the species as it is met with in a wild state, and little or no mention is made of varieties or forms which occur in some cases. Variation in the colour of the flowers, however, is usually noted. In addition, room has been found for a few facts relating to the biology of the flower, particularly regarding pollination in examples which seem sufficiently obvious to the observer. The pollination of flowers is a subject of great importance to the beekeeper, the fruit-grower, and the seedsman. In this country Charles Darwin was the foremost investigator. And there is still a good deal more to be learned.

The arrangement of the families represented by the plants illustrated follows the author's own system of classification, which aims at a sequence of increasing specialisation.* This is not very

* J. Hutchinson, *Families of Flowering Plants* (Macmillan, London). Vol. I (1926), Vol. II (1934).

difficult to understand. All those plants are grouped together which usually have *net-veined leaves* and 2 *seed-leaves* (*Dicotyledons*), and the remainder, with *parallel-veined leaves* and only 1 seed-leaf (*Monocotyledons*), come last; the latter include the Lily and Orchid families, etc., the sedges, and grasses. The *Dicotyledons* are further arranged into two main groups. First come the trees and shrubs and some herbs related to them, and secondly the purely herbaceous plants and a few related slightly woody plants. The first group embraces figures 203 to 256, and the second figures 257 to 380, whilst the *Monocotyledons* will be found from figure 381 to the end. The reader with some knowledge of botany may recognise that the families which exhibit the most primitive floral structure are placed first, and the most advanced come last in each of these groups, the Grass family being regarded as one of the most highly specialised.

The Latin names of the plants included in the book are in accordance with the International Rules of Botanical Nomenclature, so far as ascertained. A departure from common practice has been made, however, in the case of some of the names of the species. These have all been printed with a small initial letter, as is usual in zoology. Botanists generally spell certain specific names with a capital letter, especially those derived from an old genus name, and those named after persons. Thus *Sorbus Aucuparia* L., the Rowan tree, is usually so printed because *Aucuparia* is an old genus name. The " L." after the Latin name indicates that Linnaeus, the famous Swedish botanist, often spoken of as the "father of modern botany," was responsible for giving the name to the tree. The majority of the species of our commoner British plants were named by Linnaeus, as most of them are also found in Sweden. In a few cases the " L." is included in brackets after the Latin name, and the name, or abbreviated name, of another botanist follows it. This indicates that though Linnaeus first described the species, the latter is now placed under a different genus name. An example is the Stork's Bill, *Erodium cicutarium* (L.) L'Hérit. Linnaeus described it as *Geranium cicutarium*, and it was later transferred by the French botanist L'Héritier to *Erodium*.

Owing to the limitation of space, it has been possible to include few except the most common species. Some groups of plants, such as the many kinds of brambles, roses, and hawkweeds, though including some that are very common, are mostly difficult to distinguish except by intensive study, and have therefore been omitted. Nearly all the species included occur in the 112 vice-counties of Druce's *Comital Flora*, though a few less common have also been put in because of some special interest. With one or two exceptions the illustrations are original and have been drawn by the author specially for this book.

Again neither grasses nor orchids have been included in the book. It is hoped to deal with the grasses in a separate volume, and the more widely distributed orchids will find a place in the next book of this series, *Less Common Wild Flowers*.

Our wild plants are indeed a very precious possession, and great discrimination should be shown in picking them. Those in hay-fields, which will in any case be mown down by the grass-cutter, and those on rubbish-heaps and waste land, may be gathered with a clear conscience, but plants growing in other places should not be taken. Last year the author met a man descending from a Scottish mountain with a bunch of lovely Globe-flowers (*Trollius*) in his hand. He had completely stripped the banks of a stream a little farther up the mountain, and had thereby reduced its beauty for other visitors, besides destroying the chance of natural regeneration by seed for a whole year.

So do not pick the wild flowers!

The author is again indebted to those who have kindly supplied photographs. These are: Miss D. A. C. Long (Daffodils); Mr. R. M. Adam (Cowslips, Monkey Flower, Toothwort, Fuller's Teasel, Thrift, Heath Rush, Scotch Bluebell, Snowdrops, Globe Flower, and Angelica); Mr. H. Bastin (White Bryony, Wood Anemone, Stitchwort, Wood Sage, Colt's Foot, Woodruff, Lady's Mantle, Purple Loosestrife, Bugle, Wood Sanicle, and Enchanter's Nightshade).

COMPETITION FOR YOUNG PEOPLE

In order to encourage young people to study the book and become thoroughly acquainted with the subject, the author has deliberately made a mistake in one of the drawings. The drawing does not tally with the description, the latter being correct. Of course it does not follow that he has avoided making other errors, though only this one is intentional, and one which would probably lose several marks if made in an examination paper.

With the consent of the publishers, a prize is offered to the reader who detects this mistake and whose letter is opened first by the author at the address given on p. x. Only those who are less than 19 years of age will be eligible for the prize, which will be a copy of Eileen Mayo's *Story of Living Things*.*

The career of many people is quite frequently influenced by some event which may not seem of much importance at the time. The author himself, when at school, won a prize, not for botany, but for *sewing on buttons*, and the book he received was one on wild flowers. This undoubtedly helped to arouse his interest in them, with the result that he has been able to write and illustrate a book like the present volume. He likes to imagine that the winner of the prize might eventually become, if not a second Sherlock Holmes, then, perhaps, a celebrated botanist like either Bentham or Hooker.

It may be as well to add the usual condition that the decision of the author will be final, and that the name of the winner and the solution will be announced in *School Nature Study* by kind permission of the editor.

Hanover House,
  57 The Green,
    Kew, Surrey.

Books Recommended for Further Study

Among a great number of excellent botanical text-books, the following recent works are recommended for those who wish to study the subject further:—

1. Hooker, *Student's Flora of the British Islands*† (Macmillan, 1937).
2. Bentham and Hooker, *Handbook of the British Flora* (L. Reeve and Co., Sankey House, Brook, near Ashford, Kent).
3. Fitch and Smith, *Illustrations* to Bentham and Hooker's *Handbook of the British Flora* ed. 7 (L. Reeve and Co., 1924).
4. Butcher and Strudwick, *Further Illustrations of British Plants* (L. Reeve and Co., 1946).
5. Skene, *The Biology of Flowering Plants* (Sidgwick and Jackson, Ltd., London, 1932).
6. Fritsch and Salisbury, *Plant Form and Function* (G. Bell and Sons, Ltd., London, 1943).
7. Hutchinson, *British Flowering Plants* (*Evolution and Classification of Families and Genera*) (P. R. Gawthorn, Ltd., 55 Russell Square, London, W.C. 1, 1947).

The most comprehensive work on flower pollination is Knuth, *Handbook of Flower Pollination*, English translation by Ainsworth Davis (Clarendon Press, Oxford, 1908).

* Published by P. R. Gawthorn, Ltd., 55 Russell Square, London, W.C.1
† 3rd edition of 1884, reprinted in 1937; there is no up-to-date British *Flora*.

KEY FOR NAMING COMMON FLOWERING PLANTS

(For how to use the Key, see p. vi.)

A key to determine the common plants illustrated and described in this second volume is given in the following pages. With the aid of this and with that published in the first book—*Common Wild Flowers*, Pelican Book A153 (1945 and 1946)—it should be possible to determine most of the common or fairly common flowering plants which grow wild in the British Isles. When it is desired to name a common plant both books should be consulted, though plants which are only locally common and not generally distributed may not be included.

As there are no conifers described in this book, the plants are divided into only two main groups corresponding with Parts II and III of the key in the first volume.

Part I (below) is again the larger, and contains plants known as *Dicotyledons*; these have net-veined leaves, the bundles (vascular) of the stem are arranged in a circle or circles, and the seedling has 2 seed-leaves when it starts to grow. Plants of the Rose family, the Pea family, Willows, Nettles, Buttercups, the Wallflower family, Daisy family and the Hemlock family and many others come under this heading.

Part II (p. xxxviii) contains plants known as *Monocotyledons*; these have leaves with parallel veins (nerves), and are usually long and narrow, the bundles (vascular) in the stem being scattered (not in circles), and the seedling has only 1 seed-leaf. The plants belonging to this group in this book are mainly sedges and a few others, but no grasses are included, as it is hoped to publish a special volume dealing with these (see p. ix); and no orchid is common enough to appear in this part. The more generally distributed orchids, however, will be included in the next book of this series, *Less Common Wild Flowers*, and the author hopes to be able, with better means of locomotion at his disposal, to make drawings of these from living specimens.

Key, Part I (*Dicotyledons*)

1 Trees, shrubs, or shrublets, with woody stems and branches persisting for more than one season (to p. xiii) :
  2 Leaves divided into 3 or more separate leaflets:
    3 More or less branched perennial stems; shrubs or shrublets:

xi

4 Bush armed with prickles and with handsome pink or white flowers; leaflets more than 3; seeds within a hollow fleshy receptacle ("hip") with the sepals on top; Wild Roses (FIGS. 205, 206) . . . . . *Rosa*

4a Low shrublet with glandular leaves divided into 3 leaflets; branchlets ending in a sharp needle-like point; flowers irregular, pea-like; stamens united into a sheath; Spiny Rest-Harrow (FIG. 214) . *Ononis*

3a Unbranched or only slightly branched annual stems from an underground rhizome, only slightly prickly; flowers small with white petals; fruit juicy, the "seeds" exposed on a cone-like axis; Raspberry (FIG. 204) . . . . *Rubus*

2a Leaves not divided into separate leaflets, though sometimes deeply lobed:

5 Leaves opposite to each other on the shoots, not crowded:

6 Much-branched shrub; flowers white in a panicle; stamens 2 or rarely 3; Privet (FIG. 250) *Ligustrum*

6a Tall twining plant with annual stems, the lower leaves deeply 3–5-lobed; flowers unisexual, the males in loose panicles, the females in ovoid heads; Hop (FIG. 238) . . . . *Humulus*

6b Low creeping plant; flowers single, medium size, blue; stamens 5; Periwinkle (FIG. 251) . . . *Vinca*

5a Leaves alternate on the shoots, sometimes crowded:

7 Flowers neither in catkins nor in dense spikes, though sometimes crowded:

8 Flowers crowded into a terminal flat corymb rather like the May or Hawthorn blossom; leaves sharply toothed, with prominent parallel lateral nerves; stamens free; White Beam (FIG. 203) . . *Sorbus*

8a Flowers in racemes:

9 Branchlets ending in a thorn; stamens united into a sheath, the anthers alternately longer and shorter; Petty Whin (FIG. 213) . . . . . . *Genista*

9a Branchlets armed with 3-pronged thorns; stamens free, anthers opening by flaps; leaves with very prickly margins; Barberry (FIG. 269) . . . *Berberis*

8b Flowers on simple stalks in the axils of the leaves:

10 Petals free from one another:

11 Branches armed with 3-pronged spines; leaves lobed and toothed; Wild Gooseberry (FIG. 229) *Ribes*

11a Branches without spines:

12 Leaves sharply toothed, snowy-white below, petals 8;
stamens numerous; low shrublet; Mountain
Avens (FIG. 211) . . . . *Dryas*
12a Leaves not toothed; flowers in axillary clusters;
stamens the same number and opposite the
petals; Alder Buckthorn (FIG. 249) *Frangula*
10a Petals united into a short tube; barren branchlets
ending in a spine; small shrub usually on old
walls; Tea Plant (FIG. 346) . . . . . *Lycium*
7a Flowers arranged in catkins (i.e., slender narrow and
often pendulous) or in dense spikes, the individual
flowers very small; no petals:
13 Leaves about as long as broad, on longish stalks, the
blade waving about in the slightest breeze; Aspen
(FIG. 230) . . . . *Populus*
13a Leaves much longer than broad, very shortly stalked
and not waving in the slightest breeze; Willows:
14 Leaves with entire margins very narrow and elongated,
silvery silky below; Osier (FIG. 231) . . *Salix*
14a Leaves with toothed margins, or, if not toothed, then
not elongated:
15 Leaves gradually narrowed to a sharp point:
16 Leaves densely silky-hairy below; White Willow
(FIG. 232). . . . . *Salix*
16a Leaves not hairy below; Crack Willow (FIG. 233)
Salix
15a Leaves not pointed, or very slightly so:
17 Stipules large and leafy, more or less persistent;
Eared Willow (FIG. 234) . . . . *Salix*
17a Stipules small and soon falling off:
18 Much-branched shrub or small tree; fruiting catkins
about 2½ in. long; Grey Willow (FIG. 235)
Salix
18a Dwarf creeping shrublet; fruiting catkins about
1 in. long; Dwarf Willow (FIG. 236) . *Salix*

1a **Herbs with herbaceous stems and branches or, if woody, then only slightly so towards the base; fresh stems and shoots produced annually and dying down in the autumn, sometimes with a woody root-stock.**

19 FLOWERS DENSELY CROWDED INTO HEADS, MOSTLY SUR-
ROUNDED BY ONE OR MORE ROWS OF BRACTS FORMING AN
INVOLUCRE; HEADS MOSTLY FORMED ON A SIMILAR PLAN
TO THE DAISY OR CHRYSANTHEMUM (TO P. XVI):

20 Ovary of individual flowers superior, i.e., placed more or less above the insertion of the calyx and petals; bracts at most forming an imperfect involucre:
  21 Flowers bisexual (stamens and ovary in the same flowers); not twiners:
    22 Heads without a well-developed foliage leaf below the flowers, but with a digitate bract; Kidney Vetch (FIG. 216) . . . . *Anthyllis*
    22a Heads with a well-developed leaf of 3 leaflets close under it; Marsh Bird's Foot Trefoil (FIG. 215) *Lotus*
  21a Flowers unisexual (stamens and ovary in separate flowers):
    23 Twiner with 3-lobed opposite leaves; Hop (FIG. 238) *Humulus*
    23a Herb with simple alternate leaves; Sun Spurge (FIG. 245) . . . . *Euphorbia*
20a Ovary of individual flowers inferior—i.e. placed below the insertion of the calyx and corolla (calyx often composed of hair-like bristles or minute):
  24 Ovary with numerous ovules:
    25 Flowers blue, large, bell-shaped, only the terminal ones in a loose head; calyx-lobes green; Bell-flower (FIGS. 321, 322) . . . . *Campanula*
    25a Flowers blue, small, all in a small dense head; Sheep's-bit (FIG. 323) . . . . . *Jasione*
  24a Ovary with one ovule; calyx of individual flowers very small or bristly or hair-like (as in Daisy family):
    26 Leaves in whorls, narrow and entire; corolla violet or pink; Field Madder (FIG. 255) . . *Sherardia*
    26a Leaves opposite:
      26aa Leaves deeply divided into 3 main segments; achenes with 2 bristles with reflexed barbs; Trifid Bur-Marigold (FIG. 324). . . . . . *Bidens*
      26ab Leaves at most toothed; achenes without barbs; Fuller's Teasel (FIG. 320) . . . . *Dipsacus*
    26b Leaves alternate:
      27 Flower-heads with both ray and disk flowers (i.e. strap-shaped and tubular):
        28 Bracts of the involucre in one main row, with a few smaller ones at the base; species of Groundsel and Ragwort genus (FIGS. 335, 336) *Senecio*
        28a Bracts of the involucre in more than one row:

29 Ray flowers blue; fleshy plant in salt marshes near the coast; leaves not toothed; achenes with hair-like pappus; Sea Aster (FIG. 326) *Aster*

29a Ray flowers yellow; leaves coarsely toothed or lobed; achenes with no pappus; Corn Marigold (FIG. 330) . . . . . *Chrysanthemum*

29b Ray flowers white; achenes with rim-like pappus:

30 All the disk flowers in the axil of a scaly bract on the receptacle; ray flowers with a style; achenes smooth; Corn Chamomile (FIG. 332) *Anthemis*

30a Only the upper disk flowers in the axil of a scaly bract on the receptacle; ray flowers without a style; achenes prominently warted; Fetid Chamomile (FIG. 333) . . . *Anthemis*

30b Disk flowers not in the axil of a bract; flowers forming a wide corymb; Feverfew (FIG. 331) *Chrysanthemum*

27a Flower-heads with the flowers all of one kind, either all strap-shaped or all tubular, sometimes in the latter case the outer flowers female and thread-like (filiform):

31 All the flowers tubular, with a regularly lobed top (lobes not all fused into one flat blade) (to p. xvi):

32 Involucral bracts not ending in a spine, though sometimes cut up at the top like a comb:

33 Leaves divided to the middle into fine lobes; flowers arranged on a cone-like axis; achenes crowned by a slightly toothed rim at the top; leaves not covered with woolly hairs; Rayless Chamomile (FIG. 334) . . . . *Matricaria*

33a Leaves at most toothed; covered (especially below) with woolly hairs; achenes crowned with a hair-like pappus:

34 Male and female flowers in the same head (bisexual):

35 Involucral bracts not comb-like at the top:

36 Receptacles without any scales amongst the flowers; Marsh and Heath Cudweeds (FIGS. 325, 327). . . . . *Gnaphalium*

36a Receptacle with a row of scales within the outer row of flowers; Cudweed (FIG. 328) *Filago*

35a Involucral bracts cut around the top like a comb; flowers bluish-purple; Cornflower or Bluebottle (FIG. 337) . . *Centaurea*

34a Male and female flowers in separate heads and on separate plants (unisexual and dioecious); involucral bracts of the male with spreading white tips; Mountain Everlasting (FIG. 329)
Antennaria

32a Involucral bracts ending in a sharp prickly or hooked point; thistles or thistle-like plants:

37 Axis of flower-head without bristles, but honey-combed over the surface; Scotch Thistle (FIG. 338) . . . . *Onopordon*

37a Axis of flower-head with bristles amongst the flowers:

38 Bracts of the involucre hooked at the apex; strong-growing plant with large almost rhubarb-like leaves; Lesser Burdock (FIG. 340) *Arctium*

38a Bracts of the involucre not hooked at the apex:

39 Flower-heads not crowded, more or less solitary; stems winged with the prickly extensions of the leaf-bases; Musk Thistle (FIG. 339)
Carduus

39a Flower-heads densely crowded towards the top of the plant; stems closely beset with prickles; Marsh Thistle (FIG. 341) *Cirsium*

31a All the flowers strap-shaped (as in figs. 342-345):

40 Pappus-bristles with long slender side-hairs (plumose):

41 Leaves not hairy (glabrous), grass-like, entire, linear; Goat's Beard Salsify (FIG. 347)
Tragopogon

41a Leaves clothed with rather long forked hairs; leaves coarsely toothed or lobulate with reflexed lobes; Hawksbit (FIG. 345) *Leontodon*

40a Pappus-bristles without long slender side-hairs (barbellate or smooth):

42 Achenes not narrowed into a beak at the apex; Corn Sowthistle (FIG. 342) . . *Sonchus*

42a Achenes narrowed into a slender beak; Wild and Wall Lettuce (FIGS. 343, 344) . *Lactuca*

19a FLOWERS NOT CROWDED INTO HEADS, OR, IF SO, THEN NOT SURROUNDED BY AN INVOLUCRE OF BRACTS:

43 *Flowers arranged in umbels, their several stalks radiating from one point like the ribs of an umbrella:*
  44 Flowers very small and nearly hidden within the stipule opposite the leaf-stalk; tiny annual plant; Parsley Piert (FIG. 212) . . . . *Alchemilla*
  44a Flowers not hidden within the stipule:
    45 Petals absent; flowers unisexual, arranged in a cup-like involucre; Sun Spurge (FIG. 245) . . *Euphorbia*
    45a Petals present; flowers mostly bisexual:
      46 Petals united into a tube:
        47 Flowers about 5 together in a bunch at the top of a common stalk, sessile in the cluster; corolla greenish-yellow; Moschatel (FIG. 311) *Adoxa*
        47a Flowers numerous and surrounded by a whorl of leafy bracts; corolla violet or pink; Field Madder (FIG. 255) . . . . . *Sherardia*
      46a Petals free from one another; petals white:
        48 Umbels nearly sessile (stalkless), out of the axils of the leaves; Marsh Wort (FIG. 314) . . *Apium*
        48a Umbels with a distinct common stalk:
          49 Flowers sessile or nearly so within the umbel; Shepherd's Needle (FIG. 317) . . . *Scandix*
          49a Flowers (at least some) stalked within the umbel:
            50 Primary and secondary umbels with an involucre of leafy bracts; Lesser Sium (FIG. 315) . *Sium*
            50a Primary umbels without bracts:
              51 Fertile flowers sessile or nearly so; Water Dropwort (FIG. 316) . . . . . *Oenanthe*
              51a Fertile flowers stalked; Rough Chervil (FIG. 313) *Chaerophyllum*

43a *Flowers not arranged in umbels (as described above), though sometimes densely clustered in the axils of the leaves or on a peduncle:*

52 Leaves alternate on the shoots, or sometimes all the leaves confined to the base of the plant (radical), never reduced to scales and always more or less green (to p. xxiii):

  53 Female (middle) part of the flower composed of 2 or more carpels free from one another and with separate styles:
    54 Leaves without stipules:
      55 Sepals more conspicuous than the petals, the latter narrow; Globe-flower (FIG. 257) . *Trollius*

55a Sepals less conspicuous than the petals, the latter broad; species of Buttercup (FIGS. 258–265)
Ranunculus

54a Leaves with conspicuous stipules:
  56 Petals and calyx-lobes 8; leaves simple; Mountain Avens (FIG. 211) . . . . *Dryas*
  56a Petals and calyx-lobes 4–6; leaves compound:
    57 Carpels in fruit ending in a long jointed awn; Water Avens (FIG. 208) . . . . . *Geum*
    57a Carpels in fruit not awned, at most with a short beak:
      58 Leaves with 3 leaflets (FIGS. 209, 210) *Potentilla*
      58a Leaves with numerous leaflets; (pinnate) Dropwort (FIG. 207) . . . . *Filipendula*
  56b Petals absent; leaves fan-shaped, deeply lobed; Parsley Piert (FIG. 212) . . . *Alchemilla*

53a Female (middle) part of the flower composed of a single ovary (made up of 1 carpel or 2 or more united carpels):
  59 Petals present, free or united into a tube (to p. xxiii):
    60 Sepals and petals inserted below or around the ovary (ovary superior) (to p. xxii):
      61 Stamens with their stalks united into a column or sheath (in the latter case sometimes split down one side) (to p. xix):
        62 Flowers divisible into equal halves in several directions (regular); Common and Musk Mallows (FIGS. 241, 242) . . . . . . *Malva*
        62a Flowers divisible into equal halves in only one (vertical) direction; mostly plants of the Pea and Violet families:
          63 Stamens 5:
            64 Leaves not divided except for the small teeth in the margin, ovate or rounded; Violet (FIGS. 239, 240) . . . . . . *Viola*
            64a Leaves much divided into small leaflets; climbing *Corydalis* (FIG. 270) . . *Corydalis*
          63a Stamens 10, united into a sheath, or one free:
            65 Leaves simple, narrow and grass-like, with parallel nerves; Grass-leaved Pea (FIG. 228)
Lathyrus
            65a Leaves compound (or 2 or more leaflets):

66 Leaflets 3, or sometimes only a pair with the terminal modified into a tendril:

67 No tendrils:

68 Branchlets ending in a thorn; Spiny Rest-Harrow (FIG. 214) . . . *Ononis*

68a Branchlets not ending in a thorn:

69 Flowers in slender one-sided racemes; Common Melilot (FIG. 217) . *Melilotus*

69a Flowers in globose heads or short dense spikes:

70 Perennials; fruits spreading star-like, ovules and seeds numerous; Marsh Bird's Foot Trefoil (FIG. 215) *Lotus*

70a Annuals; fruits very short, 1–2-seeded; Trefoils or Clovers; (FIGS. 219, 220) *Trifolium*

67a Tendrils present; Wood Pea (FIG. 227) *Lathyrus*

66a Leaflets more than 3 (in addition to the tendril when present):

71 Common stalk of the leaves ending in a tendril or barren point:

72 Wing-petals joined to the keel petals; style thread-like throughout; Vetches (FIGS. 222, 224) . . . . . *Vicia*

72a Wing-petals free or nearly so; style flattened at the end with a beard of hairs below the apex; Wild Peas (FIGS. 225–228) *Lathyrus*

71a Common stalk of the leaves not ending in a tendril or barren point:

73 Calyx not inflated in fruit, much shorter than the seed-pod, the latter contracted between the seeds and hook-pointed; Bird's-Foot (FIG. 221). . . . . . *Ornithopus*

73a Calyx inflated, enclosing the seed-pod; Kidney Vetch (FIG. 216) . *Anthyllis*

61a Stamens not united into a column or sheath, sometimes inserted on the corolla:

74 Stamens numerous (more than double the number of the petals):

75 Land plants with pinnately divided leaves; sepals 2, soon falling off; Poppy (FIG. 268) *Papaver*

xix

75a Water plants with entire leaves:
  76 Sepals greenish outside, about the size of the outer white petals; White Waterlily (FIG. 266) . . . . *Nymphaea*
  76a Sepals yellow concealing the much smaller petals; Yellow Waterlily (FIG. 267) . *Nuphar*
74a Stamens few, not more than double the number of the petals:
 77 Petals not united into a tube (to p. xxi):
  78 Stamens 6, 4 long and 2 shorter; petals 4; Wallflower family (to p. xxi):
   79 Petals yellow:
    80 Lower leaves not pinnate; Black Mustard (FIG. 276) . . . . *Brassica*
    80a Lower leaves pinnately divided to the midrib:
     81 Fruits on long stalks, beaked, constricted between the seeds, bristly hairy; White Mustard (FIG. 275) . . . *Sinapis*
     81a Fruits very shortly stalked, linear, not constricted between the seeds; Hedge Mustard and Tumbling Mustard (FIGS. 273, 274) . . . . . *Sisymbrium*
   79a Petals white:
    82 Fruit as broad or nearly as broad as long:
     83 Small annual with a rosette of spreading pinnately lobed leaves; fruits winged; Shepherd's Cress (FIG. 283) *Teesdalia*
     83a Taller branched plants with reticulate but not winged fruits:
      84 Stem-leaves stalked, glaucous and fleshy; Sea Kale (FIG. 281) . . . *Crambe*
      84a Stem-leaves sessile, eared at the base:
       85 Fruits cordate at the base; ovary with 1 ovule in each loculus; seeds 2 in each fruit; Hoary Cress (FIG. 279) *Cardaria*
       85a Fruits not cordate; ovary with more than 1 ovule in each loculus; seeds several in each fruit; Scurvy Grass (FIG. 280) *Cochlearia*
    82a Fruit much longer than broad, long and narrow:
     86 Leaves forming a rosette, slightly toothed, clothed with forked hairs; fruits elongated; Wall Cress (FIG. 272) *Arabidopsis*

86a Leaves not forming a rosette, or, if so, then some also on the stem and pinnate:
  87 Leaves large (9 inches long or more) and crenate, elliptic, rarely lobed; Horse Radish (FIG. 277) . . . *Armoracia*
  87a Leaves much smaller, deeply pinnately divided:
    88 Fruits slender and elongated; leaves divided into distinct leaflets; Hairy Bittercress (FIG. 271) . *Cardamine*
    88a Fruits short; leaves not divided into separate leaflets; Iceland Watercress (FIGS. 278) . . . . *Rorippa*
78a Stamens more or fewer than 6; petals usually 5:
  89 Leaves in a rosette, spoon-shaped and covered with sticky hairs or processes; acid bog plant; Sundew (FIG. 312) . . *Drosera*
  89a Leaves not as above:
    90 Leaves rounded and slightly toothed, rather large:
      91 Flowers irregular; Violets (FIGS. 239, 240) *Viola*
      91a Flowers regular; Wintergreen; (FIG. 246) *Pyrola*
    90a Leaves fan-shaped and deeply divided, very small and densely hairy; Parsley Piert (FIG. 212) . . . . . *Alchemilla*
77a Petals united into a tube:
  92 Stamens placed opposite to the corolla-lobes and equal to them in number:
    93 Ovary free from the calyx; stem-leaves united (perfoliate); Perfoliate Montia (FIG. 291) *Montia*
    93a Ovary partly united with the calyx; stem-leaves not united at the base; Brookweed (FIG. 306) . . . . . *Samolus*
  92a Stamens placed alternate with the corolla-lobes, sometimes fewer in number:
    94 Ovary deeply and vertically 4-lobed, with the style inserted between the lobes (gynobasic style):
      95 Corolla-tube bent in the middle; nutlets densely warted; Bugloss (FIG. 370) *Lycopsis*

95a Corolla-tube straight:
 96 Tube of corolla more or less closed at its mouth by scales:
  97 Nut smooth or a little wrinkled; Forget-me-nots (FIGS. 368, 369) . . *Myosotis*
  97a Nut warted and burr-like; Hound's Tongue (FIG. 372) . . . . *Cynoglossum*
 96a Tube of corolla not closed at its mouth; Corn Gromwell (FIG. 371)
          Lithospermum
94a Ovary not vertically lobed or only slightly so; style terminal:
 98 Corolla spurred at the base, 2-lipped:
  99 Leaves linear, borne on the stem; flowers yellow; Yellow Toad Flax (FIG. 348)
          Linaria
  99a Leaves broad in a basal rosette; flowers blue; Butterwort (FIG. 364)
          Pinguicula
 98a Corolla not spurred at the base and not 2-lipped:
  100 Flowers numerous in a lax panicle; Black Mullein (FIG. 350) . . *Verbascum*
  100a Flowers axillary or spicate:
   101 Leaves very narrow, entire or lobulate:
    102 Flowers bisexual; Seaside Plantains (FIGS. 307, 308) . . *Plantago*
    102a Flowers unisexual; Shoreweed (FIG. 309) . . . . . *Littorella*
   101a Leaves rounded-ovate, some opposite; flowers axillary; fruit notched at the top (FIGS. 349–356) *Veronica*
60a Sepals and petals inserted above or nearly above the ovary (ovary inferior):
 103 Flowers in dense clusters or heads:
  104 Flowers with involucre of bracts, blue; Sheep's-bit (FIG. 323) . . . . *Jasione*
  104a Flowers without bracts, greenish-yellow; Moschatel (FIG. 311) . . . . . *Adoxa*
 103a Flowers not in dense clusters or heads:
  105 Stamens the same number and opposite the petals or corolla-lobes; ovary only half-inferior; Brookweed (FIG. 306) . . . *Samolus*

105a Stamens alternate with the petals or more numerous:
  106 Petals free:
    107 Ovary short, covered with glandular hairs; Saxifrage (FIG. 310) . . . *Saxifraga*
    107a Ovary elongated and stalk-like, not glandular hairy; various Willow Herbs (FIGS. 292–294) *Epilobium*
  106a Petals united into a tube; flowers blue; Bell flowers (FIGS. 321, 322) . . *Campanula*
59a Petals absent, the sepals thin, sometimes more or less coloured and petal-like:
  108 Leaves without stipules:
    109 Flowers unisexual, the males with one stamen, with the single female flower (an ovary and style) in an involucre; Spurge (FIG. 245) *Euphorbia*
    109a Flowers bisexual, racemose; leaves forming a rosette at the base of the stem; Pepperwort (FIG. 282) . . . . . . *Lepidium*
  108a Leaves with stipules:
    110 Calyx in fruit of 5 nearly equal parts; stipules sheathing the stem; species of Polygonum (FIGS. 295–298) . . . . *Polygonum*
    110a Calyx in fruit of 6 parts, 3 inner often enlarged; Docks (FIGS. 299, 300) . . . . *Rumex*
    110b Calyx of 4 small green parts; fertile stamens 1 or 2; Parsley Piert (FIG. 212) . . *Alchemilla*

52a **Leaves opposite to each other or in whorls on the stem (at any rate the lower leaves) never all at the base of the plant, rarely reduced to scales:**

  111 Petals absent (to p. xxiv):
    112 Leaves fairly large (over 1 inch) and toothed, stalked:
      113 Leaves without stinging hairs:
        114 Leaves not lobed; stems erect; Annual Dog's Mercury (FIG. 244) . . . *Mercurialis*
        114a Leaves deeply 3-lobed; stems twining; female flowers in bracteate balls; Hop (FIG. 238) *Humulus*
      113a Leaves with sharp stinging hairs, coarsely toothed; Stinging Nettle (FIG. 237) . . . *Urtica*
    112a Leaves very small, entire; tiny annual plants:
      115 Stamens opposite the sepals; Annual Pearlwort (FIG. 288) . . . . *Sagina*

115a Stamens alternate with the sepals; Sea Milkwort
(FIG. 305) . . . . *Glaux*
111a Petals present:
116 Petals separate from one another:
117 Stamens more than 10, united into bundles; St.
John's Worts (FIGS. 247, 248) . . *Hypericum*
117a Stamens 10 or fewer, not united into bundles:
118 Leaves with stipules:
119 Leaves rounded, lobed and toothed; petals large
and showy; Geranium (FIGS. 365-367)

Geranium

119a Leaves narrow and in whorls; petals small and
white; Spurry (FIG. 284) . . *Spergula*
118a Leaves without stipules:
120 Petals deeply divided into 2 lobes:
121 Ovary below the calyx and petals (ovary inferior);
Willow Herbs (FIGS. 292-294) . *Epilobium*
121a Ovary above the calyx and petals (ovary
superior):
122 Sepals free nearly to the base:
123 Styles 3; Heath Stitchwort (FIG. 285) *Stellaria*
123a Styles 5; Field Chickweed (FIG. 286)

Cerastium

122a Sepals united into a tube:
124 Styles 5; plant pubescent; White Campion
(FIG. 289) . . . . *Lychnis*
124a Styles 3-4; plant glabrous and glaucous, maritime; Sea Campion (FIG. 290) *Silene*
120a Petals not divided or only slightly notched at the
apex:
125 Ovary above the sepals and petals (ovary superior)
not united with the calyx:
126 Stem and leaves not fleshy; a very delicate little
annual; All-seed (FIG. 243) . . *Radiola*
126a Stem and leaves fleshy, maritime species with
creeping perennial root-stock; Sea Purslane (FIG. 287) . . . . *Arenaria*
125a Ovary below the sepals and petals (ovary
inferior), and united with the sepals; Willow
Herbs (FIGS. 292-294) . . *Epilobium*
116a Petals united into a tube:
127 Stamens opposite to the corolla-lobes and equal in
number to them:

128 Fruit opening into valves from the top; flowers yellow; species of Lysimachia (FIGS. 302, 303)
Lysimachia

128a Fruit opening by a transverse slit; flowers pink; filaments hairy; Bog Pimpernel (FIG. 304)
Anagallis

127a Stamens alternate with the corolla-lobes, sometimes fewer in number, rarely more numerous:

129 Ovary inserted above the calyx and corolla (ovary superior) (to p. xxvi):

130 Stamens 2:

131 Corolla not 2-lipped; stems rounded; species of Speedwell (FIGS. 349–356) . . . *Veronica*

131a Corolla 2-lipped; stems square in section; Clary (FIG. 380) . . . . . *Salvia*

130a Stamens 3 or more:

132 Style placed on top of the ovary, the latter at mostly only slightly lobed vertically (to p. xxv):

133 Corolla regular, not 2-lipped:

134 Flowers not in a head; leaves not compound:

135 Flowers yellow; leaves not toothed; Yellow-wort (FIG. 301) . . . *Blackstonia*

135a Flowers blue; leaves not toothed; Periwinkle (FIG. 251) . . . . *Vinca*

135b Flowers pink or white; leaves toothed; Vervain (FIG. 256) . . . . *Verbena*

134a Flowers in a head; leaves ternately compound; Moschatel (FIG. 311) . *Adoxa*

133a Corolla irregular, 2-lipped:

136 Parasitic plants without green parts, growing on the roots of trees and flowering in early spring; Toothwort (FIG. 363) . *Lathraea*

136a Green plants:

137 Calyx 5-lobed or 5-toothed:

138 Corolla-tube nearly globose; flowers small, in a lax panicle; Figwort (FIG. 357)
Scrophularia

138a Corolla-tube not globose; flowers axillary, large and showy, yellow and spotted; leaves toothed; Monkey Flower (FIG. 358) . . . . *Mimulus*

137a Calyx 2–4-lobed or toothed:

xxv

139 Bracteate leaves pinnate or lobulate on the margins:
  140 Flowers yellow; Common Cow-wheat (FIG. 361) . . . . . *Melampyrum*
  140a Flowers purple-red; Marsh Louse-wort (FIG. 359) . . . . *Pedicularis*
139a Bracteate leaves at most toothed:
  141 Flowers yellow; Common Corn Rattle (FIG. 362) . . . . . *Rhinanthus*
  141a Flowers purplish-red; Red Bartsia (FIG. 360) . . . . *Bartsia*
132a Style placed between the lobes of the deeply (vertically) divided ovary, the latter with rounded lobes:
  142 Stamens longer than and exserted from the corolla:
    143 Stamens 4:
      144 Flowers axillary; Wild Basil (FIG. 375) *Clinopodium*
      144a Flowers forming a dense leafy panicle; Marjoram (FIG. 374) . . *Origanum*
    143a Stamens 2, sometimes with 2 staminodes; flowers sessile in dense axillary clusters; Gipsywort (FIG. 373) . . . *Lycopus*
  142a Stamens with the anthers concealed under the upper lip of the corolla:
    145 Calyx 2-lipped:
      146 Calyx composed of 2 very short undivided lobes, the upper with a concave scale on the back; corolla mauve-blue; Skull Cap (FIG. 376) . . . . *Scutellaria*
      146a Calyx with toothed lobes; no scale on the back (FIG. 380) . . . *Salvia*
    145a Calyx equally or subequally 5-lobed, not 2-lipped:
      147 Flowers bright yellow or white; Yellow Archangel and White Dead-nettle (FIGS. 378, 379) . . . . . . *Lamium*
      147a Flowers mauve-purple; Black Horehound (FIG. 377) . . . . . *Ballota*
129a Ovary inserted below the calyx and corolla (ovary inferior):
  148 Leaves in whorls of 4 or more at each node:

149 Calyx a mere rim; flowers in lax panicles or
axillary clusters; species of *Galium* (FIGS.
252–254) . . . . *Galium*

149a Calyx 4–6-toothed; flowers in a terminal bunch
surrounded by bracts; Field Madder (FIG.
255) . . . . *Sherardia*

148a Leaves in pairs at each node:

150 Flowers in dense heads surrounded by an involucre of bracts:

151 Bracts not spine-like; Field Scabious (FIG. 318)
Knautia

151a Bracts spine-like; Fuller's Teasel (FIG. 320)
Dipsacus

150a Flowers in a head without an involucre; leaves
ternately compound; Moschatel (FIG. 311)
Adoxa

150b Flowers in panicles without an involucre of
bracts; Valerian (FIG. 319) . *Valeriana*

Key, Part II (*Monocotyledons*)

1 Leaves arrow-shaped (sagittate) at the base; aquatic plant
with large white petals, the flowers arranged in distant
whorls of 3, some male, some female; Arrowhead (FIG.
382) . . . . *Sagittaria*

1a Leaves not arrow-shaped, often sheathing at the base:

2 Crocus-like plant, flowering in the autumn and fruiting in the
following early summer; flowers pale-purple or mauve;
stamens 6; Autumn Crocus (FIG. 383) . *Colchicum*

2a Not Crocus-like:

3 Flowers with a distinct coloured perianth (sepals and
petals):

4 Flowers umbellate, pink; carpels free from one another;
Flowering Rush (FIG. 381) . . . *Butomus*

4a Flowers racemose, bright-yellow; carpels united into an
ovary; Bog Asphodel (FIG. 384) . . *Narthecium*

3a Flowers without a perianth or the latter very small and inconspicuous; mostly grass-like plants (Sedges, etc.):

5 Flowers in globose balls, the males and females separate
but in the same inflorescence; aquatic plant; Burreed (FIG. 385) . . . . *Sparganium*

5a Flowers in spikes or clusters (not in balls):

6 Flowers with a distinct perianth of 6 glume-like parts;
stamens 6 or 3; Rushes (FIGS. 386–390) . *Juncus*

6a Flowers without a perianth, or the latter represented by bristles or hairs, sometimes the ovary hidden in a bottle-shaped structure (utricle); stamens 3; Sedges:

7 Stamens and ovary in the same flower (i.e. within the same glume-like bract and bisexual):

8 Spikelets solitary at the top of the peduncle:

9 Bristles not exserted from the glumes, barbed; Marsh Club Rush (FIG. 394) . . . *Eleocharis*

9a Bristles, not barbed; Deer's Grass (FIG. 393)
Scirpus

8a Spikelets clustered or more than one on each flowering stem:

10 Spikelets clustered into an umbel-like inflorescence with radiating stalks:

11 Hypogynous bristles long and hair-like (woolly), much exserted from the glumes in fruit; Cotton Grass (FIG. 396) . . . . . *Eriophorum*

11a Hypogynous bristles not exserted, barbed; Bulrush (FIG. 391) . . . . . . *Scirpus*

10a Spikelets sessile in a head-like cluster at the apex of the peduncle:

12 Several of the lower bracts (glumes) without flowers inside; Black Bog Rush (FIG. 395) . *Schoenus*

12a Only the lowermost bract (glume) without a flower inside; leaves very small and slender (awl-shaped); Bristly Scirpus (FIG. 392)
Scirpus

7a Stamens and ovary in different flowers (flowers unisexual), though both sexes sometimes in the same spikelet; Sedges (FIGS. 397–408) . . *Carex*

MORE COMMON
WILD FLOWERS

The numbering of the flowers
is continued from the previous
volume, *Common Wild Flowers*
(Pelican Book, A 153)

WHITE BEAM, *Sorbus aria* (L.) Crantz.

203. White Beam, *Sorbus aria* (L.) Crantz ($\times \frac{1}{2}$); a shrub or moderate-sized tree up to about 40 ft. high, easily recognised by the snow-white under-surface of the leaves; branchlets brownish-crimson, marked with very small rounded pore-like lenticels; leaves simple, ovate to slightly obovate, shortly wedge-shaped at the base, rounded or slightly pointed at the apex, averaging about 3 in. long and 2 in. broad, woolly-hairy on both surfaces when young, but the hairs only persisting below, rather coarsely and doubly crenate-dentate, with 6–9 pairs of nearly straight prominent nerves; flowers (A, $\times 1\frac{1}{4}$) arranged in a terminal corymb (see figure) at the end of the new shoots, covered

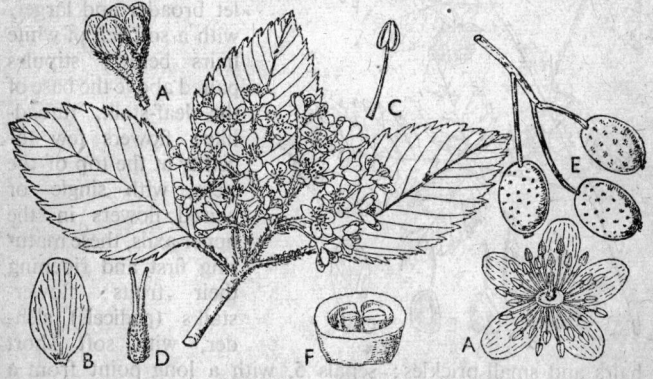

all over with cottony white hairs; petals (B, $\times 2$) white; stamens (C, $\times 2$) about 25, in two rows; styles (D, $\times 2\frac{1}{2}$) 2, hairy at the base; fruits (E, $\times \frac{1}{2}$) ellipsoid, red, $\frac{1}{2}-\frac{3}{4}$ in. long (F, $\times 1\frac{1}{4}$ section of fruit) (synonym *Pyrus aria* L. J. Ehrh.) (family *Rosaceae*).

The White Beam is a tree in woods, on good soil reaching 40–50 ft. or sometimes a little higher. In rocky mountainous situations, however, it is usually shrubby. It is easily recognised by the snowy-white under-surface of the leaves, but outside Britain it exhibits a great variety of forms in a wild state, ranging as it does over a wide area throughout Europe, Algeria, Asia Minor, and as far east as Siberia and Central China.

RASPBERRY, *Rubus idaeus* L.

204. Raspberry, *Rubus idaeus* L. (× ⅓); stems biennial, flowering and fruiting the second season, woody, to about 5 ft. high, prickly (A, × 0); root-stock short; leaves pinnate, the lower often with two pairs, the upper with one pair of leaflets and an end leaflet; leaf-stalk sometimes with a few short prickles; leaflets broadly ovate, doubly cut into sharp-pointed teeth, end leaflet broader and larger, with a soft felt of white hairs below; stipules paired above the base of the leaf-stalk, thread-like; flowers few together at the top of the stem, with single or paired flowers in the upper axils, these maturing first and ripening their fruits; flower-stalks (pedicels) slender, with soft short hairs and small prickles; sepals 5, with a long point from a triangular base, softly hairy (B, × 0); petals 5, white (C, 1⅓); stamens (D, × 3) numerous; carpels (E, × 3) numerous on a conical receptacle, free and woolly when young, becoming red or yellow and juicy in fruit; style slender (F, seed × 5) (family *Rosaceae*).

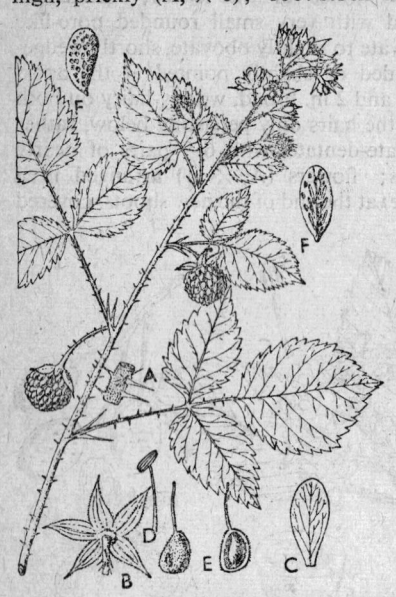

The Raspberry is easy to recognise among the many British species, forms and hybrids of the genus *Rubus*. It grows in partially open spots in woods and is often common on the sides of railway embankments and cuttings. It flowers from June onwards, and soon produces a crop of the juicy red berries so much sought after by country people. Nectar is secreted in a fleshy ring on the margin of the flower-axis (receptacle) within the stamens. The styles form a convenient landing-place for insects, which effect cross-pollination, but self-pollination may also take place.

SCOTCH ROSE, BURNET ROSE, *Rosa spinosissima* L.

205. Scotch Rose, Burnet Rose, *Rosa spinosissima* L. (× ⅓); shrublet usually not much more than 1 ft. high, much branched, the branches densely covered with unequal-sized prickles mixed with shorter gland-tipped hairs; leaves with 3–5 pairs of leaflets and an odd stalked leaflet at the end; leaflets sessile, almost orbicular, about ½ in. long, rather sharply toothed, not hairy: stipules green, joined (adnate) to the stalk, about ½ in. long, finely glandular-toothed; flowers mostly solitary at the end of short shoots, stalked, about 1½ in. diam.; calyx-lobes narrow, ½ in. long, margins at most finely toothed but not lobed as in some

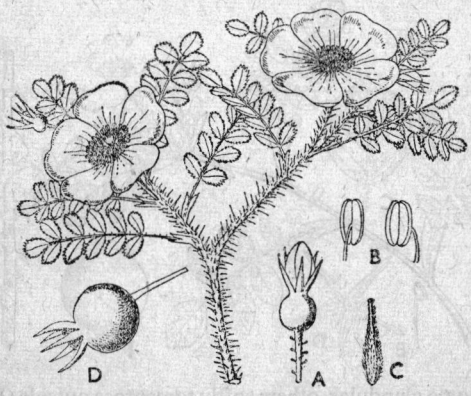

other roses; petals pink or white, spreading widely; stamens numerous, the stalks very short; carpels numerous, enclosed by the enlarged floral receptacle which really forms a false fruit around the little fruitlets (achenes) lining the inside; false fruit globose, purplish-black, crowned by the persistent calyx-lobes (family *Rosaceae*).

This pretty little rose grows on sandy heaths, especially near the sea, and is to be found on some of the commons around London. In its widest (i.e., aggregate) sense it is distributed in the cooler parts of Europe, Northern Asia and south to the Himalayas. There are several varieties, and it hybridises freely with other species; var. *pimpinellifolia* has smooth flower-stalks, though intermediate states are found.* Rose flowers have no nectar, but are sweetly scented, and attract insects by their abundant pollen.

* See Wolley-Dod, *Journal of Botany*, 1930, *Suppl.*, p. 10.

SWEET BRIAR, *Rosa rubiginosa* L.

206. Sweet Briar, *Rosa rubiginosa* L. (× ⅓); shrub with woody root-stock; young stems (A, × ⅓) succulent and very prickly, with downwardly curved prickles mixed with slender straight prickles here and there; leafy branchlets also armed with slender straight prickles; stipules (B, × 0) large, adnate to the leaf-stalk and densely margined with glands; leaf-stalk glandular and prickly; leaflets 3 pairs and a terminal leaflet (C, × ⅔), rounded, sharply and doubly serrate, rather densely glandular below and aromatic when rubbed; flowers pink, solitary or in threes, about 1½ in. diam.; usually 3 calyx-lobes pinnately lobed,

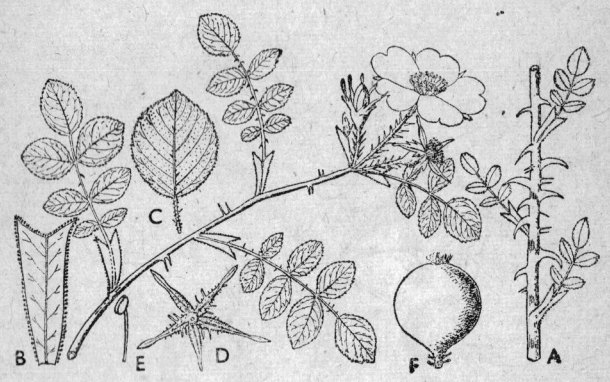

2 entire, some glandular, others softly tomentose outside (D, × ½); petals rather deeply notched; stamens (E, × 2) numerous; carpels numerous inside the receptacle; fruit (F, × ⅔) rounded, smooth or occasionally with very few slender prickles, the stalk armed with stiff gland-tipped prickles, sepals at length falling off (family *Rosaceae*).

This differs from the Dog Rose (*Common Wild Flowers* fig. 9) by the densely glandular leaflets, which are sweet scented when rubbed, and, like the fragrant flowers, help to attract insects.

In most roses nectar is not secreted in the flowers, insects visiting them for their pollen, but the Sweet Briar is an exception. On the broad fleshy margin of the receptacle or calyx-tube there is a thin layer of nectar. The flowers appear in early summer and are open from very early morning until about 9 p.m., the stigmas being receptive before the stamens release their pollen.

DROPWORT, *Filipendula hexapetala* Gilib.

207. Dropwort, *Filipendula hexapetala* Gilib. ($\times \frac{1}{2}$); perennial with the roots swollen here and there into oblong tubers (A, $\times \frac{1}{2}$) (hence the common name Dropwort); stems erect, up to about 2 ft. high, but usually about 1 ft.; leaves mostly crowded at the base of the stem, pinnately divided into several separate often alternately longer and shorter segments, which increase in length upwards and are coarsely toothed, glabrous or nearly so; stipules broad and adnate to the leaf-stalk nearly their full length; flowers (B, $\times 1\frac{1}{2}$) in a terminal cyme with raceme-like branches, and the flowers on one side, the lateral ones very shortly stalked; calyx 5-lobed, lobes oblong, rounded at the apex, glabrous; petals 5, rounded-obovate, shortly clawed, pure white or sometimes tinged with red; stamens numerous; carpels (C, $\times 3$) free, 6–12, not twisted in fruit (D, $\times 4$), shortly hairy (synonym *Spiraea filipendula* L.) (family *Rosaceae*).

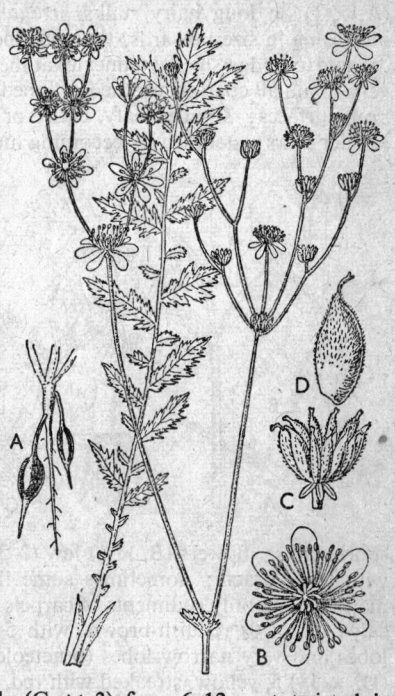

This plant bears various names in different Floras, such as *Spiraea filipendula* L., *Ulmaria filipendula* Hill, and the one used for it here. The companion species in the British flora, the Meadow Sweet, is shown in fig. 10 in our *Common Wild Flowers*, and it is there explained why a separate generic name is necessary for them. *F. hexapetala*, so named from having usually six petals, ranges right across Europe and Asiatic Russia, and flowers in summer. It is found mainly in dry chalky and limestone pastures. The flowers have a faint scent, but secrete no nectar.

WATER AVENS, *Geum rivale* L.

208. Water Avens, *Geum rivale* L. (× ½); perennial herb with a rather slender rhizome covered with persistent leaf-sheaths fringed with hairs; roots sometimes hairy; basal leaves (A, × ½) on long hairy stalks, irregularly pinnate, the leaflets increasing in size upwards, the end one the largest, and widely cordate to wedge-shaped (cuneate) at the base, the lower becoming very small, all coarsely toothed or lobed, finely but thinly hairy on both surfaces; stipules leafy, entire or lobed, clothed with long slender hairs; stem-leaves becoming much smaller and with very

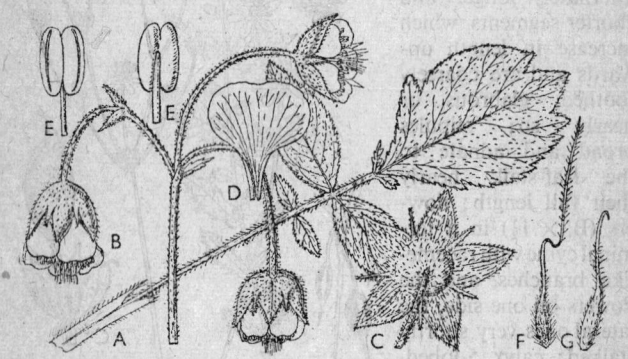

short stalks; flowers (B, × ½) few (2–3) at the top of the stems, with leafy bracts; sometimes some flowers are unisexual, the males having only rudiments of carpels; stalks very softly hairy; calyx (C, × 0) reddish-brown, with 5 ovate-triangular pointed lobes and very narrow lobes (bracteoles) between them; petals (D, × 1½) 5, yellow, streaked with red, obovate, narrowed into a claw, strongly nerved; stamens (E, × 4) numerous; carpels arranged in a stalked bunch, densely covered with long soft hairs, with a long slender style which in fruit (F, G, × 2) becomes bent like a hook in the upper part and clothed with long spreading hairs (family *Rosaceae*).

Grows in marshy places and ditches, and widely distributed in the temperate regions all around the northern hemisphere; common in northern Britain and in Eire. Nectar is stored in numerous drops in the receptacle. Either cross- or self-pollination is possible, some humble bees stealing nectar by inserting their proboscis between the calyx and petals.

ERECT POTENTILLA, *Potentilla erecta* (L.) Rausch.

209. **Erect Potentilla**, *Potentilla erecta* (L.) Rausch ($\times \frac{1}{3}$); perennial herb with numerous slender erect pubescent stems from a thick many-headed root-stock; leaves nearly sessile, divided to the base into 3 narrowly wedge-shaped segments, with a pair of leafy lobulate stipules at the base, the segments coarsely and sharply toothed; pedicels axillary and terminal, often collected into a loose leafy cyme, very slender; sepals (A, $\times 2$) 4, narrowly triangular-lanceolate, acute, with a narrow bracteole between each; petals (B, $\times 1\frac{3}{4}$) 4 or rarely 5, yellow, broadly obovate, veiny; stamens (C, $\times 3$) 15–20; carpels (D, $\times 4$) few, obliquely obovoid, hairy around the base, with a slender lateral style, glabrous; fruits (E, $\times 3$) ovoid, reticulate (F, fruits, $\times$ 0) (family *Rosaceae*).

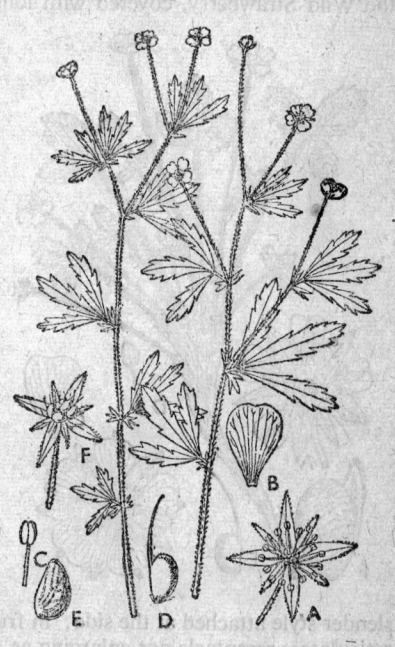

On heaths and dry pastures, widely distributed; flowering in summer. In most British floras this is usually included in the aggregate species, *P. tormentilla*. Nectar is secreted on the inner side of the calyx-tube (receptacle), and the anthers are only covered with pollen on their narrow outer edges. Cross-pollination is effected by insects, but during dull weather the flowers are half shut, when self-pollination may take place.

Although most of the British species of *Potentilla* are herbs, many of the exotic species are shrubs. The herbaceous species, therefore, are probably the most highly evolved, for their shrubby ancestry is indicated by the possession of a woody underground root-stock, a device which ensures their preservation in winter and during excessive droughts.

STRAWBERRY-LEAVED POTENTILLA, BARREN STRAWBERRY, *Potentilla sterilis* (L.) Garcke.

210. Strawberry-leaved Potentilla, Barren Strawberry, *Potentilla sterilis* (L.) Garcke ($\times \frac{1}{3}$); perennial with the habit of the Wild Strawberry, covered with long silky hairs; leaves on long stalks, divided into 3 leaflets, these broadly obovate, nearly sessile, wedge-shaped at the base, very coarsely toothed, silky hairy on both surfaces; stipules large and thin, joined to the leaf-stalks, persisting on the older part of the stem; flowers (B, $\times$ 0) solitary, on long slender stalks, nearly $\frac{1}{2}$ in. diam.; calyx (A, $\times$ 0) of 5 narrowly triangular lobes with a narrow bracteole between each almost as long; petals (C, $\times 1\frac{1}{2}$) white, broadly obovate; stamens (D, $\times$ 3) about 20; anthers elliptic; carpels (E, $\times$ 4) rounded, glabrous, with a long slender style attached at the side; in fruit (F, $\times$ 5) obovoid and reticulate; receptacle not enlarging as in the Strawberry (synonym *Potentilla fragariastrum* Ehrh.) (family *Rosaceae*).

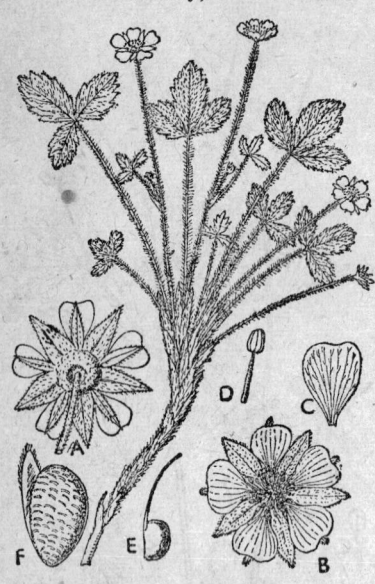

This species flowers in early spring, and grows on banks, dry pastures and in open woods in Europe, extending eastwards as far as the Caucasus; it is rare in northern districts of Britain. It greatly resembles the wild Strawberry (*Common Wild Flowers*, fig. 14), having very similar white flowers but borne singly, and with quite different fruits. Between the stamens and the carpels is a pentagonal hairy coloured nectar-ring. After a time the stamens bend inwards and touch the stigmas, when self-pollination results. The hairs on the upper surface of the leaves have a bulbous swelling at the base.

MOUNTAIN AVENS, *Dryas octopetala* L.

211. Mountain Avens, *Dryas octopetala* L. ($\times \frac{1}{2}$); woody perennial with short much-branched prostrate or creeping stems and forming dense tufts; leaves (A, $\times 1\frac{1}{4}$) alternate, on fairly long hairy stalks, oblong or ovate-oblong in outline but deeply toothed on the margin and rounded-cordate at the base, glabrous and green above with impressed nerves and veins, snowy-white below with woolly hairs, $\frac{1}{2}-\frac{3}{4}$ in. long; stipules thin, united to the leaf-stalks, but with free linear tops; flowers on long slender hairy stalks terminating the short leafy shoots; sepals (B, $\times 1\frac{1}{4}$) about 8, narrow, nervose on the inside, woolly hairy outside; petals (C, $\times 0$) white, about 8 to 10 or rarely fewer, narrowly obovate, veiny; stamens (D, $\times 6$) very numerous, with slender filaments and rounded anther-loculi; achenes (E, $\times 2$) numerous, free, silky hairy, each in fruit ending in a long plumose tail like that of " Traveller's Joy," *Clematis vitalba* (*Common Wild Flowers*, fig. 73) (family *Rosaceae*).

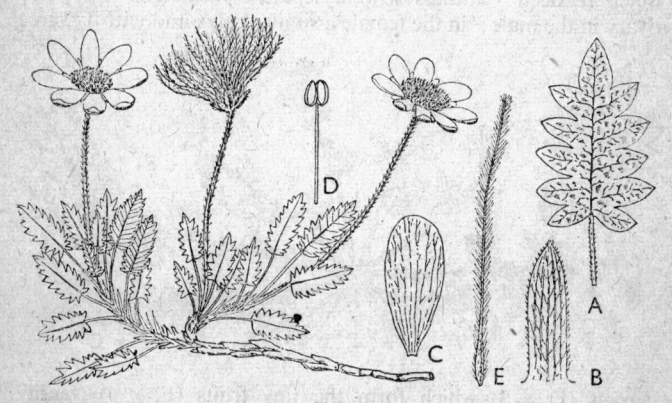

This lovely and distinctive plant is not found over the whole of Britain, but is frequent in northern England, northern and western Eire, and the mountains of northern Scotland, especially on limestone soil. It is widely distributed in arctic and alpine regions of the northern hemisphere.

PARSLEY PIERT, *Alchemilla arvensis* (L.) Scop.

212. Parsley Piert, *Alchemilla arvensis* (L.) Scop. ($\times \frac{1}{3}$); low-growing annual forming a flat carpet, with numerous branches radiating from the root; stems softly hairy with very delicate hairs; leaves (A, $\times 2\frac{1}{2}$) fan-shaped, stalked, divided into 3 main parts, each part deeply lobed, thinly hairy; stipules (B, $\times 2$) encircling the stem and adnate to the leaf-stalk, with a bunch (fascicle) of unisexual flowers in the axil and opposite to the leaf (leaf-opposed); pedicels short; calyx-lobes (C, $\times 5$) 4, ovate, ciliate; no petals; fertile stamens 1 or 2, the others much reduced; anthers with 2 separate loculi (D, $\times 8$); no ovary in the male; in the female a similar calyx and with 1–3 free

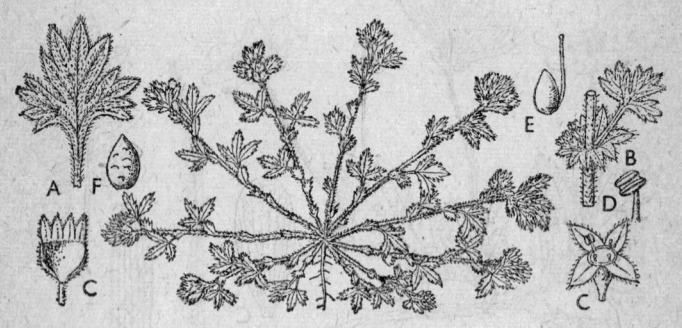

carpels (E, $\times 3$) which form the tiny fruits (F, $\times 4$) (family *Rosaceae*).

In fields and waste places, and often on lawns; widely distributed over the world by cultivation. The tiny flowers are hidden by the large leafy stipules, in the axil of which they are bunched together, and on the side of the stem opposite to the leaf. The small greenish semi-unisexual flowers have no petals, and the nectar is secreted by a fleshy ring on the inner wall of the floral axis (receptacle).

In many families, and even in some genera, one or more species often show considerable reduction in their flowers, especially by dispensing with their petals; or the flowers have become unisexual. Both these conditions are found in this interesting little species, an additional advanced character being its annual habit, most of the other species being perennials.

PETTY WHIN, NEEDLE FURZE, *Genista anglica* L.

213. Petty Whin, Needle Furze, *Genista anglica* L. (× ½); a tiny shrub up to about a foot high; roots long and creeping; stems woody, branched from the base, branches armed with long slightly curved sharp spines, these being the hardened leafless branchlets of the previous season; young leafy shoots produced below the spines, some barren, some bearing flowers; leaves small, simple, obovate, acute; no stipules; flowers yellow, about ½ in. long; calyx (A, × 2½) bell-shaped, shortly 5-toothed; standard-petal (B, × 2) ovate; wing-petals (C, × 2½) obliquely oblong, shortly clawed; keel-petals (D, × 2½) very similar but

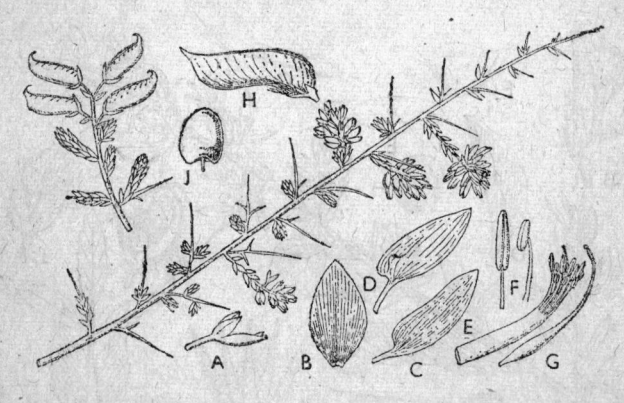

with a lobule towards the base; stamens (E, × 2½) 10, united into a single tube; anthers (F, × 6) alternately short and attached in the middle (versatile) and long and attached at the base; ovary (G, × 2½) glabrous; style longer than the stamen, glabrous; fruits (H, × 1½) inflated like short broad pea-pods and tipped by the curled style, obliquely nerved; seeds (J, × 5) rounded, dark brown and shining (family *Papilionaceae*).

This small shrublet grows on heaths and moors, flowering in spring and early summer and sometimes again in the autumn. It is confined to western Europe, extending eastward only to Denmark and north-west Germany. It is absent from Eire. As in other species of the genus, there is no nectar secreted in the flowers, which discharge their pollen by an explosive mechanism on to the ventral surface of visiting bees, which collect the pollen in their pollen-baskets.

SPINY REST-HARROW, *Ononis spinosa* L.

214. Spiny Rest-Harrow, *Ononis spinosa* L. (× ⅓); shrublet to about 2 ft. high, much branched and leafy, with short branchlets ending in a sharp needle-like point; stems crimson, covered with curly and gland-tipped hairs; leaves (A, × 0) alternate, most on the long shoots with 3 leaflets, on the short shoots with 1 leaflet; stipules leafy, joined to the leaf-stalk, rather sharply toothed like the leaflets, these jointed at the base; flowers (B, × 0) axillary on the short spine-tipped branchlets, bright pink; standard and keel streaked with numerous crimson lines; or rarely all pure white; calyx (C, × 0) green, with numerous gland-tipped hairs and a few longer hairs, 2-lipped, the upper lip of 4 equal narrow lobes, the lower of 1 slightly longer lobe; standard (vexillum) (D, × 0) recurved in the open flower, slightly glandular outside, pink (or white), ¾ in. long; wing-petals (alae) (E, × 2) a little shorter than the sharply beaked keel-petals (F, × 1⅓); stamens (G, × 1⅓) 10, united into a sheath open along the top; anthers equal; ovary (H, × 1⅓) with long gland-tipped several-celled hairs; ovules 6–8; style thread-like, stigma terminal; fruit (J, K, × 0) ellipsoid, densely glandular; seeds (L, × 2) rounded, finely warted (family *Papilionaceae*).

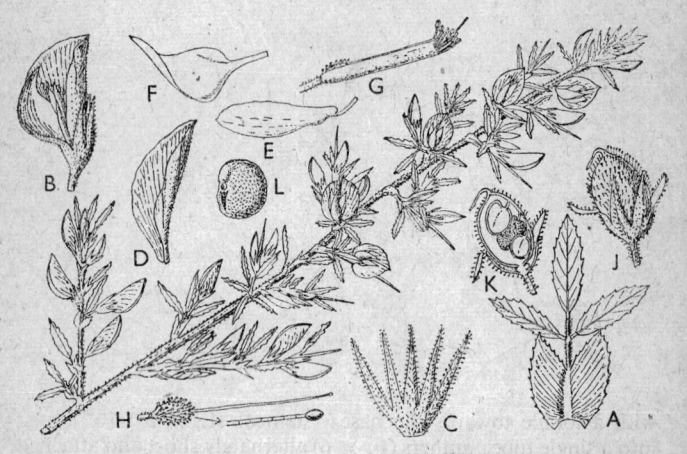

A very pretty plant with a profusion of bright pink, rarely white, pea-like flowers. They are without nectar, but are visited mainly by bees which set in motion the pumping arrangement, when threads of pollen are thrown off.

MARSH BIRD'S FOOT TREFOIL, *Lotus uliginosus* Schkuhr.

215. Marsh Bird's Foot Trefoil, *Lotus uliginosus* Schkuhr ($\times \frac{2}{5}$); perennial; stems erect or ascending, up to about 2 ft. long, rather zigzag, glabrous or thinly pilose; leaves petiolate, trifoliolate, leaflets very shortly stalked, obovate to oblanceolate, glabrous to thinly pilose; stipules large and leafy, elliptic to obovate, looking like a pair of basal leaflets; flowers orange-yellow, several in a head on a long slender peduncle, the head about 1 in. diam. and with a trifoliolate leafy bract (A, $\times 1\frac{2}{5}$) at the base; calyx (B, $\times 1\frac{2}{5}$) bell-shaped, equally 5-lobed, lobes narrow, ciliate; standard-petal (vexillum) (C, $\times 1\frac{3}{5}$) obovate, gradually narrowed into the rather broad claw, notched at the apex; wing-petals (D, $\times 1\frac{2}{5}$) oblong-elliptic, produced on one side at the base, with a slender claw; keel-petals (E, $\times 1\frac{4}{5}$) ovate-acuminate; stamens (F, $\times 1\frac{4}{5}$) in 2 bundles, 1 stamen free, the other 9 united in a sheath open along the top; filaments alternately longer and shorter, but anthers equal; ovary (G, $\times 1\frac{4}{5}$) long and narrow, glabrous, with a longish smooth style bent at an angle; ovules numerous; fruits (H, $\times \frac{3}{5}$) spreading in star fashion, about 1 in. long, almost rounded, slightly keeled, slightly reticulate, at length splitting with the halves slightly curled; seeds (J, $\times 3$) very small, globose, greenish, with a very small circular scar (family *Papilionaceae*).

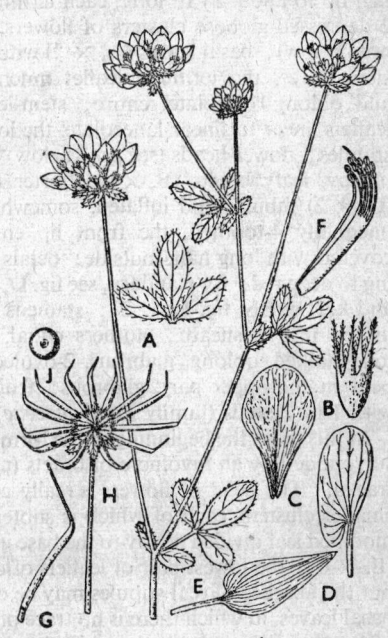

The pollen mechanism is similar to that described in the Bird's-Foot Trefoil in *Common Wild Flowers*, fig. 27; as in that species the stalks of 5 of the stamens are club-shaped at the top.

KIDNEY VETCH, LADY'S FINGERS, *Anthyllis vulneraria* L.

216. Kidney Vetch, Lady's Fingers, *Anthyllis vulneraria* L. (× ⅔); perennial herb covered with very short appressed hairs; root-stock woody, branched; stems annual, spreading or ascending, up to about 1½ ft. long, each terminating in 1 or more often 2 depressed-globose clusters of flowers, girt by leafy bracts (see note below); basal leaves (A, × ⅔) with broader leaflets than the stem-leaves, the terminal leaflet much larger than the others and oblong-lanceolate, entire; stem-leaves subsessile, pinnate, leaflets linear to linear-lanceolate, the lowermost pair resembling stipules; flower-heads (see note below) up to 1½ in. diam. girt by narrow leafy bracts (B, × 0) shorter than the flowers; calyx (C, × 2) tubular and inflated, somewhat 2-lipped, the back lip unequally 4-toothed, the front lip entire or slightly toothed, covered with long hairs outside; petals usually yellow, but varying to deep red; for standard, see fig. D, × 2½, wing, fig. E, × 2½, and keel petals, fig. F, × 2½; stamens (G, × 1½) 10 their stalks united into 1 sheath; anthers equal, short; ovary (H, × 4) long-stalked, oblong, glabrous, 2-ovuled (J, × 6); style slender, bent in the upper part, glabrous; fruits enclosed in the calyx, with 1 or 2 seeds (family *Papilionaceae*).

In this plant the beginning of the formation of a head of flowers surrounded by an involucre of bracts (capitulum) may be clearly traced. The head of flowers is really composed of a number of smaller clusters, each of which is subtended by a much-reduced modified leaf divided nearly to the base into several narrow leaflets (B, × 0); the lowest pair of leaflets often look very like stipules, but the absence of real stipules may be checked by examining the basal leaves, in which there is no trace of them; a striking feature of the floral structure is the stalked (stipitate) ovary (H, × 4).

The pollen is collected into threads and is discharged from the flowers by a pumping arrangement, the ends of the filaments of the stamens being thickened and club-like. The pollen is stored up in the tip of the keel-petals before the flower opens, and is released by insect visitors. Not until the pollen is carried away does the stigma of the same flower become receptive, and this is caused by insects rubbing against it. The species is found chiefly in hilly districts throughout Europe and western Asia. It flowers in early summer.

45

COMMON MELILOT, *Melilotus altissima* Thuill.

217. Common Melilot, *Melilotus altissima* Thuill ($\times \frac{1}{2}$); annual or biennial herb up to 4 ft. high, sometimes much branched; stems glabrous, ribbed; leaves alternate, divided into 3 separate leaflets, the lateral pair nearly sessile, the end leaflet stalked but jointed near the top; leaflets oblong to narrowly obovate, narrowed to but rounded at the base, shortly dentate, with several straight side nerves; stipules 2 to each leaf, awl-shaped, about $\frac{1}{4}$ in. long; flowers in slender one-sided axillary racemes, reflexed; calyx (A, $\times 4$) with 5 awl-shaped lobes; petals yellow, the standard, wings and keel equal in length and as shown in figs. B, C, D, $\times 2\frac{1}{2}$; stamens 10, 1 free from the others (E, $\times 2\frac{1}{2}$); ovary (F, $\times 2\frac{1}{2}$) shortly stalked, with a style about as long; fruit (G, $\times 2\frac{1}{2}$) transversely nerved, shortly beaked, 1-seeded; seed (H, $\times 3$) ellipsoid, smooth (synonym *Melilotus officinalis* Willd.) (family *Papilionaceae*).

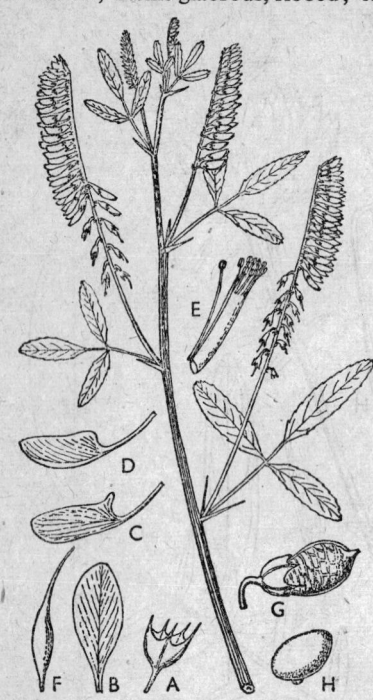

Found mostly in waste places, ranging throughout Europe and Russian Asia. The flowers are produced in summer, secrete nectar, and smell like cumarin. Cross-pollination is effected by insects, which dust the stigma projecting beyond the anthers. The wing- and keel-petals are loosely fused together on each side and are depressed by the weight of the insect, when the stamens and pistil are exposed.

BLACK MEDICK, NONSUCH, *Medicago lupulina* L.

218. Black Medick, Nonsuch, *Medicago lupulina* L. ($\times \frac{1}{2}$); annual, with slender mostly procumbent branches from the base and up to 2 ft. long; stipules large and toothed; leaflets 3, obovate, shortly toothed (dentate), apiculate; common stalk short; flowers (A $\times$ 3) in small rounded heads in the axils of the leaves, heads on slender stalks (peduncles); calyx (B, $\times$ 5) equally, 5-lobed to the middle, lobes lanceolate, hairy on the margins (ciliate); petals yellow, the standard (C, $\times 2\frac{1}{2}$) broadly obovate; keel and wings blunt at the apex, free from the staminal tube; 1 stamen free, the other 9 united in a sheath split along the top (D, $\times$ 5); anthers small and equal; ovary with a glabrous style, stigma terminal; fruits (E, $\times 1\frac{1}{2}$) crowded into an oblong cluster, very short, curved, black when ripe, reticulate, 1-seeded; seed (F, $\times 3\frac{1}{2}$) kidney-shaped, straw-coloured, smooth (family *Papilionaceae*).

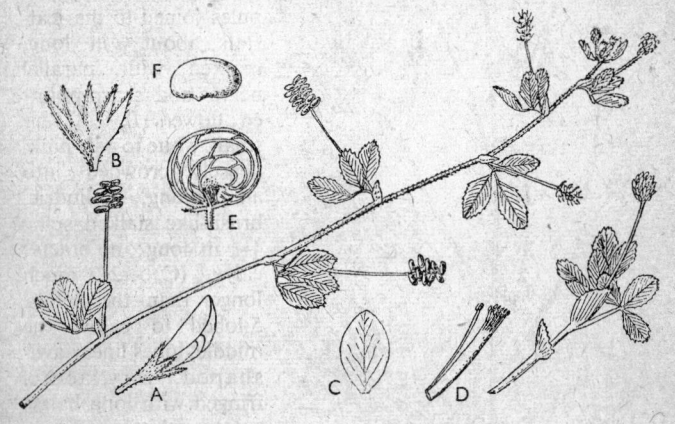

A weed in waste places and fields, widely distributed in temperate regions and naturalised in many countries.

The chief pollinator of this plant is the honey-bee, which does not disdain even this flower's tiny store of honey. The whole inflorescence is pulled down by the weight of the insect, which then sucks the flower's head downwards. It visits a few flowers at a time, and then flies away to another plant. On alighting the insect causes the column of reproductive organs (stamens and style) to spring out of the keel, to which in this case it does not return after the pressure is removed.

HARE'S-FOOT TREFOIL or CLOVER, *Trifolium arvense* L.

219. Hare's-foot Trefoil or Clover, *Trifolium arvense* L. ($\times \frac{2}{5}$); annual herb with erect slender root; stems wiry, slender, much branched, softly pubescent with appressed hairs; leaves (A, $\times 1\frac{1}{2}$) divided into 3 separate leaflets on a very short common stalk, the leaflets oblanceolate, entire or slightly toothed near the apex, softly hairy below; stipules joined to the leaf-stalk, about $\frac{1}{3}$ in. long, marked with parallel nerves and sharp-pointed; flowers (B, $\times 3$) very small, white to pale pink, densely crowded into an oblong, cylindric, brush-like stalked spike $\frac{1}{2}$–$\frac{3}{4}$ in. long; no bracts; calyx (C, $\times 2$) much longer than the petals, 5-lobed to below the middle, lobes linear-awl-shaped, very acute, fringed with long hairs; petals white or pale pink, very small; standard (D, $\times 3$) obovate, with a very broad claw; wing- and keel-petals as shown in figs. E, F, ($\times 3$); stamens (G, $\times 4$) 10, the upper one free, the remainder united in a sheath (diadelphous); anthers minute, rounded; ovary (H, $\times 4$) very small, shortly stalked (stipitate), containing 1 ovule; fruit a tiny 1-seeded pod embraced by the calyx (family *Papilionaceae*).

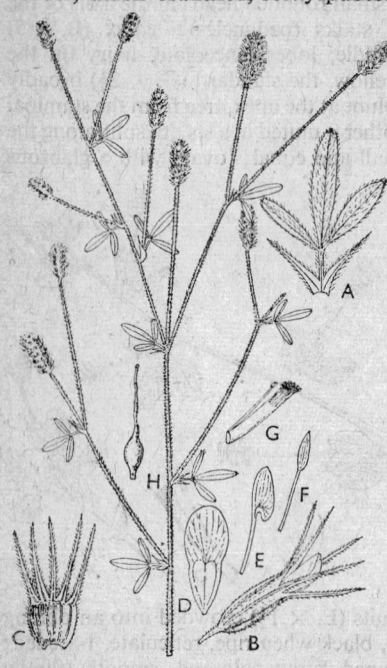

Grows in dry sandy fields, flowering from July to September; widely distributed across the northern hemisphere.

As in most other species of Clover, the flowers secrete nectar. Cross-pollination is effected mainly by bees, though self-pollination also produces fertile seed.

HOP TREFOIL or CLOVER, *Trifolium campestre* Schreb.

220. **Hop Trefoil or Clover,** *Trifolium campestre* Schreb. (× ½); annual, on dunes, waste places and in fields; stems wiry, much branched and procumbent and clothed with very short hairs; leaves (H, × 0) divided into 3 separate leaflets (trifoliolate), the end leaflet with a longer stalk than the others, all obovate and broadly wedge-shaped (cuneate) in the lower half, upper half shortly toothed; nerves numerous and parallel, each ending in a tooth; stipules large and leafy, united for a short distance to the stalk, narrowly ovate, clothed with a few long hairs; flowers (A, × 3) very small in a congested head-like raceme, greenish-yellow, the standard petal enlarging and becoming membranous over the ripe fruit; calyx with 5 very narrow lobes of unequal length; standard petal (B, × 5) slightly toothed in the upper part; wing- and keel-petals partly united (C, × 3); stamens (D, × 3) 10, 1 free, the others united into a sheath; anthers very small and rounded; ovary (E, × 4) shortly stalked, with 1–2 ovules; fruit ovoid-ellipsoid, 1- or rarely 2-seeded; seed ovoid, yellowish and shining (family *Papilionaceae*).

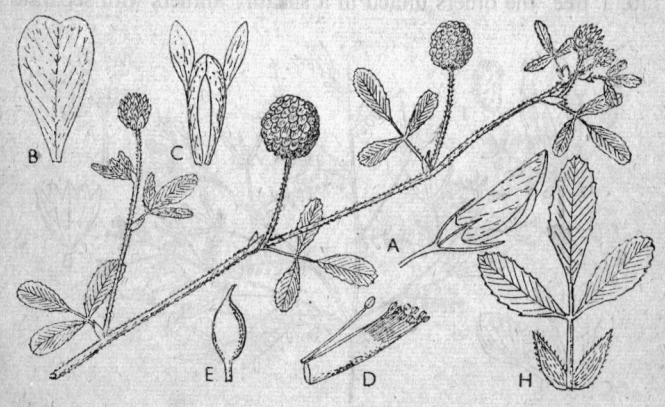

Widely spread in Europe, Asia and North Africa and the Atlantic Islands, and introduced into North America.

Trifolium is the largest genus of *Papilionaceae* represented in the British flora, there being 23 species in the latest list of plants. Included in these are 5 species which are introduced, either as crop plants or weeds of cultivation.

BIRD'S-FOOT, *Ornithopus perpusillus* L.

221. Bird's-foot, *Ornithopus perpusillus* L. ($\times \frac{1}{3}$); much-branched prostrate annual with slender leafy stems; leaves alternate, pinnate, with about 6–8 pairs of almost stalkless elliptic leaflets and an odd terminal leaflet, all slightly hairy; flowers in a cluster at the end of axillary branchlets and subtended by a small pinnate leaf (A, $\times$ 2); calyx (B, $\times$ 4) tubular, with 5 equal lobes, pubescent; petals yellowish white or tinged with pink; standard petal (C, $\times$ 3) spoon-shaped with a long claw and streaked with purple; wing-petal (D, $\times$ 3) very similar but a little broader; keel-petals (E, $\times$ 3) also similar but with a rounded auricle (ear) on one side at the base; stamens (F, $\times$ 3) 10, 1 free, the others united in a sheath; anthers with separate loculi (G, $\times$ 10); ovary with several seeds, hairy; style incurved; fruits (H, $\times$ 0) curved, about $\frac{3}{4}$ in. long, breaking up into about 5–7 1-seeded joints, thinly hairy, terminated by the hook-like stigma; seeds (J, $\times$ 3) ellipsoid, brown and mottled (family *Papilionaceae*).

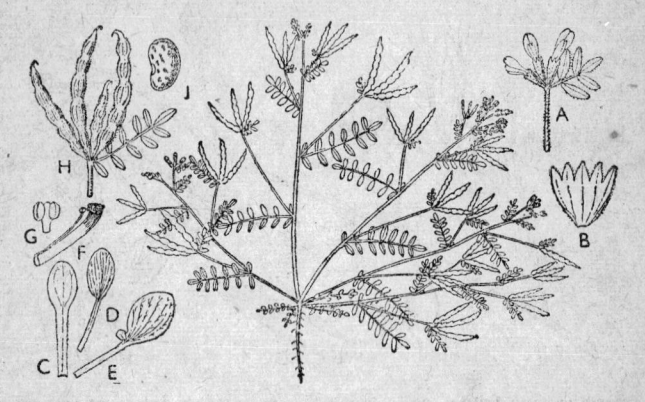

This is called Bird's-Foot because the fruits with their hooked tips resemble birds' claws. The plant belongs to the interesting tribe *Hedysareae*, mostly found in the tropics, and distinguished at once in the family by the jointed pods, which split up into 1-seeded units.

It grows in dry pastures, and flowers in spring and summer. The stamens and stigma are mature at the same time, and automatic self-pollination is quite effective. As there is no nectar secreted in the flowers, insect visitors are very few.

BUSH or HEDGE VETCH, *Vicia sepium* Linn.

222. Bush or Hedge Vetch, *Vicia sepium* Linn. ($\times \frac{2}{5}$); perennial with creeping root-stock; stems slightly zigzag, glabrous except towards the top; leaves rather distant, spreading or recurved, pinnate, branched at the end into slender threads (tendrils); leaflets nearly opposite, ovate to ovate-lanceolate, rounded at the base, rounded and mucronate at the apex, glabrous or thinly pubescent; stipules divided into 2 lobes, more or less dentate, green but small; flowers dull lilac to pale purple, yellowish at the base, few in very short subsessile racemes in the upper axils; stalks and calyx pubescent; calyx (A, $\times$ 0) with 5 almost equal sharp teeth; standard (B, $\times$ 0) obovate, contracted in the middle; wing-petals (C, $\times$ 0) obliquely obovate, with a reflexed lobe; keel-petals (D, $\times$ 0) golf-club-shaped; stamens (E, $\times$ 2) 10, all but one united in a sheath; ovary (F, $\times$ 3) stalked, glabrous; style with 2 brushes of hairs below the stigma, the inner of shorter hairs (G, $\times$ 5); fruits (H, $\times \frac{3}{5}$) 1–1½ in. long, like small pea-pods, sharply pointed, glabrous, the valves curling after opening; seeds (J, $\times$ 2½) purple-black, with a broad hilum reaching more than half the way around (family *Papilionaceae*).

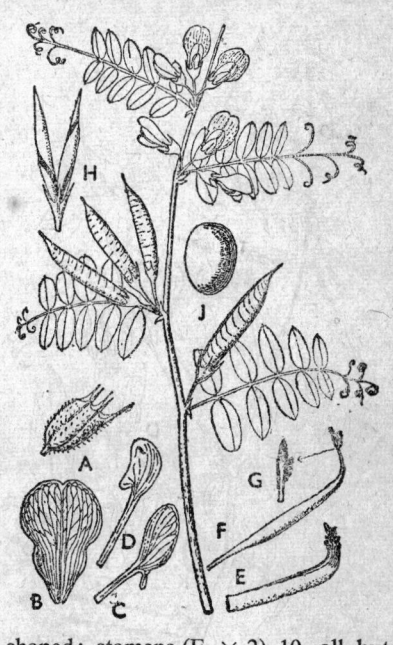

In this species the style is provided with 2 brushes just below the stigma; that on the inside of the bend is shorter than that on the outer side, as shown in fig. G, $\times$ 5; the latter encloses a plate-like depression; access to the nectar is much the same as described for the Tufted Vetch (*Common Wild Flowers*, fig. 24).

WOOD VETCH, *Vicia sylvatica* L.

223. Wood Vetch, *Vicia sylvatica* L. ($\times \frac{2}{5}$); climber over bushes up to 8 ft. high; stems and leaves glabrous; leaves pinnate with about 6 pairs of opposite or subopposite elliptic leaflets (A, $\times \frac{4}{5}$) rounded to a short point at the apex, the main stalk ending in a branched tendril; stipules (B, $\times 1\frac{1}{2}$) leafy, rounded and deeply cut into sharp lobes; flowers white with blue veins, arranged in axillary one-sided racemes; peduncle as long or longer than the leaves; stalks shorter than the calyx, slightly hairy; calyx (C, $\times 1\frac{1}{2}$) oblique, with short narrow teeth; standard-petal (D, $\times \frac{4}{5}$) narrowly obovate; wing-petals (E, $\times 0$) half spoon-shaped; keel-petals (F, $\times 0$) narrower, with a reflexed lobe on one side near the middle; stamens (H, $\times 3$) in 2 bundles, the upper one free except in the lower part; ovary (G, $\times 1\frac{1}{2}$) glabrous; style with a brush of hairs all around below the stigma; fruits (J, $\times \frac{4}{5}$) about 1 in. long, with several seeds (K, $\times 1\frac{1}{4}$), these rounded and with a circular depression on one side and a long hilum (family *Papilionaceae*).

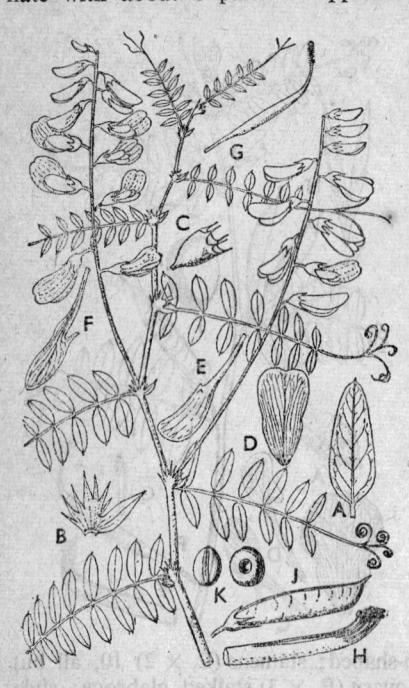

Mostly in woods in hilly districts, flowering in summer; widely distributed into Asiatic Russia and Central Asia.

All species of this genus are nectar-yielding bee-flowers, with a brush of hairs on the style. In addition there are often extra-floral nectaries, sometimes indicated by deeply coloured spots on the under-side of the stipules. These secrete nectar in sunny weather. This nectar is eagerly sought for by ants, which in turn serve to protect the plant from caterpillars and such-like.

HAIRY VETCH, *Vicia hirsuta* (L.) S. F. Gray

224. Hairy Vetch, *Vicia hirsuta* (L.) S. F. Gray ($\times \frac{2}{5}$); slender annual with weak stems rambling among grasses and other herbs; stems ribbed, hairy to nearly glabrous; stipules (B, $\times 1\frac{3}{5}$) deeply divided into very narrow parts; leaves pinnate, nearly sessile, the common stalk ending in a branched tendril; leaflets (A, $\times$ 0) 6–10 pairs, narrow, scooped out at the apex and with a sharp point; flowers very small, few on axillary peduncles shorter than the leaves, pale blue; calyx (C, $\times$ 3) deeply and equally 5-lobed, hairy outside; petals about a third longer than the calyx (for shapes see figures), standard (D), wings (E) and keel (F) $\times$ 2; stamens (G, $\times$ 8) 10, the upper partly free, the other united; ovary (H, $\times$ 3) pubescent; style glabrous, very short; fruit (J, $\times \frac{4}{5}$) a small pod, at length twisted (K, $\times 1\frac{1}{5}$), reticulate and hairy all over, with 2 rounded slightly flattened seeds (L, $\times 2\frac{1}{2}$) mottled with dark purple (family *Papilionaceae*).

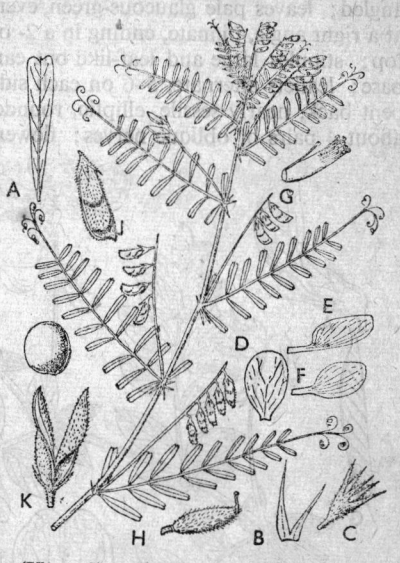

A widely distributed species, and recognised by its small 2-seeded fruits; the style is very short and not hairy below the tip, as in several other species of the genus.

The small bluish flowers secrete abundant nectar, which collects in the form of a large drop and emerges on each side of the base of the free filament. Insect-visitors are numerous, and they effect cross- and self-pollination with equal facility.

SEA PEA, *Lathyrus japonicus* Willd.

225. Sea Pea, *Lathyrus japonicus* Willd. (× ⅓); perennial with a long thick black root-stock (rhizome); stems several, procumbent, usually not hairy, pale glaucous-green, very sharply angled; leaves pale glaucous-green, even paler below, spreading at a right angle, pinnate, ending in a 2- or 3-forked tendril at the top; stipules large and leaf-like but ear-like (auriculate) at the base; leaflets alternate, 5-6 on each side, sometimes somewhat bent back, nearly sessile, elliptic, rounded to an acute tip, with about 4 pairs of oblique nerves; flowers (A, × 0) few in erect stalked racemes, purple and fading to blue; calyx unequally 5-lobed, 2 upper broadly triangular, the 3 lower narrowly so, acute, and longer; standard (vexillum) (B, × 0) about 1 in. long, rounded, with a short broad claw and with 2 oblique lumps just below the middle, notched at the apex and arched with crimson lines like a butterfly; wing (C, × 0) and keel-petals (D, × 0), smaller and paler blue or violet; stamens (E, × 0) 10, united into a sheath except the upper one; style bent upwards at a right angle, bearded along the inner side; ovary (F, × 0) very finely hairy, containing about 8 ovules; fruit (G, × ½) compressed, pea-like, nearly 2 in. long, with oblique branched nerves; seeds (H, × 1½) nearly black, rounded, with a fairly long scar (hilum), about ¼ in. diam. (family *Papilionaceae*).

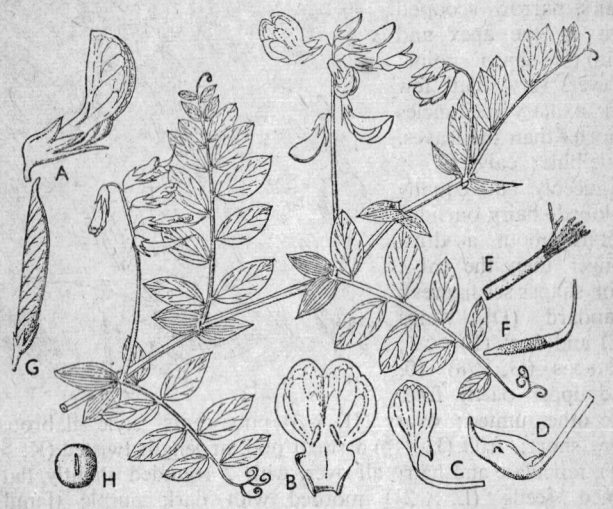

WOOD PEA, *Lathyrus sylvestris* L.

227. **Wood Pea**, *Lathyrus sylvestris* L. ($\times \frac{1}{3}$); perennial with a creeping root-stock; stems climbing by tendrils, green and broadly winged between the nodes; stipules narrow, acute, with 1 side-lobe at the base; leaves with a single pair of leaflets; the stalk winged, the upper portion ending in a 3-forked tendril; leaflets forming a V, lanceolate, very acute, up to about 4 in. long, with 3 parallel nerves, not hairy, but microscopically dotted; main flower-stalk (peduncle) axillary, usually accompanied by a short branchlet, few-flowered, up to about 6 in. long; flowers (A, $\times \frac{2}{3}$) on rather recurved stalks; calyx (B, $\times$ 1) bell-shaped, with 2 short triangular upper teeth, the lowest tooth about twice as long; petals of rather indeterminate colour, the standard (vexillum) (C, $\times \frac{2}{3}$) broad and more or less flushed with pink, the wings (alae) (D, $\times$ 1) purplish in the upper half, the keel-petals (E, $\times$ 1) united on the upper side and dull green; stamens (F, $\times 1\frac{1}{2}$) 10, in 2 bundles (diadelphous), the upper one completely free, the others united in a tube open along the top; ovary (G, $\times 1\frac{1}{2}$) not hairy; style up-curved, hairy below the apex; fruit (H, $\times \frac{1}{3}$) flattened, loosely net-veined (reticulate), about $2\frac{1}{2}$ in. long; seeds (J, $\times 1\frac{1}{2}$) $\frac{1}{4}$ in. nearly globular, purple-black, with a broad scar nearly their whole length (family *Papilionaceae*).

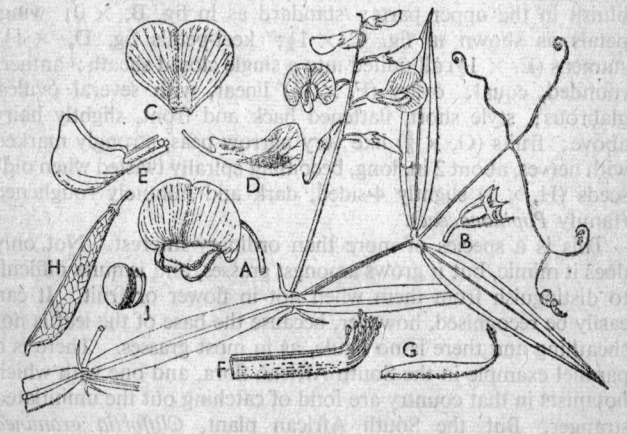

Grows in hedges, woods and copses, flowering during summer; widely distributed in Europe.

GRASS-LEAVED PEA, *Lathyrus nissolia* L.

228. Grass-leaved Pea, *Lathyrus nissolia* L ($\times \frac{1}{2}$); slender annual up to about 3 ft. high and very grass-like; stems slender, green, ribbed, not hairy; stipules minute, soon falling off; true leaves not present, but represented by the leaf-like stalk, these much like the leaves of a grass, very narrow and tapered to the apex, with 5–7 nerves parallel with the margins; flower-stalks solitary in the axils of the leaves and about equal in length, bearing 1 or 2 flowers; calyx (A, $\times 6$) obliquely bell-shaped, with 5 narrow lobes slightly hairy on the margin, the lowermost lobe a little longer than the others; petals bright red, turning crimson or bluish in the upper parts; standard as in fig. B, $\times 0$; wing-petals as shown in fig. C, $\times 1\frac{1}{2}$; keel-petals fig. D, $\times 1\frac{1}{2}$; stamens (E, $\times 1\frac{1}{2}$) all united into a single closed sheath; anthers rounded, equal; ovary (F, $\times 1\frac{1}{2}$) linear, with several ovules, glabrous; style short, flattened back and front, slightly hairy above; fruits (G, $\times \frac{2}{5}$) like very narrow peas, strongly marked with nerves, about 2 in. long, becoming spirally twisted when old; seeds (H, $\times 3$) slightly 4-sided, dark and minutely roughened (family *Papilionaceae*).

This is a species of more than ordinary interest. Not only does it mimic, but it grows amongst grasses, and is quite difficult to distinguish from them when not in flower or fruit. It can easily be recognised, however, because the base of the leaf is not sheathing and there is no ligule, as in most grasses. There is a parallel example in the South African flora, and one with which botanists in that country are fond of catching out the uninitiated stranger. But the South African plant, *Cliffortia graminea* Linn. f., belongs to the family *Rosaceae*. Secondly, this species exhibits a very high stage in evolution, having completely dispensed with its leaflets and tendrils, and developed the leaf-stalks to function as leaves, whilst the several- or many-flowered raceme characteristic of most other species of this genus is here reduced to 1 or 2 flowers. Indeed, if plants could divulge their pedigree, this would have a very interesting story.

The flowers contain nectar and have a brush of hairs on the style below the stigma to sweep out the pollen. Sometimes, however, the flowers do not open, though they set fertile fruits.

This plant is only locally common in Britain, but ranges into western Asia and North Africa.

59

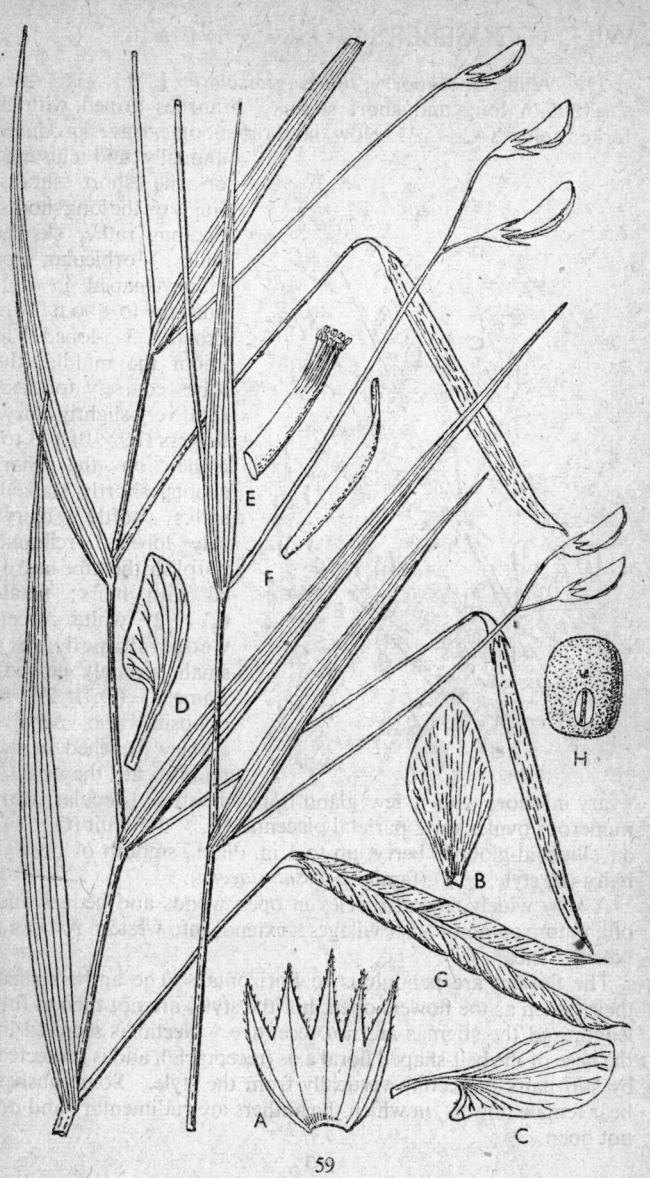

WILD GOOSEBERRY, *Ribes grossularia* L.

229. Wild Gooseberry, *Ribes grossularia* L. (× ½); small shrub with long and short shoots; branches armed with 3-forked spines (A, × 3½) below the short shoots; leaves produced annually and clustered on the short shoots, singly on the long shoots, on long rather slender stalks, orbicular or kidney-shaped in outline, up to about 2 in. broad, 3–5-lobed to about the middle, the lobes coarsely toothed, thin, very slightly hairy; flowers (B, × 0) 1–3 together on the short shoots, shortly stalked, stalks softly hairy; calyx-lobes reflexed, purplish, the tube bearded with hairs; petals (C, × 2) white, erect, wedge-shaped, very small, strongly nerved; stamens (D, × 2) 5, opposite the sepals; anthers attached in the middle at the back; ovary inferior, with a few gland-tipped bristles, 1-locular, with numerous ovules on 2 parietal placentas (E, × 3); fruit (G, × ½) an ellipsoid-globose berry, up to 1 in. diam., smooth or bristly-hairy (F, style, × 2) (family *Grossulariaceae*).

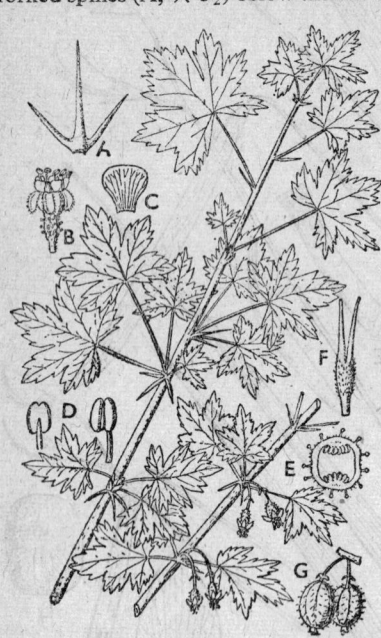

A very widely spread species in open woods and hedges and often more common near villages; extends into western Asia and North Africa.

The flowers are pendulous to horizontal. The anthers shed their pollen as the flowers open, but the styles are not then at full length and the stigmas are not receptive. Nectar is secreted in the base of the bell-shaped floral axis (receptacle), and is protected by stiff hairs projecting vertically from the style. Some bushes bear female flowers, in which the anthers are rudimentary and do not open.

ASPEN, *Populus tremula* L.

230. Aspen, *Populus tremula* L. ($\times \frac{1}{3}$); an erect tree up to 80 ft. high, the leaves of which are rarely still, shaking or "trembling" in the slightest disturbance of air, due to the very slender compressed leaf-stalks and wide almost orbicular blade; older branchlets rough with the knobs of the old leaf-scars, with shining bark; leaves 2-3 in. wide, prominently 3-nerved from the base, finely reticulate; flowers unisexual, the males and females on separate trees (dioecious); male catkins (A, $\times \frac{1}{3}$) enclosed in bud by shining sticky scales, about 3 in. long; bracts (B, $\times 1\frac{1}{3}$) deeply incised and fringed with long hairs; stamens about 8-10, inserted on an obovate flat scale; female catkins and bracts (C, $\times 1\frac{1}{3}$) very similar to the male; ovary inserted on a fleshy obovoid "disk"; style short, 2-lobed (family *Salicaceae*).

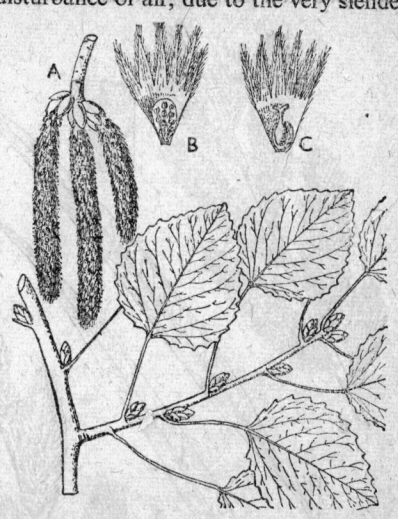

This fine tree is widely distributed through Europe, northern Africa, Asia Minor, the Caucasus and into Siberia. It covers extensive tracts in Scandinavia, Russia and Siberia. In Britain it is most abundant in the Highlands of Scotland, where it ascends to the limit of tree-growth. The tree is short-lived, however, and is one of the most beautiful in northern latitudes on account of the splendid red and yellow tints assumed by the leaves in the autumn, though such colours are rarely seen in this country. The wood is soft, and is largely used in Sweden for making matches and for wood-pulp in the manufacture of paper.

OSIER, *Salix viminalis* L.

231. Osier, *Salix viminalis* L. ($\times \frac{1}{2}$); a shrub or small tree up to 30 ft., with long slender branches minutely hairy; leaves produced after flowering, linear to very narrowly linear lanceolate, narrow at the base, very acutely acuminate, glabrous above, softly silvery silky below, with very short hairs, with numerous arched lateral nerves; stipules linear, sub-persistent; winter catkin-buds (A, $\times$ 0) ovoid, $\frac{1}{2}$ in. long, covered with a rather thin shining scale; male catkins (B, $\times \frac{1}{2}$) sessile, with or without a few very young leaves at the base, and with scattered short shoots here and there between them, about 1 in. long; bracts (C, $\times$ 3) narrowly ovate, long-ciliate; scale rod-like; stamens 2; anthers on long filaments; female catkins (D, $\times \frac{1}{2}$) sessile, with no leaves developed at flowering time, about 1 in. long; bracts densely silky with long hairs; female flowers (E, $\times$ 3) stalked within the bract (family *Salicaceae*).

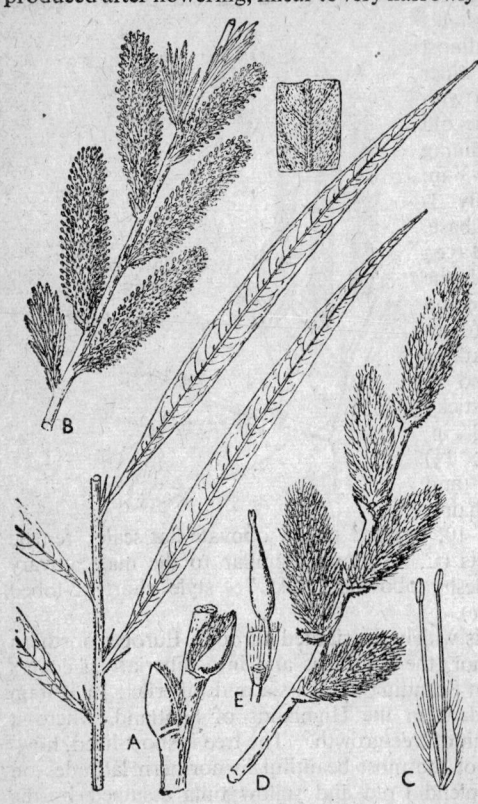

This is the true Osier extensively cultivated for its long pliant shoots, which are longer than those of any other native species and are the best for basket-making.

WHITE WILLOW, *Salix alba* L.

232. White Willow, *Salix alba* L. (× ⅓); a fairly large tree, silvery in colour because of the dense silky hairs on the lower surface of the leaves; young twigs green, purplish or bright yellow; flowers developed with the leaves on short leafy softly hairy shoots; axillary buds of the mature leafy shoots narrow and silky hairy; mature leaves (A, × ⅓) shortly stalked, narrowly lanceolate, acute at both ends and tapered to a slender point at the apex, usually about 4 in. long and at most 1 in. broad, finely toothed on the margin, soon becoming glabrous or nearly so above, closely silky hairy below and nearly white; male catkins (B, × ⅓) stalked, about 1½ in. long; floral bracts (C, × 2) elliptic, fringed with hairs; stamens 2, with a pair of glands at the base; female catkins (D, × ⅓) very slender and loosely flowered; ovary (E, × 2) glabrous, with a very short bifid style, and a fleshy gland at the base; capsule glabrous (family *Salicaceae*).

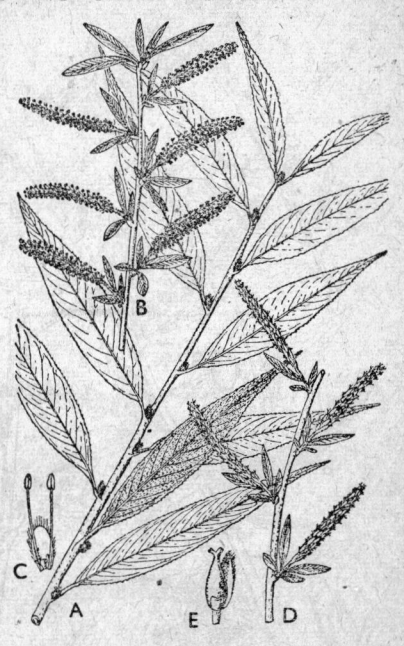

This Willow is widely spread through central and southern Europe, south to Algeria and Morocco, and eastwards to western and northern Asia. In Britain it is supposed to be native from Sutherland southwards, and it is found in Eire.

It is a tree up to 90 ft. high and with a stem as much as 20 ft. in circumference. The wood is tough and valuable, but the best cricket-bats are made from that of *S. caerulea*, formerly considered to be a variety of *S. alba*.

CRACK WILLOW, *Salix fragilis* L.

233. Crack Willow, *Salix fragilis* L. ($\times \frac{1}{2}$); a bushy tree differing in aspect from *S. alba* (fig. 232) in its green and glabrous (not white and hairy) leaves; young twigs brown or purplish, slightly hairy towards the tips; flowers developed with the leaves on short leafy shoots; axillary buds (A, $\times 0$) of the mature leafy shoots narrowly ovoid, keeled, hairy at the tip; mature leaves on fairly long stalks, broadly oblong, taper-pointed, rather coarsely toothed on the margins, glabrous on both surfaces, very finely reticulate below, with numerous lateral nerves; male catkins (B) stalked, slender, about 2 in. long; male flowers (C, $\times 3$) with oblong-elliptic silky-hairy bracts; stamens 2, with 2 unequal-sized glands (D, $\times 6$) at the base; female catkins (E, $\times \frac{1}{2}$) $2\frac{1}{2}$–3 in. long, very slender and loosely flowered; bracts narrow, pubescent; ovary (F, $\times 3$) stalked, very slender, and with a slender style, glabrous; capsules stalked, tapered to the apex (G, gland of female) (family *Salicaceae*).

This is a tree up to 70 ft. high, with the bark rough, strongly ridged and divided into broad deep fissures.

EARED WILLOW, *Salix aurita* L.

234. Eared Willow, *Salix aurita* L. ($\times \frac{1}{2}$); a bushy shrub, with short twiggy branchlets knotted with the prominent leaf-scars of previous seasons; leaves developed after the flowers, elliptic, more or less rounded at each end, wrinkled (bullate) above, shortly toothed, densely covered below with soft short hairs; stipules large and leafy; catkins flowering before the leaves, sessile on the shoots and with a few densely silky-hairy bracts at the base, $\frac{3}{4}$–1 in. long; floral bracts very silky hairy (C, $\times$ 4), each enclosing a stalked bottle-shaped gland (D, $\times$ 7) and a pair of stamens; female flowers (E, $\times$ 2½) stalked; ovary shortly hairy, ending in a short 2-lobed style; the two halves of the capsule (F, $\times$ 3) diverging and recurving, releasing the tiny seeds (G, $\times$ 5) bearing a basal tuft of long fine silky hairs (A, male, B, female catkins) (family *Salicaceae*).

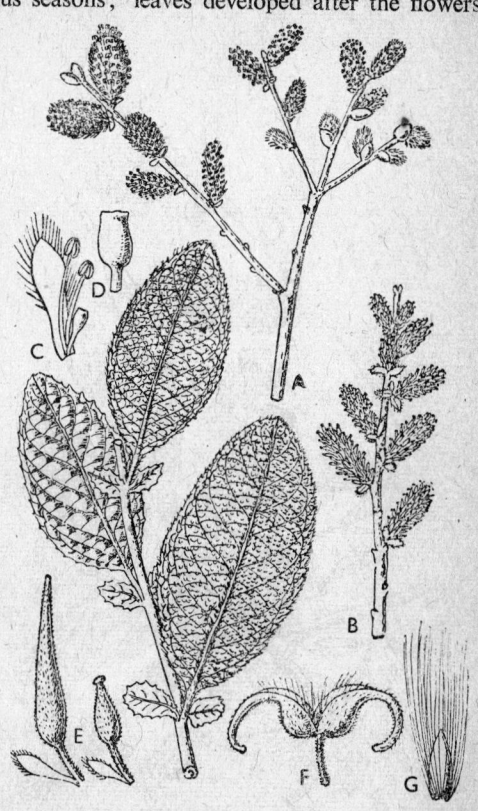

In moist woods and bushy places on damp heaths, flowering in early spring; widely distributed into Asiatic Russia, from the Mediterranean to the Arctic.

c (A180)

GREY WILLOW, *Salix atrocinerea* Brot.

235. Grey Willow, *Salix atrocinerea* Brot. ($\times \frac{1}{2}$); a much-branched shrub or small tree; leaves developed after the catkins, oblanceolate to obovate, triangular at the base and apex, covered on both surfaces with very short soft hairs, not toothed or very minutely so; stipules kidney-shaped, soon falling off; male catkins (A, $\times \frac{1}{2}$) on short stalks with a few small partially developed leaves at the base, the males about 1–1¼ in., the females (B, $\times \frac{1}{2}$) about the same length when in flower but elongating to 2 in. long in fruit (C, $\times \frac{1}{2}$), with small silky leaves towards the base; male flowers (D, $\times 2\frac{1}{2}$) with a narrowly elliptic bract, 2 stamens, and a thick fleshy bottle-shaped gland (E, $\times 10$); female flowers (F, $\times 2\frac{1}{2}$) stalked within the bract, with a very small gland at the base (G, $\times 5$); ovary shortly hairy; fruits (H, $\times 2$) with recurved halves, silky-pubescent; seeds with a coma of pure white hairs (J, $\times 4$) (family *Salicaceae*).

Like many other species of willow, this grows where there is plenty of moisture in the soil. The wood was formerly used for charcoal in the manufacture of gunpowder (see foot of next page).

CREEPING or DWARF WILLOW, *Salix repens* L.

236. **Creeping or Dwarf Willow,** *Salix repens* L. ($\times \frac{1}{2}$); a low straggling shrublet with decumbent branches, these rooting at the lower nodes, minutely hairy in the upper parts; winter-buds covered with smooth leathery scales; mature leaves (A, $\times \frac{1}{2}$) elliptic, about 1 in. long, becoming glabrous above, remaining grey-silky below with appressed hairs; male catkins (B, $\times \frac{1}{2}$) about $\frac{1}{2}$ in. long, at flowering time with a few partially developed silky leaves at the base (sub-precocious); male flowers with a flask-shaped scale at the base (C, $\times 5$); bract elliptic, fringed with long hairs; stamens 2; anthers on long slender filaments; female catkins (D, $\times \frac{1}{2}$) also sub-precocious (see above), shorter when in young flower than the male, about 1 in. long in fruit; ovaries (E, $\times 2\frac{1}{2}$) pubescent; fruits (F, $\times 3$, G, $\times 1\frac{1}{2}$) splitting into 2 recurved halves; seeds (H, $\times 6$) with a fringe of long delicate hairs (family *Salicaceae*).

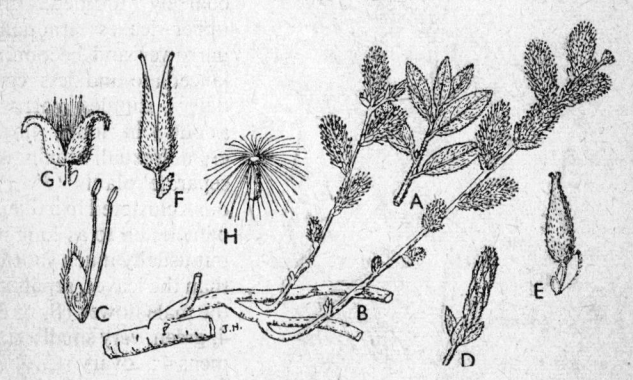

This is the smallest and dwarfest British species of willow and grows on heaths, moors, and in sandy places flowering in spring; widely distributed in the Arctic regions of the Old World, extending into Asiatic Russia.

Salix atrocinerea (contd.) :—

For a long time this species was known as *Salix cinerea*. Then it was shown that the British shrub was different from the Grey Sallow that is widely distributed on the continent of Europe, from France and Germany eastwards. Our shrub is the same as that which grows in western France, Portugal and Spain.

STINGING NETTLE, *Urtica dioica* L.

237. Stinging Nettle, *Urtica dioica* L. (male plant × 2⅖); a strong-growing perennial with creeping root-stock; stems erect, 2-3 ft. or more in rich soil or shade, covered all over with stinging bristly hairs (A, × 3), 4-angled; leaves opposite, stalked, the lower widely ovate and cordate at the base, pointed and coarsely toothed, the upper leaves gradually narrower and becoming lanceolate and less cordate; stipules narrow, about ⅓ in. long; flowers unisexual, usually on separate plants (dioecious), clustered in axillary panicles up to as long as but usually much shorter than the leaves, sepals of the male flower (B, × 3) 4, green, very small; stamens 4; ovary (C, × 3) with a single tufted stigma; fruit (D, × 2½; E, section, × 5) a flattened seed-like nutlet enclosed in the calyx (family *Urticaceae*).

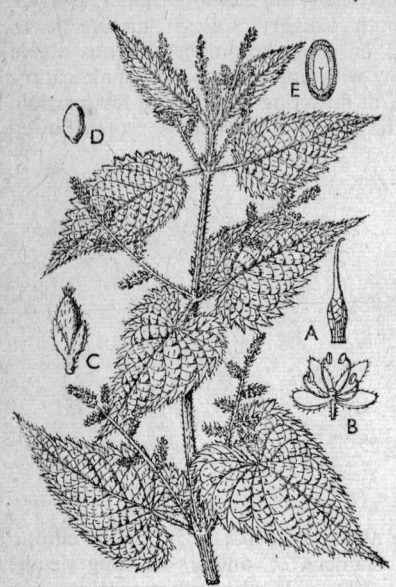

The common stinging nettle will be known to everyone, and it need only be touched by the hand to distinguish it from the somewhat similar leaves of the White Dead Nettle shown in fig. 379, when the difference will be at once apparent, for the latter does not sting.

HOP, *Humulus lupulus* L.

238. Hop, *Humulus lupulus* L. ($\times \frac{1}{3}$); perennial herb with a thick branched root-stock; stems annual, twining to a considerable height over other plants and in hedges, very tough and rough; leaves opposite, stalked, deeply and broadly heart-shaped at the base, the larger ones deeply 3–5-lobed and sharply toothed (serrate), the floral leaves less divided or only toothed, rough to the touch (scabrid); stipules in pairs; flowers unisexual, dioecious, the males (A, $\times \frac{1}{3}$) in loose panicles with small bracts, small and yellowish-green; sepals (B, $\times$ 3) 5; petals none; stamens (C, $\times$ 3) 5, the large anthers on very short filaments and opening by terminal pore-like slits; female flowers in shortly stalked axillary ovoid heads covered with green overlapping bracts (D, $\times$ 3), each bract with 2 sessile female flowers (E, $\times$ 8) in its axil; calyx much reduced and scale-like; ovary crowned by a pair of long styles free from the base; fruiting cone (F, $\times \frac{1}{3}$) covered with broad green or yellow bracts hiding the fruits, the scales covered with resinous glands at the base, as also the fruits (G, H) (family *Cannabinaceae*).

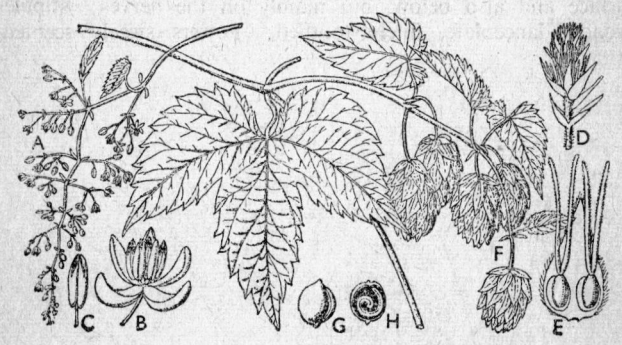

The Hop plant is well known for its use in brewing, being widely cultivated in certain counties, such as Kent and Worcestershire; it is considered to be native from Yorkshire southwards, and is widely distributed in Europe and Asia.

SWEET VIOLET, *Viola odorata* L.

239. Sweet Violet, *Viola odorata* L. (× ½); perennial with a short root-stock covered with the persistent bases of the old leaf-stalks and stipules, giving it a knotted appearance; runners (A) freely produced; leaves all borne on the main shoot (all radical) on long stalks, the latter covered with very short deflexed hairs; leaf-blade ovate to almost orbicular, widely cordate at the base, rounded or very bluntly triangular at the apex, averaging about 1¼–1¾ in. long (sometimes up to 3 in. when growing in shade), crenate on the margin, very shortly pubescent on the upper surface and also below, but mainly on the nerves; stipules broadly lanceolate, finely toothed; flowers sweely scented, axillary, on stalks mostly exceeding the leaves, the stalks with a pair of opposite bracts about half-way up (sometimes not quite opposite), glabrous or at most very slightly hairy; sepals oblong, obtuse, with narrow thinner margins; petals bluish-purple or sometimes white, the lowermost with a blunt round spur at the base; anthers forming a ring around the ovary, the connective produced at the apex; ovary 1-locular, with the ovules on 3 placentas on the walls; capsule (B, × 1½) opening by 3 boat-shaped valves, thinly hairy; seeds (C, × 2½) along the middle of the valves, smooth, attached by a short spongy stalk (D, cross-section of ovary) (family *Violaceae*).

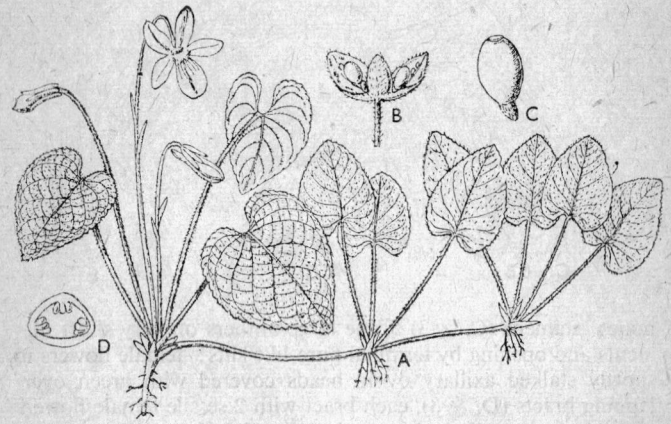

The Sweet Violet is well known to most people, though there are several species closely related to it. It flowers in early spring.

MARSH VIOLET, *Viola palustris* L.

240. Marsh Violet, *Viola palustris* L. (× ½); perennial herb with a creeping root-stock covered with the remains of hard scale-like leaf-bases and a tangle of fine roots; runners very short and few; leaves few in a bunch at the end of the root-stock, on slender stalks, quite glabrous, the blade almost orbicular except the deeply cordate base, averaging 1½–2 in. diam., thin, very obscurely and distantly crenate on the margin, in a dried state with minute brown markings on the lower surface; stipules broadly lanceolate, acute, fringed with glands; flowers not scented, on slender stalks longer than the leaves, the stalks bearing a pair of opposite or nearly opposite bracts below the middle; sepals oblong, obtuse, glabrous; petals pale blue, with purple streaks, the lowermost with a short and very broad spur; anthers (A, × 6) forming a cone around the ovary (B, × 8), their tops, orange-coloured; ovary not hairy; capsule (D, × 3) also not hairy, splitting into 3 boat-shaped parts with the seeds along the middle of each (C, cross-section of ovary) (family *Violaceae*).

This species grows in a different habitat from that of the Sweet Violet (see fig. 239), being partial to spongy bogs and swampy places in woods. It is very widely distributed in northern latitudes all around the northern hemisphere, and is common in Scotland and Eire, but less so in England and Wales. Like the Sweet Violet, it also produces flowers without petals and stamens (*cleistogamous* flowers), but both kinds bear fruits and seeds.

COMMON MALLOW, *Malva sylvestris* L.

241. Common Mallow, *Malva sylvestris* L. ($\times \frac{2}{5}$); biennial or perennial herb; stems, leaf-stalks and flower-stalks clothed with long spreading hairs with swollen bases; leaves alternate, on long stalks, 3–7-lobed but usually 3- or 5-lobed, widely heart-shaped (cordate) at the base, lobes rounded-ovate and crenate-dentate, hairy mainly on the nerves; nerves radiating from the base; stipules (A, $\times 1\frac{2}{3}$) large and pointed, fringed with long hairs; flowers several in a cluster, axillary, but only one or two in bloom at a time; calyx (C, $\times \frac{2}{3}$) of 5 lobes with 3 additional parts (bracteoles) below (B, $\times 1\frac{1}{3}$), all fringed with long hairs; petals (D, $\times$ 0) 5, pale reddish-purple or blue, marked with darker circles, nearly 1 in. long, unequally 2-lobed; stamens united into a column (E, $\times \frac{2}{3}$), each filament bearing a 1-locular anther (F, $\times 2$); carpels about 10, united into a flat disk-like reticulate structure (G, $\times 1\frac{1}{2}$); style-branches the same number as the carpels; fruit (H, $\times 1\frac{2}{3}$) about $\frac{1}{3}$ in. diam.-grooved between the carpels (J, $\times 3$), strongly reticulate; seeds (K, $\times 4$) flattened and with a V-shaped slit on one side (family *Malvaceae*).

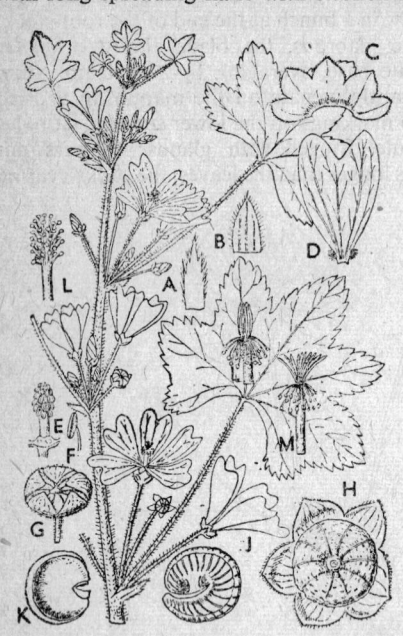

Mainly in waste places and by roadsides, flowering from about the middle of June. The petals are marked with darker circles, which serve as nectar-guides, the nectar being protected by hairs. At first the anthers are crowded in the middle of the flower and completely cover the still immature stigmas (E, $\times \frac{2}{3}$). After the anthers open they curve downwards (L, $\times 1\frac{1}{2}$), and their place is taken by the stigmas (M, $\times 1\frac{1}{2}$), which become receptive.

MUSK MALLOW, *Malva moschata* L.

242. Musk Mallow, *Malva moschata* L. ($\times \frac{1}{3}$); perennial herb about 1½ ft. high; stems and leaf-stalks clothed with slender hairs with swollen bases; leaves alternate, on longish stalks, divided nearly to the base into several segments, these again deeply and irregularly lobed, thinly hairy below or nearly glabrous; a form with nearly undivided (though toothed) leaves is called var. *heterophylla*; stipules (A, $\times \frac{2}{3}$) lanceolate, fringed with hairs; flowers in a bunch at the top of the stem and lateral shoots; stalks longer than the calyx, with long hairs; calyx (B, $\times 0$) divided into 5 broad lobes, with 3 additional parts (bracteoles) towards the base of the tube, all clothed with long slender hairs; petals rose-coloured or rarely pure white, about 2 in. diam.; stamens united into a column (C, $\times 0$), each filament bearing a 1-locular anther; carpels (D, $\times 0$) about 15, united and arranged in a circle; style branches as many as carpels; fruit (F, $\times 1\frac{1}{4}$) consisting of a low ring of about 15 united carpels with a hump in the middle, the carpels softly hairy (E, cross-section of ovary) (family *Malvaceae*).

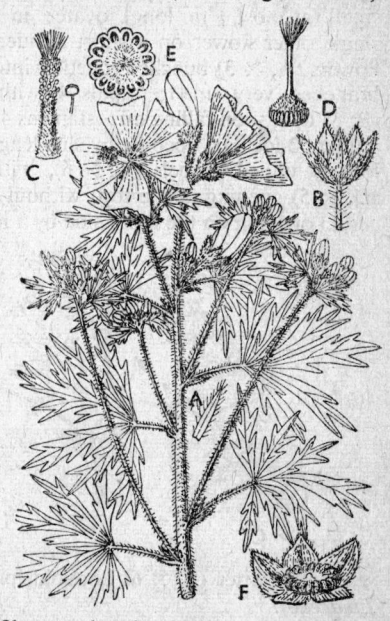

The arrangement for cross-pollination in the flowers of this species is the same as for *M. sylvestris* (fig. 241). In most of the *Malva* family, *Malvaceae*, the stamens are united into a column in the middle of the flower, the anthers being peculiar in that they are 1-locular. This is due to the splitting of the connective and filament resulting in the separation of the 2 loculi. Another good spotting feature is shown by the calyx, the lobes of which are *valvate* in bud, i.e. they do not overlap one another.

ALL-SEED, *Radiola linoides* Roth.

243. All-seed, *Radiola linoides* Roth. ($\times \frac{3}{5}$); a diminutive annual, much branched from the base, the branches repeatedly forked and thread-like, glabrous; leaves opposite, sessile, very small (at most $\frac{1}{8}$ in. long), ovate; in the middle of each fork a single older flower on a short slender stalk; remainder of the flowers (A, $\times$ 3) bunched together into a cyme at the top of the branches, very small; sepals 4, with 2–4 small teeth; petals (B, $\times$ 6) 4, soon falling off; stamens 4, alternate with the petals; anthers 2-locular, opening by slits lengthwise; ovary of 4 rather loosely united carpels (C, $\times$ 6), with 4 free styles; capsule (D, $\times$ 5) opening at the top, without any central column, each carpel opening on the inner side by a longitudinal slit and with 2 seeds, the latter (E, $\times$ 6) obovoid, pale brown, shining (family *Linaceae*).

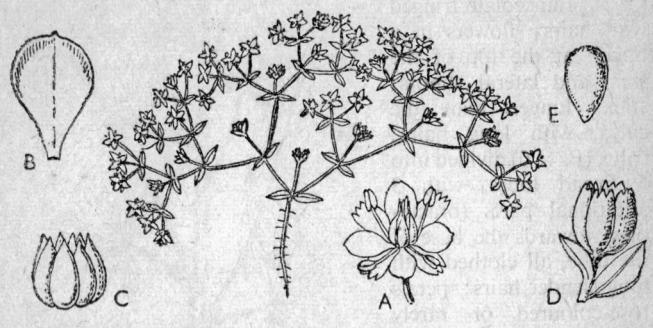

One of the smallest of British annual plants, growing in damp sandy and gravelly places, flowering from July to August. It may easily be mistaken for a small member of the *Caryophyllaceae*, but can be recognised especially by the 4-locular ovary (in *Caryophyllaceae* the ovary is 1-locular), and the seeds have no reserve food material (endosperm).

The genus *Radiola* is monotypic, i.e., it is represented by only one species, though it is very widely distributed. It ranges from northern Europe to the island of Madeira, and is even found in the mountains of tropical Africa, and eastward into Asia. The correct name according to international rules is used here, but in most British botanical books it is called *Radiola millegrana* Sm. Bentham remarked that *R. linoides* was an earlier name, " but very inapplicable " !

ANNUAL DOG'S MERCURY, *Mercurialis annua* L.

244. Annual Dog's Mercury, *Mercurialis annua* L. ($\times \frac{1}{3}$); annual and mostly as a weed in cultivated or waste ground; stems glabrous, with a thick rib running between the nodes and between the leaf-stalks; leaves opposite, stalked, each with a pair of stipules, lanceolate, rather irregularly crenate, glabrous; stalk with a pair of minute glands at the top (A, $\times \frac{3}{4}$); flowers unisexual, mostly each sex on a different plant (dioecious), sometimes the two sexes mixed; male flowers (B, $\times 2$) numerous, clustered on long-stalked axillary spikes; sepals 4, ovate; no petals; stamens (C, $\times 6$) several, with 2 divergent rounded loculi; female flowers sessile or shortly stalked, axillary, solitary or 2 or 3 together on separate stalks; sepals as in the male; no petals; ovary 2-locular, covered on the shoulders by conical warts, each tipped by a hair; fruit (D, $\times 2$) slightly 2-lobed, tuberculed; seeds brown, reticulate (family *Euphorbiaceae*).

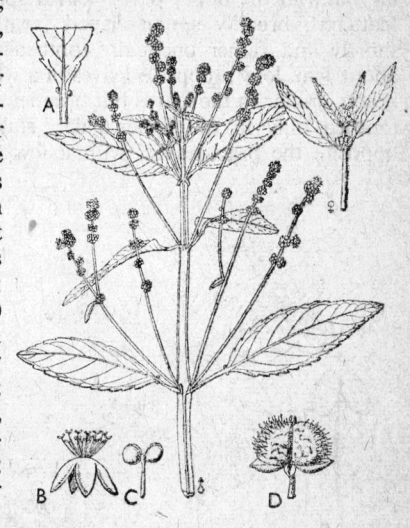

Though rather a troublesome weed, this plant has an interesting structure, the flowers being of one sex only and usually confined to different plants, and the leaf-stalks have a pair of glands (extra floral nectaries) at the apex.

A characteristic feature of the stem is the thick rib which traverses the internode between each pair of leaves. The two halves of the anther (loculi) are quite separate on the filament, and open by a slit across the top. The pollen discharged from them is conveyed from the male to the female by the wind (anemophilous).

SUN SPURGE, *Euphorbia helioscopia* L.

245. Sun Spurge, *Euphorbia helioscopia* L. ($\times \frac{1}{3}$); annual up to about 1½ ft. high, with milky juice; stems unbranched or with 2 weaker branches at the base, rounded, with a few weak spreading hairs in the upper part; leaves spirally arranged, few and scattered, broadly spoon-shaped (spathulate), glaucous-green, shortly and rather unequally toothed only in the upper half, about 1 in. long; upper 5 leaves in a whorl and forming ring of bracts similar to the leaves but broader and rounded at the base, toothed only in the upper half; stalks of flower-clusters 5, opposite the bract-leaves, with a few slender spreading hairs, bearing at the top 3 leaf-like bracts, one smaller than the other two; secondary branches repeat the above description but with smaller bract-leaves and surrounding the flower-clusters (inflorescences) (A, $\times$ 2); glands of the involucre broadly elliptic, green; male flowers (B, $\times$ 6) several; female solitary in the middle of the males but sharply bent away from them; ovary green, 3-lobed and 3-locular (D, $\times$ 2), smooth; fruits (C, $\times$ 5) 3-lobed; seeds (E, $\times$ 8) broadly obovoid, closely reticulate (family *Euphorbiaceae*).

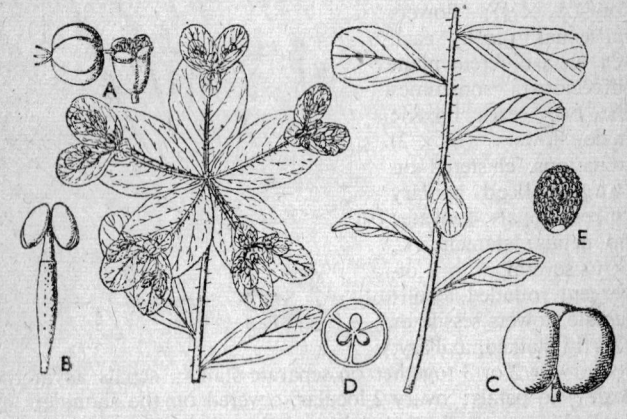

Grows in fields and waste places, frequently as a garden-weed; it is widely distributed in the northern hemisphere and is introduced into North America; one of the most easily recognised of the Spurges, the involucre of leafy bracts forming a pretty pattern with an equal number of rays, the whole ensemble glowing with yellowish-green.

SMALL WINTERGREEN, *Pyrola minor* L.

246. Small Wintergreen, *Pyrola minor* L. ($\times \frac{1}{2}$); root-stock perennial, decumbent, bearing long narrow chaffy scales amongst the leaf-stalks; leaves crowded towards the base of the stem, long-stalked, broadly elliptic to nearly orbicular, minutely toothed on the margin, glabrous, very laxly veiny and with 4–6 pairs of divided lateral nerves; flowers in a short-stalked raceme; bracts as long as the pedicels; calyx deeply 5-lobed; petals 5, white or pale pink, quite free, rounded; stamens (A, $\times$ 4) 10, not on the corolla; anthers opening by pores; ovary (B, $\times 1\frac{1}{3}$) depressed-globose, 5-locular, with numerous ovules on axile placentas; style short, straight, with a 5-lobed stigma; fruit (C, D, $\times 1\frac{1}{4}$) a 5-lobed capsule, opening by slits into the chambers, with the persistent style much shorter than the fruit; seeds (E, enlarged) numerous, very minute, shortly tailed at each end (family *Pyrolaceae*).

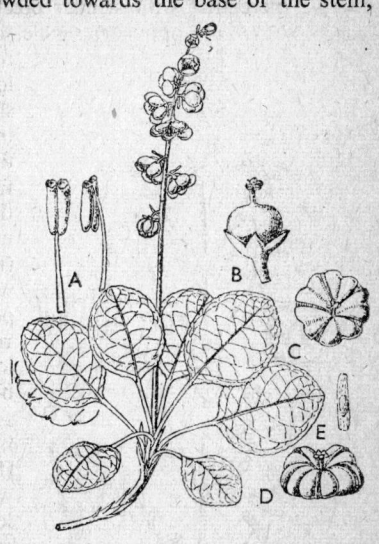

Distinguished from other species by the style, which is shorter than the corolla and much shorter than the capsule (fruit); in woods and moist shady places mostly in Scotland and northern England; rare in Eire; flowers during summer.

Some species of *Pyrola* do not secrete nectar, and this is one of them. Instead, however, the 5 stigmatic lobes exude a sticky fluid which appears to be licked by insects before they search for pollen and thereby bring about cross-pollination.

The family *Pyrolaceae* was formerly often included in *Ericaceae*, but is now generally regarded as distinct. As in *Ericaceae*, the anthers open by pores, and the pollen-grains are in tetrads. A striking feature of the fruit of *Pyrola* is that the margins of the valves are connected by web-like threads.

UPRIGHT ST. JOHN'S WORT, *Hypericum pulchrum* Linn.

247. Upright St. John's Wort, *Hypericum pulchrum* Linn. ($\times \frac{1}{2}$); perennial with slender erect glabrous rounded stems; leaves (A, $\times 1\frac{1}{2}$) opposite, sessile, ovate, cordate at the base, rounded at the apex, $\frac{1}{2}$–$\frac{3}{4}$ in. long, those on the lateral shoots much smaller, with transparent glands towards the margins; flowers rather few in a loose oblong cyme, the lower stalks the longest, usually 3-flowered; sepals (B, $\times 0$) 5, obovate, fringed with sessile black glands; petals (C, $\times 1\frac{1}{2}$) yellow, narrowly obovate, about $\frac{1}{2}$ in. long, margined with sessile black glands; stamens (D, $\times 2$) shortly united into bundles; anthers red; ovary (E, $\times 2\frac{1}{2}$) glabrous, 3-locular, with 3 slender styles nearly as long as the stamens; fruit a capsule wrapped in the persistent petals; seeds (F, $\times 7$) narrowly oblong, finely pitted (family *Hypericaceae*).

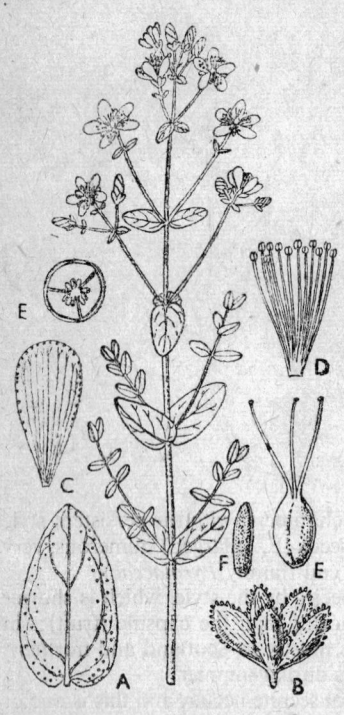

This species favours dry woods, and open heaths and waste land, flowering in summer; it is widely dispersed over Europe.

Different theories are held by botanists as to whether the bundles of stamens so common in this family are due to fusion or to branching. In most British textbooks they are described as being fused, thus implying that their ancestral types had free stamens. This view is held by the present author, because the fusion of stamens is a common tendency in many families, and he sees no reason for an exception to be made for the family *Hypericaceae*.

CREEPING ST. JOHN'S WORT, *Hypericum humifusum* L.

248. Creeping St. John's Wort, *Hypericum humifusum* L. ($\times \frac{1}{2}$); low decumbent, much-branched herb, sometimes forming dense spreading tufts; root-stock perennial, but sometimes flowering in the seedling stage; stems slender, green or suffused with dull crimson, rounded and without ridges, glabrous; leaves (A, $\times$ 2) sessile, opposite, broadly elliptic, rounded at each end, pale glaucous-green, glabrous, with about 3 pairs of transparent nerves and with numerous transparent dots, besides a few black glands below along the margin; flowers in short, loose, leafy cymes; pedicels suffused with crimson; a pair of small leaf-like bracts below each flower; sepals (B, $\times$ 3) 5, shortly united at the base, unequal-sized, 2 larger than the others, all slightly toothed and with here and there a small black gland; petals (C, $\times$ 4) 5, free, rich cream-yellow, with streaks of red outside, about 5 mm. long, with a few small black glands on the margin; stamens (D, $\times$ 5) about 15, in 3 bundles; ovary (E, $\times$ 5, F, $\times$ 7) 3-locular; styles 3, between the bundles of stamens; fruit a capsule wrapped in the dry persistent petals and by the sepals (family *Hypericaceae*).

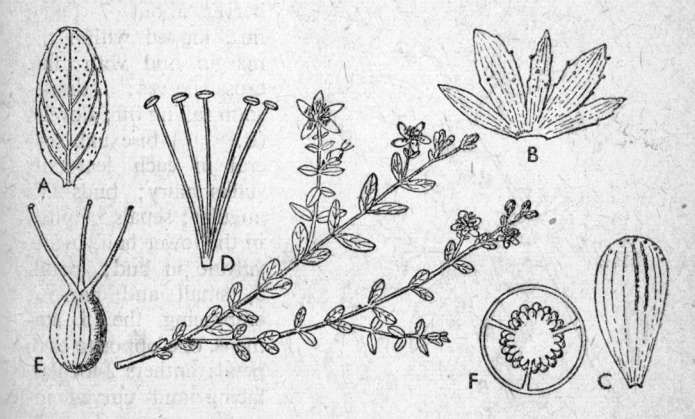

This pretty little plant grows in a variety of places, stony heaths, and bogs, fields and waste places, sometimes on lawns; it flowers from early summer until the autumn. The flowers do not open in unfavourable weather, and automatic self-pollination then takes place.

ALDER BUCKTHORN, BLACK ALDER, *Frangula alnus* Mill.

249. Alder Buckthorn, *Frangula alnus* Mill. ($\times \frac{2}{5}$); shrub; branches alternate, without thorns, hairy when young; winter buds not covered with scales; leaves broadly elliptic to obovate, rounded at the base, triangular at the apex, 1½–2 in. long, entire, glabrous above, pubescent on the nerves below when young, lateral nerves about 7 pairs, fine, looped within the margin and with fine cross nerves; stipules soon falling off; flowers (B, $\times 1\frac{1}{2}$) bisexual, several in each leaf-axil; stalks hairy; buds (A) angular; sepals 5, united in the lower half, ovate, valvate in bud; petals 5, small and narrow, embracing the 5 stamens, one opposite each petal; anthers 2-locular, facing and curved inwards; ovary (C, $\times 2$) in the base of the calyx and surrounded by nectar, 3-locular; style undivided; fruit (D, $\times 1\frac{1}{2}$) globose, black when ripe, about ¼ in. diam. (synonym *Rhamnus frangula* L.) (family *Rhamnaceae*).

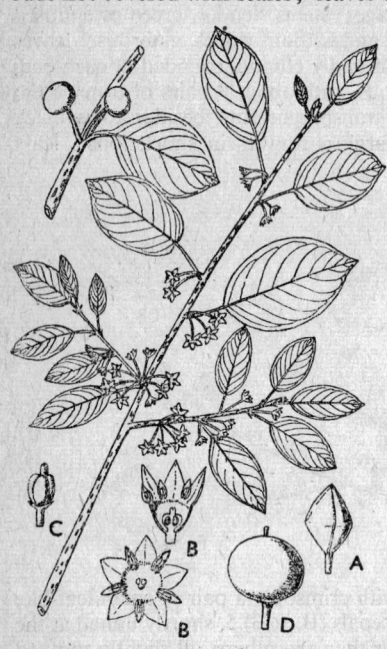

Compared with the drawing of *Rhamnus cathartica* L., shown in fig. 56 in *Common Wild Flowers*, it will be seen that the species described above differs in having bisexual flowers, with 5 sepals, 5 petals and 5 stamens. On account of these differences the Alder Buckthorn is now often referred to a separate genus, *Frangula*.

The anthers are ripe before the stigma of the same flower is receptive, so that cross-pollination is effected when insects visit to suck the nectar, which is secreted within the base of the calyx and around the ovary.

PRIVET, *Ligustrum vulgare* L.

250. Privet, *Ligustrum vulgare* L. ($\times \frac{1}{2}$); a much-branched shrub with slender whip-like branchlets; leaves opposite or nearly so, shortly stalked, lanceolate to oblong-elliptic, rounded or tapered to an acute point, more or less acute at the base, entire, glabrous and with very obscure nerves; no stipules; flowers (A, $\times$ 2) scented, crowded in pyramidal panicles at the ends of the branchlets; lower bracts somewhat leafy, upper small and awl-shaped (subulate); calyx cupular, minutely toothed; corolla white, shortly tubular with 4 or rarely 5 obovate lobes; stamens (B, $\times$ 3) 2 or rarely 3, inserted in the corolla-tube but protruding from it; ovary (C, $\times$ 3) superior, 2-locular, with 2 pendulous ovules (D, $\times$ 5) in each loculus; style undivided, with an oblong stigma; fruit a purple-black globose berry (E, $\times \frac{2}{5}$) about $\frac{1}{3}$ in. diam., 2-locular, loculi 1–2-seeded (family *Oleaceae*).

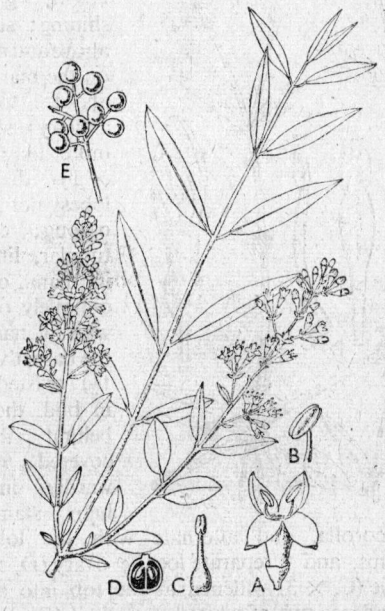

Grows in hedges and woods, especially on chalk downs, extending into western Asia, often employed as a hedge.

Nectar is secreted by the ovary and stored in the base of the corolla-tube.

PERIWINKLE, *Vinca minor* L.

251. Periwinkle, *Vinca minor* L. ($\times \frac{1}{2}$); perennial with creeping root-stock and trailing glabrous shoots rooting at the lower nodes; leaves opposite, stalked, the stalks connected at the base by a rim, ovate or ovate-elliptic, rounded at the base and apex, with 5–6 pairs of spreading looped nerves less prominent below, glabrous and shining; stalks flattened above and minutely hairy on the margins; flowers about 1 to each shoot, axillary; stalks 1 in. or more long; calyx (A, $\times 1\frac{1}{2}$) deeply 5-lobed, lobes not overlapping, oblong; corolla blue, tubular, limb about $1\frac{1}{4}$ in. diam., divided into 5 obliquely obovate lobes with a narrow rim at the base, the lobes (A, $\times 1\frac{1}{2}$) twisted to the left in bud, the tube inside behind the stamens covered with downwardly directed white hairs; stamens (B, $\times 3$) 5, on the corolla, and alternate with the lobes; anthers with hairy tips, and 2 separate loculi; ovary (D, $\times 3$) laterally 2-lobed; style (C, $\times 3$) widened at the top into a broad rim, crowned by a dense tuft of white hairs; fruit (E, $\times 0$) composed of two divergent parts (family *Apocynaceae*).

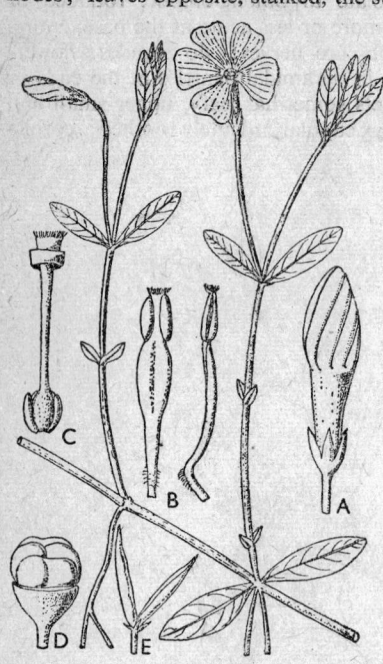

The "Periwinkle" is of strong sentimental interest to the writer. It grew in the garden of his country home, and was one of the earliest of which he learned both the common and Latin names. It rhymed with that favourite "bedtime story" in the peaceful days of Queen Victoria, which was chanted into the ears of children by devoted mothers: "Twinkle, twinkle, little star"! If for no other reason, then, it finds a place in this second little book, though it is by no means a common wild plant.

CROSSWORT, *Galium cruciata* (L.) Scop.

252. Crosswort, *Galium cruciata* (L.) Scop. ($\times \frac{1}{2}$); perennial with creeping root-stock; stems weak and slender, up to 2 ft. long, trailing, quadrangular, angles rounded, loosely covered with long bristly white hairs, green but tinged with crimson just above the leaves; leaves (A, $\times$ 0) in whorls of 4, 2 being real leaves and 2 leafy stipules exactly similar, elliptic-lanceolate, narrowed to the base, not pointed, 3-nerved from the base, bristly hairy on both surfaces; flowers (B, $\times$ 2) few in a 3-forked cluster from each real leaf with 2 or 3 leafy erect bracts on the top side at the base of the flowerstalks, the outer flowers bisexual (C, $\times$ 4), the inner male (D, $\times$ 4); calyx not evident; corolla yellow, of 4 petals united at the base, spreading; stamens 4, between the corolla-lobes; ovary below the corolla (inferior), with a 2-lobed style, 2-locular, smooth; fruit (E, $\times$ 2) globose, the stalk soon deflexed (family *Rubiaceae*).

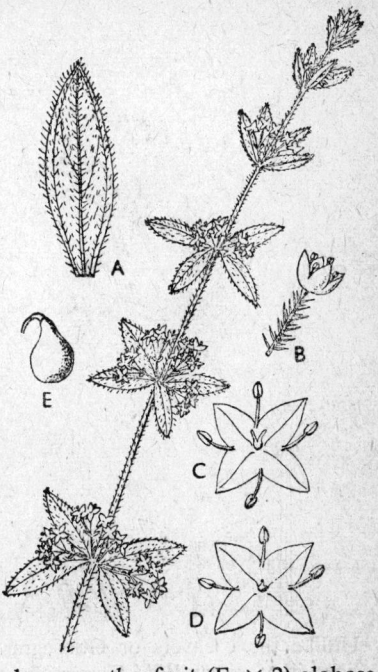

Grows in woods and hedges, but rare in Eire; extends to Siberia. It is not easy to explain in simple words the rather complicated and quite fascinating morphology of this species. For botanical examination purposes it is as well to know that only 2 of the leaves in each whorl are real, the others being leafy stipules resembling them in every respect except that they have no buds in their axils such as the real leaves have. And the flowers are of 2 sexes, the outer being bisexual and producing the fruit, which is soon deflexed, the inner males and soon falling off. They smell like honey, and are pollinated mainly by means of the feet of insect visitors crawling about amongst them.

GREAT HEDGE BEDSTRAW, *Galium mollugo* L.

253. Great Hedge Bedstraw, *Galium mollugo* L. (agg.) (× ½); perennial; stems up to about 4 ft. high, erect or trailing, obtusely 4-angled, smooth or rather softly hairy; leaves usually 8 in a whorl (half really stipules), narrowly oblanceolate, rounded to a very sharp tip, minutely bristly on the margin, otherwise glabrous; flowers numerous in leafy cymes, the ultimate branches of the cymes bearing 1 or a pair of leafy bracts; pedicels about as long as the bract; calyx reduced to a mere line on top of the ovary; corolla white, 4-lobed, lobes spreading from the base, ovate-lanceolate, acute; stamens 4, inserted between the corolla lobes; a nectariferous ring around the base of the two styles, these with rounded stigmas; fruit small and smooth or nearly so (family *Rubiaceae*).

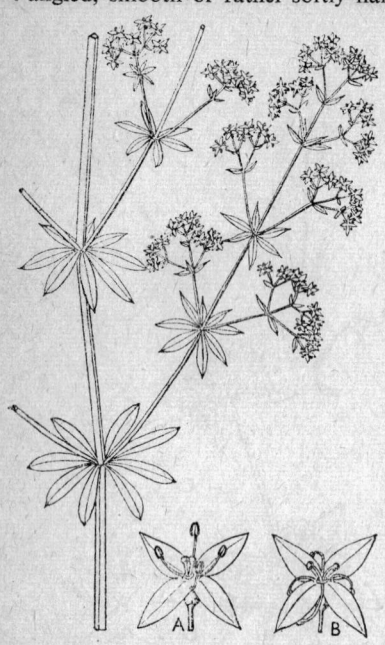

Unlike the Cleavers or Goosegrass, *Galium aparine* L., described in *Common Wild Flowers*, fig. 61, this is a perennial, and the stems are not, as in that species, provided by hook-like hairs. It grows in hedges and woods, and has a wide range into western Asia.

The anthers are mature before the stigmas are receptive. At first the stamens are erect, while the 2 head-like stigmas are close together, as shown in fig. A (× 3). After the anthers have shed their pollen, the filaments bend away between the lobes of the corolla, as shown in fig. B (× 3), when the styles diverge into the position previously held by the anthers. Thus cross-pollination is easily brought about by visiting insects.

MARSH BEDSTRAW, *Galium palustre* L.

254. Marsh Bedstraw, *Galium palustre* L. ($\times \frac{1}{2}$); perennial with weak stems slightly rough on the angles; leaves (including the similar stipules) often 6 in a whorl, sometimes 4, narrowly oblanceolate, narrowed to the base, blunt at the apex, about $\frac{3}{4}$ in. long, glabrous except the slightly rough margins, 1-nerved; flowers (A, $\times$ 5) in lax leafy straggly panicles, each final cluster with a pair of leafy bracts at the base; stalks thread-like; ovary below the corolla (inferior), 2-locular; calyx completely reduced (really encircling the ovary); corolla white very short, 4-lobed, lobes ovate, not overlapping in bud; stamens 4, alternate with the lobes; styles 2, with a rounded stigma; fruit (B, $\times$ 2) deeply 2-lobed, lobes rounded, almost smooth (family *Rubiaceae*).

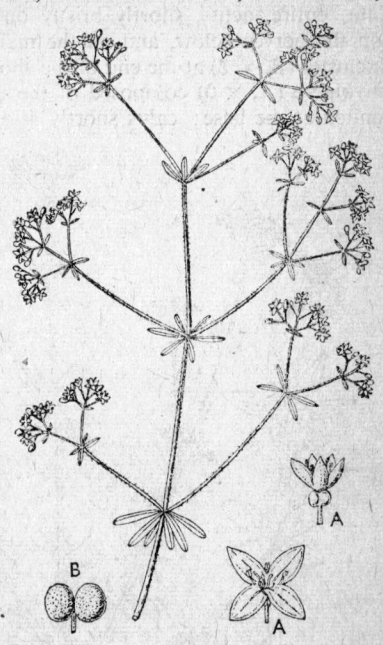

As implied by the specific name, this plant usually grows in marshy and wet places, sometimes quite in the water; it flowers during the summer months.

The student who has seen only the British examples of the family *Rubiaceae* can have only a very imperfect idea of the family as a whole. Among many others it includes the *Gardenia*, the Coffee plant, Ipecacuanha, and the Quinine tree (*Cinchona*). All the British genera belong to the tribe *Galieae*, distinguished from the others by the stipules being leaf-like and not distinct from the true leaves. The leaves of *Rubiaceae* are never lobed, not even toothed, and the stipules are between (inter-) or within (intra-) the leaf-stalks.

FIELD MADDER, *Sherardia arvensis* L.

255. Field Madder, *Sherardia arvensis* L. ($\times \frac{1}{2}$); a small annual, very much branched from the base; branches bristly with stiff short hairs; leaves usually 6 in a whorl, sessile, lanceolate, entire, acute, shortly bristly on both surfaces, especially on the nerves below, and on the margin; flowers (D, $\times$ 4) in a cluster (B, $\times$ 2) at the end of the shoots and surrounded by an involucre (A, $\times$ 0) composed of the upper leaves more or less united at the base; calyx shortly 4-lobed, adnate to the ovary, the lobes becoming more distinct in fruit; corolla violet or pink, on top of the ovary, tubular, 4-lobed, lobes valvate in bud (C, $\times$ 4); stamens 4, exserted, inserted between the base of the lobes; ovary inferior; style surrounded by a fleshy disk; fruit (E, vertical section) crowned by the leafy calyx-lobes (family *Rubiaceae*).

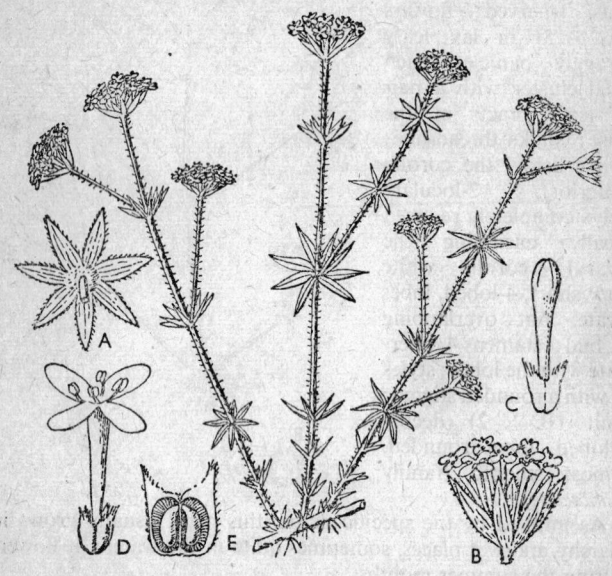

This is a typical cornfield weed, and is seldom found elsewhere. The flowers are gynodioecious (see p. 219), the bisexual being somewhat larger than the females. In the former the stigmas are often receptive at the same time as the anthers open at the same level, when automatic self-pollination takes place. The nectar is secreted by a fleshy disk surrounding the base of the style.

VERVAIN, *Verbena officinalis* L.

256. Vervain, *Verbena officinalis* L. ($\times \frac{1}{2}$); perennial with a woody root-stock; stems 4-angled, sparingly clothed with very short bulbous-based hairs; leaves opposite, connected at the base by a slight ridge, oblanceolate in outline but deeply pinnately lobed and coarsely toothed, shortly hairy on both surfaces and with almost sessile glands; flowers (A, $\times 2\frac{1}{2}$) arranged in axillary and terminal glandular spikes, bracts lanceolate, pointed; calyx with 5 narrow lobes, pubescent; corolla (B, $\times 3\frac{1}{2}$) pale violet, tube slightly wider above the middle, with white hairs at the mouth; lobes 5, spreading; stamens 4, included in the tube below the hairs; anthers rounded; disk fleshy below the ovary; ovary (C, $\times 5$) superior, 4-locular (D, $\times 7$), each chamber with 1 erect ovule; fruit of 4 granular nutlets (family *Verbenaceae*).

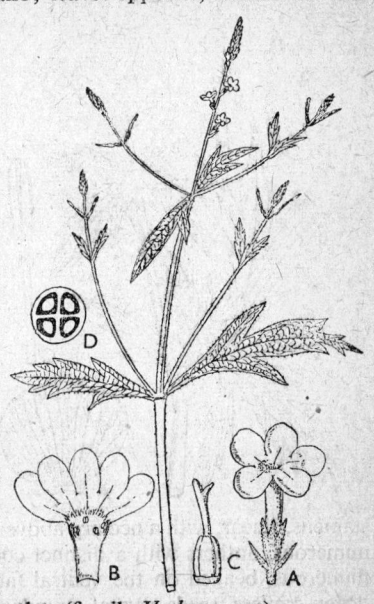

This is the only representative in the British flora of this large and mainly tropical family, which is here regarded as a parallel group with the Dead-Nettle family, *Labiatae*. Nectar is secreted below the ovary, and protection against unbidden guests is provided by a ring of white hairs at the mouth of the corolla-tube. Either cross- or self-pollination may take place.

To the *Verbena* family belongs one of the hardest-wooded and most valuable trees in the world. This is the Teak-tree, *Tectona grandis*, which grows wild in the forests of Burma and provides one of the major industries in that country.

GLOBE-FLOWER, *Trollius europaeus* Linn.

257. Globe-flower, *Trollius europaeus* Linn. ($\times \frac{1}{2}$); perennial up to about 2 ft. high; basal leaves on very long hollow stalks broadly sheathing at the base; blade palmately divided into about 5 main segments, these in turn deeply lobed and coarsely toothed, glabrous, main nerves parallel and lighter green (almost translucent), upper leaves nearly sessile, with a broad almost membranous base; flowers solitary, terminal, 1–1½ in. diam.; sepals (A, $\times$ 0) 10–15, overlapping and crowding together into a depressed-globose mass, rich cream-yellow, the outer tinged with green and toothed on the margin; petals (B, $\times$ 2) almost hidden among the stamens, linear, with a nectary above the base; stamens (C, $\times$ 2) numerous, anthers with a distinct connective; carpels (D, $\times$ 4) numerous, beaked on the ventral (anterior) side, with about a dozen ovules; seeds several, angular (family *Ranunculaceae*).

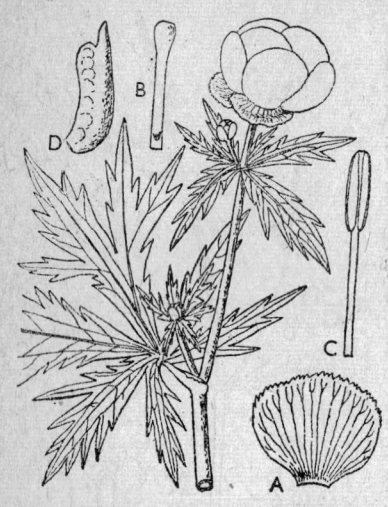

This is a very lovely wild flower which should not be picked (see p. ix); wild flowers are much more pretty growing in their native habitat, and few last for any length of time in a vase; there are plenty of garden flowers for home decoration!

In the Globe-flower it is not the petals but the large rich cream-yellow sepals which serve as the means of attraction to insects. They are folded together into a sphere, and hide the small narrow petals, which bear an unprotected nectariferous pit near the base (fig. B). If cross-pollination is not effected by insects, automatic self-pollination is inevitable, as the outer of the numerous stamens lie above the stigmas.

MEADOW CROWFOOT, *Ranunculus acris* L.

258. Meadow Crowfoot, *Ranunculus acris* L. ($\times \frac{1}{3}$); perennial with very short root-stock; basal leaves on long stalks with sheathing hairy bases, more or less orbicular in outline, usually 5-lobed nearly to the base, the lobes again deeply divided and lobulate with rather narrow acute divisions, softly hairy on both surfaces, finely mealy below; stem leaves gradually merging into bracts and becoming stalkless (sessile) and divided into 2 or 3 segments; flowers about 1 in. diam., on long stalks forming a lax panicle; stalks not grooved, but covered with very short appressed hairs; sepals (B, $\times$ 2) 5, spreading in the open flower but not becoming reflexed (as in *R. bulbosus*), yellowish-green, covered with rather long hairs; petals (C, $\times \frac{3}{4}$) 5, broadly clawed, shining except for a large patch at the base, with a scale in front of the nectary and hiding 2 dark spots (C, $\times \frac{3}{4}$); stamens (D, $\times \frac{3}{4}$) numerous; carpels (E, $\times$ 3) numerous, with recurved stigma; fruit a bunch of achenes, not hairy (glabrous) (A, flower bud) (family *Ranunculaceae*).

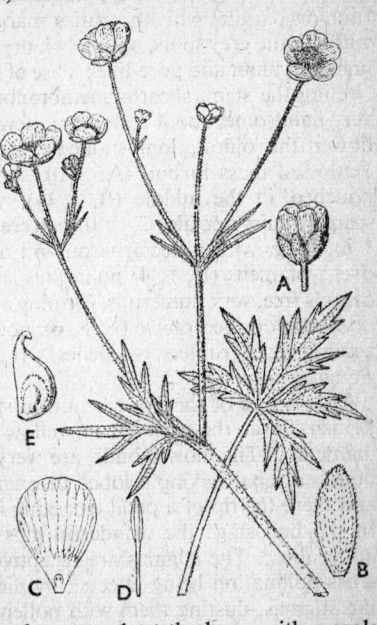

Rather like *R. bulbosus* (*Common Wild Flowers*, fig. 69), but the stem not swollen at the base and the sepals are spreading and not reflexed as in that species.

The bright-yellow very glossy petals are very conspicuous, and attract hover flies, small bees, and other insects, which collect the nectar protected by a scale at the base. As the stigmas mature before any of the anthers open, they are easily brushed with pollen from older flowers, and by the time the anthers are open the carpels are already swollen and the stigmas shrivelled.

GREAT SPEARWORT, *Ranunculus lingua* L.

259. Great Spearwort, *Ranunculus lingua* L. (× ½); perennial in marshes and ditches; leaves all borne on the rather thick quite hollow green stems, linear-lanceolate, with faint nerves running parallel with the entire margins, closely covered above with minute grey spots, minutely hairy below with short appressed hairs, tip blunt and pore-like; base of leaves sheathing and almost circling the stem, sheaths membranous on the margin; flowers very handsome, about 2 in. diam., few in a loose panicle; middle flower the oldest, long-stalked; sepals 5, forming a 5-lobed depressed mass in bud (A, × 0), spreading, deeply and widely pouched in the middle (B, × 1½), yellow tinged with green, scarcely hairy; petals (C, × 0) rich cream-yellow, widely obovate, 1 in. long, with a nectariferous pit at the base, very glossy all over; stamens (D, × 4) numerous, anthers opening at the side; carpels free, very numerous, forming a globose mass and arranged on an oblong receptacle (E, × 6), not hairy; ovule 1 (G, × 10), ascending; fruitlets (achenes) (F, × 10) glabrous (family *Ranunculaceae*).

This is one of the most beautiful species of Buttercup in the British flora, the rich cream-yellow flowers being quite 2 in. diameter. The flower-buds are very distinctive, the rounded pouched sepals giving a lobed or angular appearance, with here and there the tip of a petal emerging from the tight flower-pack. In the bud stage the wonderful gloss on the petals is scarcely noticeable. The stigmas are receptive before the anthers open, cross-pollination being effected by flies, which usually alight on the stigmas, dusting them with pollen from another flower.

Flower-lovers in numerous countries can enjoy the sight of this lovely plant which has a wide range from Eire eastward into temperate Asia and as far south as the Himalayas.

91

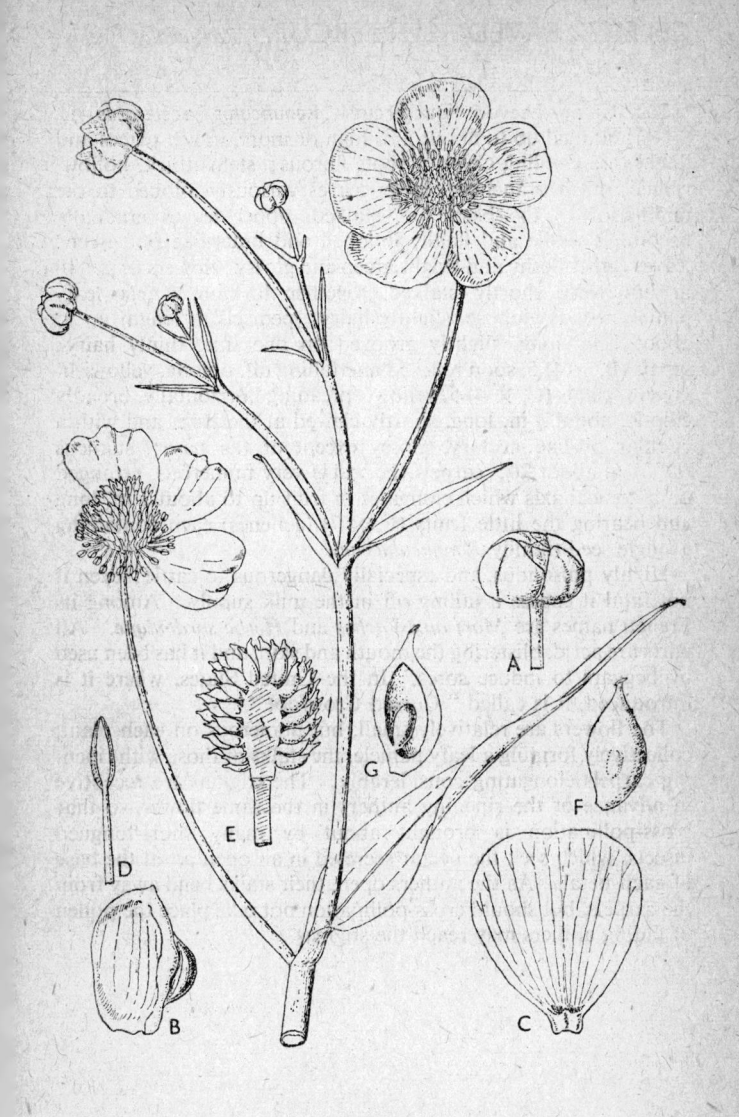

CELERY-LEAVED BUTTERCUP, *Ranunculus sceleratus* L.

260. Celery-Leaved Buttercup, *Ranunculus sceleratus* L. ($\times \frac{1}{2}$); annual up to about 2 ft. high or more, in wet places and ditches, resembling Celery; roots fibrous; stems thick, hollow, ribbed, much branched; lower leaves variously 3-lobed to the middle or to the base, long-stalked, upper leaves gradually becoming sessile and finally unlobed and bract-like but green; leaves rather fleshy and bright green and glossy; flowers (A, $\times$ 0) in bud very shortly stalked, together forming a lax leafy panicle; buds globose, slightly hairy; pedicels at length up to about 1 in. long, slightly grooved on one side, thinly hairy; sepals (B, $\times$ 4) 5, soon reflexed and falling off, oblong, yellowish-green; petals (C, $\times$ 4) 5, yellow, spreading horizontally, broadly elliptic, about $\frac{1}{4}$ in. long, shortly clawed at the base, and with a circular pit-like nectary, glossy except at the base; stamens (D, $\times$ 6) about 20; carpels (E, $\times$ $1\frac{1}{2}$) very numerous, arranged on a conical axis which elongates in fruit up to about 1 in. long and bearing the little fruits (F, $\times$ 7) (achenes) each containing a single seed (family *Ranunculaceae*).

Highly poisonous, and especially dangerous to cattle; even if not fatal it causes a falling off in the milk supply. Among its French names are *Mort aux Vaches* and *Herbe sardonique*. All parts are acrid, blistering the mouth and skin, and it has been used by beggars to induce sores. In the United States, where it is introduced, it is called " Cursed Crowfoot "!

The flowers are relatively small, but numerous on each plant, collectively forming a leafy panicle, the stalks of those with ripening carpels elongating considerably. The stigmas are receptive in advance of the ripening anthers in the same flower, so that cross-pollination is brought about by many short-tongued insects, which seek the nectar secreted in an open pit at the base of each petal. As the anthers open, their stalks bend away from the carpels, but should cross-pollination not take place the pollen of fading anthers may reach the stigmas.

93

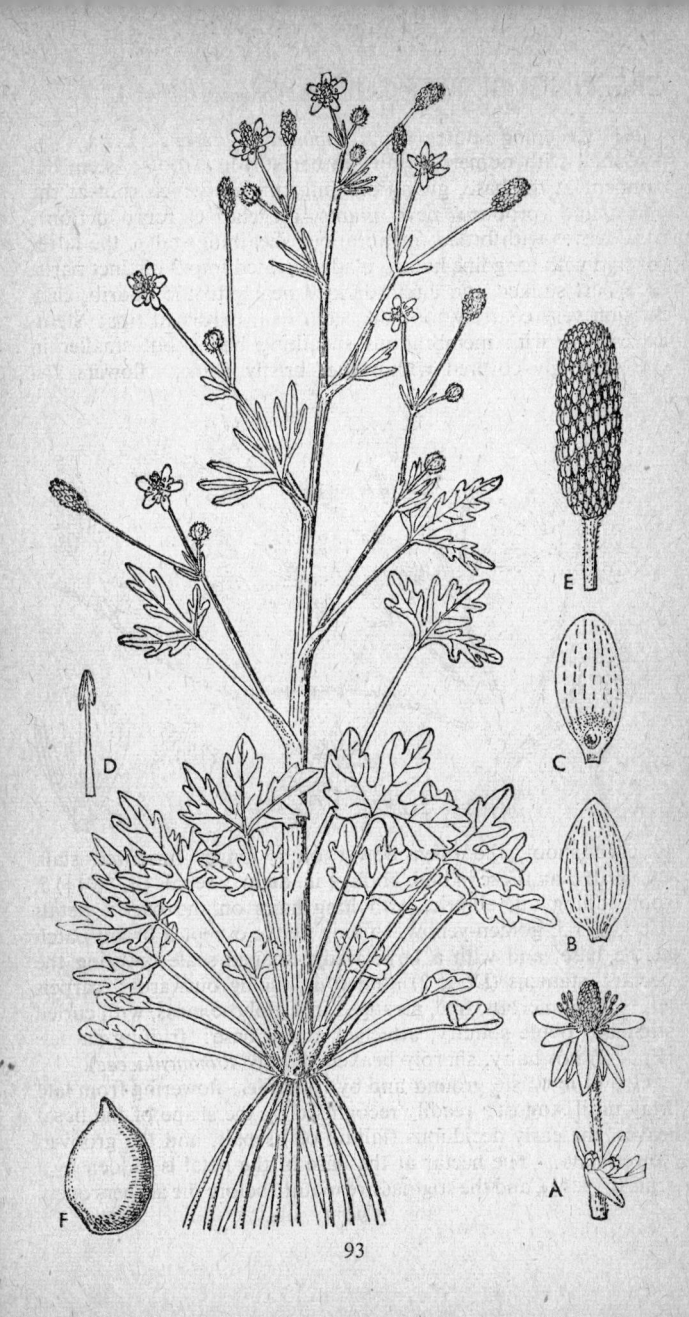

CREEPING BUTTERCUP, *Ranunculus repens* L.

261. Creeping Buttercup, *Ranunculus repens* L. ($\times \frac{1}{3}$); perennial with numerous long rather stilt-like roots; stem decumbent at the base, giving off long runners which root at the nodes and produce new plants (vegetative reproduction); basal leaves with broad membranous sheathing stalks, the latter covered with long fine hairs; blades divided into 3 distinct parts, each part stalked and again divided nearly to the midrib, each division very coarsely toothed, teeth with hardened tips; stem-leaves also with membranous sheathing bases, but smaller in size sparingly covered with rather bristly hairs; flowers 2–4 to each shoot, the open flower on a longer furrowed stalk (A, $\times$ 0) than those in bud, about 1 in. diam.; sepals (B, $\times 1\frac{1}{4}$) 5, soon falling off, elliptic, with long hairs on the back; petals (C, $\times 1\frac{1}{4}$) 5, golden-yellow, shining above except a broad patch at the base, and with a large wedge-shaped scale covering the nectar; stamens (D, $\times$ 2) numerous, facing outwards; carpels (E, $\times$ 4) numerous, free, arranged in a globose mass, with curled stigmas; ovule solitary, attached at the base; fruiting carpels (F, $\times$ 2) not hairy, sharply beaked (family *Ranunculaceae*).

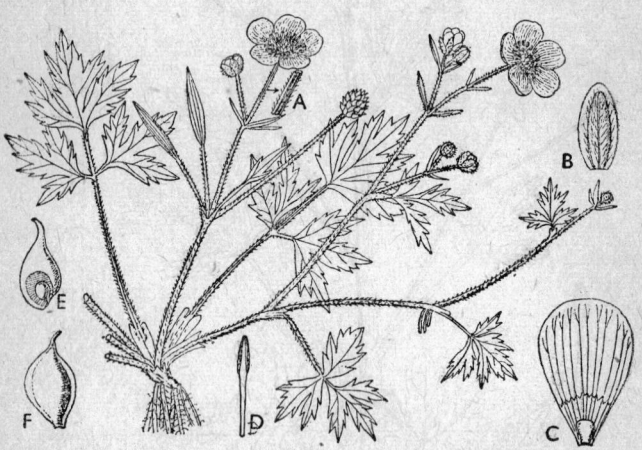

Grows in waste ground and by roadsides, flowering from late May until August; readily recognised by the shape of the basal leaves, the early deciduous (falling off) sepals, and the grooved flower-stalk. The nectar at the base of the petal is hidden by a scale (C, $\times 1\frac{1}{4}$), and the stigmas are mature before the anthers open.

GOLDILOCKS, *Ranunculus auricomus* L.

262. Goldilocks, *Ranunculus auricomus* L. ($\times \frac{2}{5}$) perennial; basal leaves very variable, long-stalked, kidney-shaped and irregularly and coarsely toothed, or deeply 3-lobed; stem-leaves sessile, cut nearly to the base into 5 segments, the lowermost with narrowly wedge-shaped stalked segments, the upper with linear irregularly lobed segments, bright green, glabrous below but very minutely pubescent above; flowers terminal and axillary, on slender stalks; sepals 5, or sometimes 4 where only 1 petal, mixed with green and yellow, more green when there are all 5 petals; petals (C, $\times 1\frac{1}{4}$) 5, or sometimes fewer or absent, and then the sepals more yellow, shining on the upper surface, with a nectariferous pit at the base; stamens (D, $\times 3\frac{1}{2}$) numerous; carpels (E, $\times 3\frac{1}{2}$) shortly stalked, numerous, conspicuously beaked, shortly pubescent (family *Ranunculaceae*).

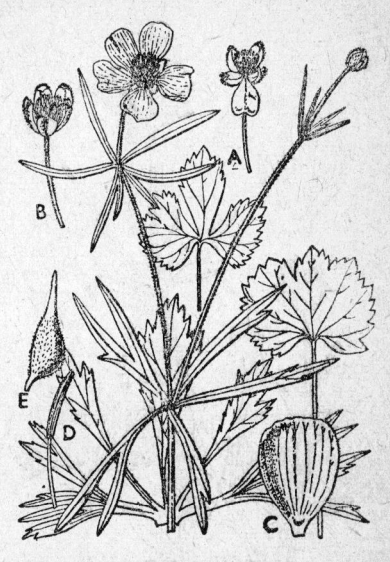

This is very variable with regard to the presence or absence of petals; sometimes there is only one petal (A, $\times \frac{2}{5}$) and then the sepals are more or less half green and half yellow. In a large batch growing in the grass at Kew I found only a very occasional flower with a petal, all the others being without petals (apetalous) (B, $\times \frac{2}{5}$), and then the sepals nearly completely yellow. The apetalous condition therefore approaches very near to Anemone, which is also without petals, the function of these being carried out by the sepals. Goldilocks seems to represent an intermediate and indeterminate stage between the two genera *Ranunculus* and *Anemone*, and shows clearly how the latter genus has been evolved.

HAIRY BUTTERCUP, *Ranunculus sardous* Crantz

263. Hairy Buttercup, *Ranunculus sardous* Crantz ($\times \frac{2}{5}$); an erect annual, but mostly much branched from the base and resembling a perennial, softly hairy all over, though less hairy states occur; basal leaves (A, $\times \frac{2}{5}$) with a broadly sheathing stalk, the sheath fringed with long hairs; stalks also fringed with hairs; blade divided into 3 separate parts, each part again very coarsely toothed or lobulate to about the middle, softly hairy all over; stem-leaves gradually becoming sessile upwards and forming leafy bracts, deeply divided; flowers numerous, the first opening soon fruiting whilst the remainder are still in bloom; stalks scarcely grooved; sepals 5, clothed with very long slender hairs in bud (B, $\times 1\frac{1}{4}$), becoming sharply reflexed as the flower opens (C, $\times \frac{4}{5}$); petals (D, $\times 0$) pale yellow, glossy, the nectary at the base covered with a rounded scale; stamens (E, $\times 2$) about 25-30; carpels numerous, in fruit (F, $\times 2$) compressed and rounded, with a row or 2 of small tubercles within the margin (family *Ranunculaceae*).

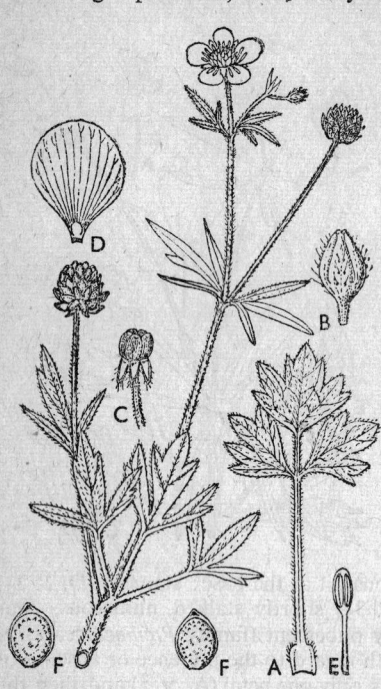

This species may easily be mistaken for the more common *Ranunculus bulbosus* L., having, like that species, reflexed sepals, but it is an annual and the carpels are flattened with 1 or 2 rows of small tubercles with the margin. In *R. bulbosus* the carpels have no tubercles.

HUNGER-WEED, CORN BUTTERCUP, *Ranunculus arvensis* L.

264. Hunger-weed, Corn Buttercup, *Ranunculus arvensis* L. (× ⅓); an erect annual with rather thick roots; stems up to 1½ ft. high, branched in the upper part, and very slightly hairy in the upper part; basal leaves deeply pinnately lobed, the lobes broader than those of the stem leaves, with a few rounded teeth; stem leaves with narrow linear segments; flowers small, the lower developing into fruit before the others have faded; stalks clothed with reflexed hairs; sepals (A, × 3) 5, spreading, hairy; petals (B, × 3) 5, pale yellow, with a wedge-shaped scale over the nectary at the base; stamens (C, × 5) rather few; carpels (D, × 2½) few, free, in fruit compressed and covered with sharp-pointed warts and with bristly margins (family *Ranunculaceae*).

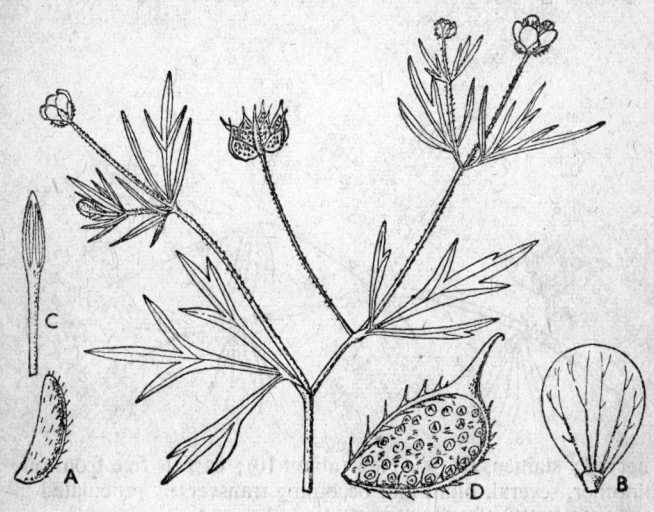

A common weed, and often abundant in neglected cornfields, flowering and ripening its seed with the corn. It is a regular companion of Fool's Parsley, Venus' Comb, and other similar followers of the plough, and it often frequents stackyards. It proves a pest to farmers because it gets bound up with the straw in harvesting, being tall when growing in the shelter of the corn. The prickly fruits are unique among our native buttercups, and are readily spread by means of the hooked tubercles.

IVY-LEAVED CROWFOOT, *Ranunculus hederaceus* L.

265. Ivy-Leaved Crowfoot, *Ranunculus hederaceus* L. ($\times \frac{1}{2}$); in muddy places in ditches or floating in water; stems rooting at the nodes; leaves opposite or alternate, kidney-shaped, shallowly 5–7-lobed, widely heart-shaped at the base, on long stalks, rather fleshy and glabrous green, with a half-moon shaped darker patch; stalks expanded at the base into a broad membranous sheath; flowers (A, $\times 1\frac{1}{2}$) solitary from near the axil of the leaf-stalk, about $\frac{1}{4}$–$\frac{1}{3}$ in. diam., rather long-stalked, but the stalks shorter than those of the leaves and recurving in fruit; sepals 5, green, shorter than the petals; petals 5, white, 3–5-nerved; stamens (B, $\times 6$) few (about 10); carpels free from one another, several, blunt and becoming transversely reticulated in fruit (C, $\times 10$) (family *Ranunculaceae*).

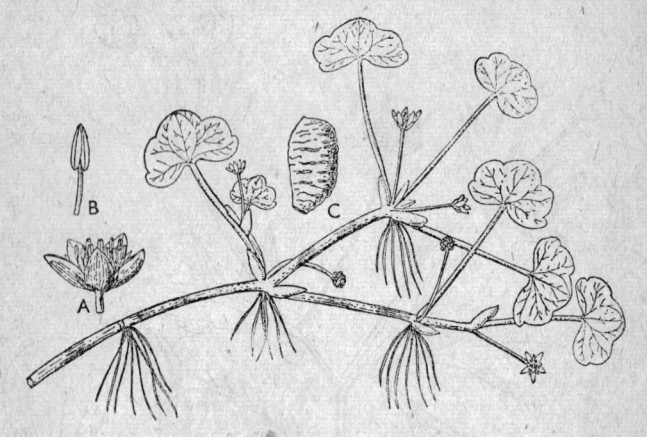

This species is rather intermediate between the Field and the Water Buttercups, but the leaves are never finely divided, as in the latter. It also shows some relationship with the Lesser Celandine, *Ficaria verna* Huds. (*Common Wild Flowers*, fig. 71).

The anthers of the 8–10 stamens shed their pollen on the stigmas when the flower opens, and self-pollination is effective; afterwards the stamens move outwards. Nectar is sparingly secreted in a pit at the base of the petals.

WHITE WATER-LILY, *Nymphaea alba* L.

266. **White Water-Lily,** *Nymphaea alba* L. ($\times \frac{1}{3}$); aquatic perennial with thick fleshy root-stock; leaf-stalks rounded, with 4 large and several smaller intercellular spaces with internal hairs (K, $\times 1\frac{1}{2}$); leaf-blade floating on the water, rounded, deeply cordate, with several radiating nerves; flowers on long stalks, lying on the surface of the water, white, not scented, 3–4 in. diam.; sepals (A, $\times \frac{1}{3}$) 4, greenish-white; petals (B, C, $\times \frac{3}{4}$) numerous, white or tinged with pink downwards, the outer broadly lanceolate and gradually transformed into stamens (D–G, $\times \frac{3}{4}$); carpels about 20, united into an ovary with spreading united yellow stigmas, each ending in an incurved rich cream-yellow appendix; ovary (H, $\times \frac{1}{2}$) with as many loculi as stigmas, with numerous ovules on the walls (J, $\times \frac{1}{2}$); fruit a pulpy berry, ripening under water (family *Nymphaeaceae*)

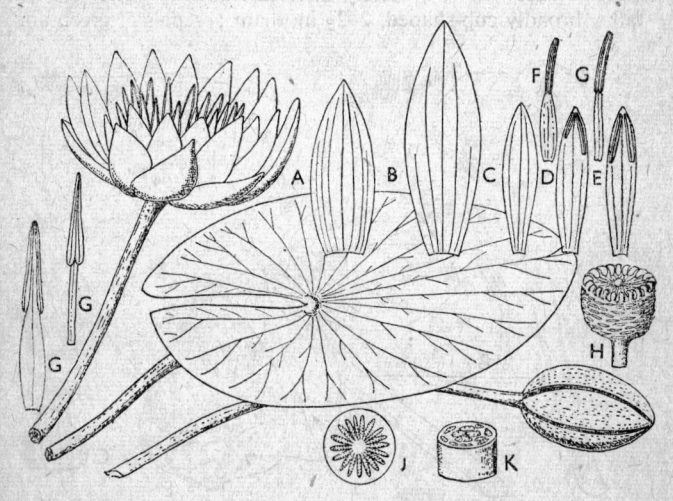

In lakes, ponds and backwaters, flowering from June to September; widely distributed in the temperate northern hemisphere.

Although clearly related to the Buttercup family (*Ranunculaceae*), the Water-Lily family, *Nymphaeaceae*, shows a considerable advance in some parts of its floral structure. Its more primitive features are the scarcely perceptible difference between the sepals and petals; the latter are numerous and grade into the also numerous stamens.

BRANDY BOTTLE, YELLOW WATER-LILY, *Nuphar lutea* (L.) Sm.

267. Brandy Bottle, Yellow Water-Lily, *Nuphar lutea* (L.) Sm. ($\times \frac{1}{3}$); in lakes, ponds and ditches; rhizome creeping; submerged leaves on rather short stalks, very thin, floating leaves rather leathery, deeply 2-lobed at the base, lobes contiguous, blade in outline broadly obvate, with a wide midrib and many slender side-nerves; leaf-stalk thick and fleshy, flattish on the upper surface; flowers shortly exserted from the water on long stalks, broadly cup-shaped, 2–2½ in. diam.; sepals 5, green and yellow outside, yellow inside, thick and fleshy; petals (A, $\times$ 0) 12–15, broadly obovate-wedge-shaped, about ½ in. long and broad, closely and strongly nerved; stamens (B, $\times$ 0) numerous, in about 6 rows, facing inwards (introrse), curving outwards as they ripen; anther-lobes separate, connective produced and very blunt (truncate); ovary (C, $\times \frac{1}{3}$) ovoid, style short, thick, top composed of about 15 united stigmas radiating from the middle; fruit (E, $\times \frac{2}{3}$) ovoid, with numerous seeds (F, $\times$ 0) (D, cross-section of ovary, $\times \frac{1}{2}$) (family *Nymphaeaceae*).

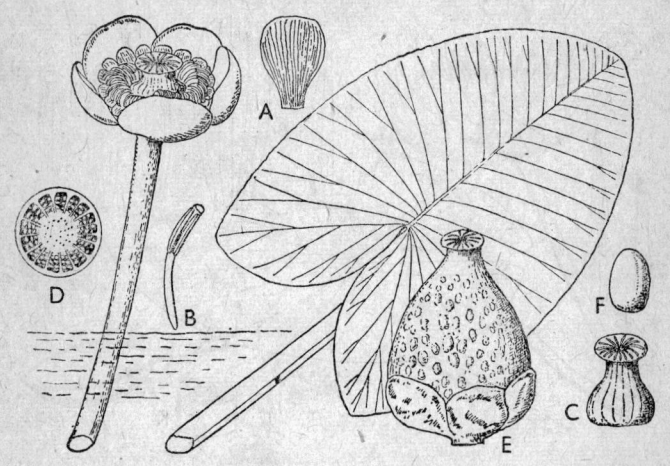

The name "Brandy Bottle" is given to this plant probably in reference to the shape of the fruit (E, $\times \frac{1}{2}$), and not because of the flower-scent. The radiating stigmas recall those of the poppy capsule.

LONG-HEADED POPPY, *Papaver dubium* L.

268. Long-Headed Poppy, *Papaver dubium* L. ($\times \frac{2}{5}$); annual with a narrow carrot-like root, up to about 1½ ft. high; leaves (A, $\times \frac{2}{5}$) up to 1 ft. long, pinnately divided almost to the midrib, the lobes again deeply cut into oblong segments, loosely covered with long bristle-like hairs; stems leafy in the lower part, also bristly-hairy; flowers salmon-red, 1½–2 in. diam., on long slender stalks; sepals 2, falling off as the flower opens (B, $\times \frac{2}{5}$), egg-shaped, ¾ in. long, loosely covered with long bristle-like hairs; petals 4, veiny; stamens numerous, their stalks and anthers dark purple; no nectary; ovary longer and narrower than in the Field Poppy (*Common Wild Flowers*, fig. 74), narrowed to the base, smooth, 1-locular with 6–12 intruding placentas (C, $\times$ 3) and numerous ovules; stigmas about 6–12 radiating on the flat top of the ovary; fruit (D, $\times \frac{4}{5}$) tapered to the base (narrowly obconic), capped by the radiating stigmas and opening by "windows" between each rib; seeds (E, $\times$ 8) numerous, deeply pitted (family *Papaveraceae*).

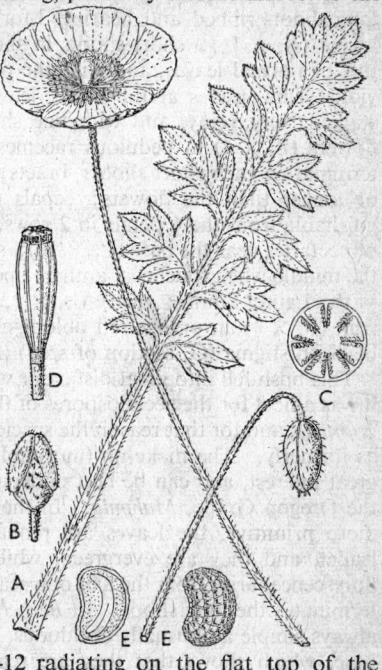

Grows in old quarries, in fields and amongst rubbish-dumps. Like the Field Poppy, it is poisonous to stock, and remains so if mixed with hay. It is readily recognised, especially by its fruit, which is long and narrowed to the base, with fewer stigmatic rays (usually about 8) than in the Field Poppy. As in the latter, there are no nectaries in the flower, insects visiting them to collect the pollen for food.

BARBERRY, *Berberis vulgaris* L.

269. Barberry, *Berberis vulgaris* L. ($\times \frac{2}{3}$); a shrub up to several feet high in hedges and copses; wood yellowish in section; branches of two kinds, of long and short shoots, the long shoots ribbed and bearing 3-forked, prickle-like, modified leaves (A, $\times 1\frac{1}{3}$); short shoots in the axils of these, bearing a tuft of normal leaves, and with the persistent stalks of the previous years' leaves at the base; leaves spoon-shaped-obovate, stalked, very veiny, and with fine sharp teeth on the margin; flowers (B, $\times 4$) in pedulous racemes, each raceme apparently terminating each short shoot; bracts very small; stalks as long or longer than the flowers; sepals usually 9, scarcely distinguishable from the 6 petals in 2 rows, but the latter with a pair of nectaries near the base (C, $\times 10$); stamens 6, moving towards the middle when touched; anthers opening by flaps (D, $\times 6$), as in the Laurel family; ovary (E, $\times 12$) with a few basal ovules; fruit (F, $\times \frac{1}{2}$) an orange-red oblong-elliptic berry, with a broad blackish stigma (G, section of seed) (family *Berberidaceae*).

This bush fell into great disfavour when it was discovered that it was a host for the aecidiospores of the Rust of wheat, *Puccinia graminis*, and for that reason the species is not nearly so common as formerly. The make-up (morphology) of the Barberry is of great interest, and can be best understood when compared with the Oregon Grape, *Mahonia*. In the latter genus, which is the more primitive, the leaves are pinnate with an odd terminal leaflet, and they are evergreen, whilst the flower-clusters (inflorescence) arise from the axil of a scale of the winter-bud which terminates the long shoot. In *Berberis*, however, the leaves are always simple and usually deciduous, but they are jointed at the base, which shows that they are really a compound leaf like *Mahonia*, but reduced to a single leaflet; and the inflorescence is at the apex of a short shoot, which arises in the axil of a leaf-thorn.

Honey is produced in abundance in swellings on the petals and is eagerly sought by bees. As soon as they touch the lower part of the stamen, the latter moves towards it, and showers the pollen on the head of the insect, which transfers it to the stigma of another flower. The movement of the stamens may be observed by touching the anther of a newly opened flower with the tip of a pencil.

103

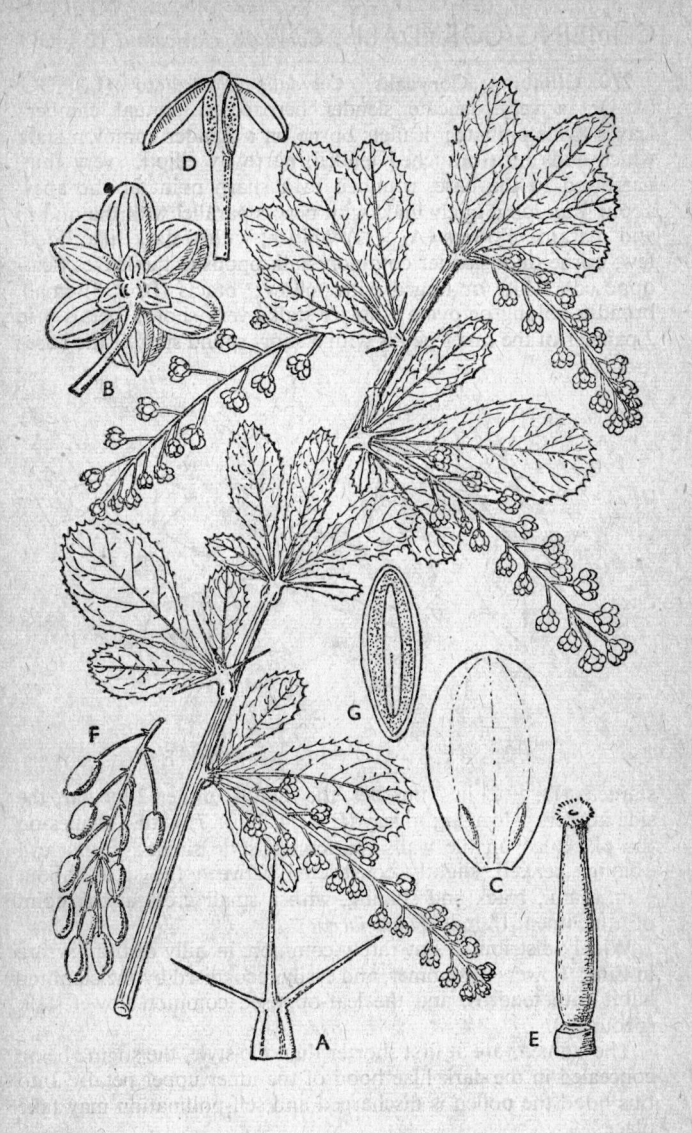

CLIMBING CORYDALIS, *Corydalis claviculata* (L.) DC.

270. Climbing Corydalis, *Corydalis claviculata* (L.) DC. ($\times \frac{1}{2}$); a very delicate slender herbaceous annual climber; leaves twice pinnate; leaflets borne on a slender common stalk which ends in a branched tendril, narrowly elliptic, very thin, narrowed to the base, rounded to a sharp point at the apex, about $\frac{1}{2}$ in. long, finely lined with nerves parallel with the midrib and margin; flowers (A, $\times$ 2) whitish, with a dark lilac hood, few, borne on a slender common stalk opposite the leaves (leaf-opposed), white or tinged with yellow; bracts (B, $\times$ 3) small, broadly oblong or ovate; flower-stalks very short; petals 4 in 2 pairs, 1 of the outer petals with a short round spur at the base;

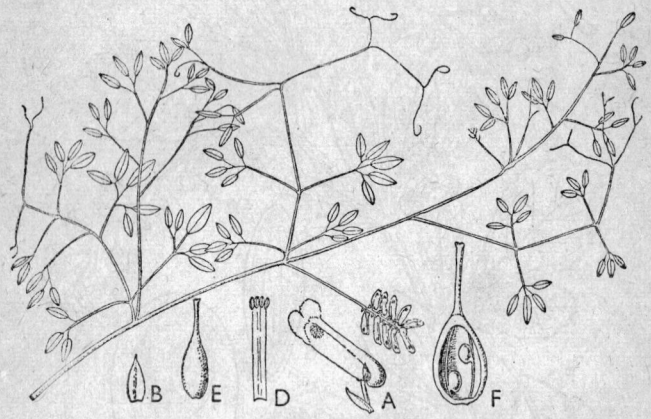

stamens (D, $\times$ 2) in 2 bundles, the middle anther 2-locular, the side anthers 1-locular; ovary (E, $\times$ 4, F, $\times$ 7) with 2 ovules on the placentas on the walls (parietal); style single; fruits few, oblong, beaked, slightly constricted between the seeds, about $\frac{1}{4}$ in. diam., black and shining, with a small crest at the point of attachment (family *Fumariaceae*).

Widely distributed but rarely common, in hilly districts; rare in Eire; flowers in summer, and easily recognised by the climbing habit with tendrils, and the leaf-opposed common flower-stalk (peduncle).

The stamens are at first shorter than the style, the stigma being concealed in the dark lilac hood of the inner upper petal. Into this hood the pollen is discharged and self-pollination may take place.

HAIRY BITTERCRESS, *Cardamine hirsuta* L.

271. Hairy Bittercress, *Cardamine hirsuta* L. ($\times \frac{1}{2}$); a rather dark green annual, on moist or shady banks, and in waste and cultivated places throughout temperate regions, usually about 6 in. but sometimes nearly a foot high, glabrous (in spite of the specific name) or very slightly hairy; lower leaves forming a loose rosette, pinnate, with a few rounded stalked lateral leaflets and a broader rounded or kidney-shaped end leaflet; a few stem leaves with rather narrower and smaller leaflets; flowers very small, white, few, in terminal racemes, soon developing into fruit (A, $\frac{1}{2}$); petals about twice as long as the sepals; stamens often only 4; ovary linear, with a sessile stigma; fruits (B, $\times$ 2) on slender stalks up to $\frac{1}{2}$ in. long and remaining erect, usually about 1 in. long, the valves not keeled; seeds brown, compressed, almost square in outline, smooth (family *Cruciferae*).

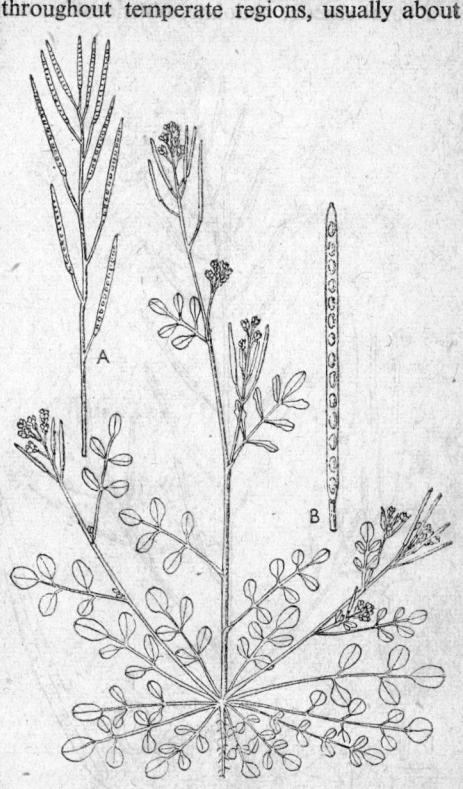

This species has a very unsuitable specific name, for it is only slightly hairy and certainly not *hirsute*, which means covered with hair. When botanists were free to choose what they considered to be the most suitable name, this one would have been objected to, especially by R. A. Salisbury, who gained notoriety in this practice early last century.

WALL CRESS, *Arabidopsis thaliana* (L.) Heynh.

272. Wall Cress, *Arabidopsis thaliana* (L.) Heynh. ($\times \frac{2}{5}$); slender erect annual sometimes branched from the base; leaves in a basal rosette, petiolate, oblanceolate, dentate especially in the lower half, sprinkled on both surfaces with stiff simple or 2–3-armed hairs (A, $\times 8$); stem-leaves very few and sessile; branches ending in a bunch of flowers, the main axis elongating as the fruits soon ripen; sepals 4, elliptic; petals (B, $\times 4$) 4, white, narrowly obovate, clawed, faintly nerved; stamens (C, $\times 4$) 6, 4 long and 2 short; anthers ovoid, short; ovary (D, $\times 4$) elongated, with numerous ovules, and a nearly sessile stigma; fruits (E, $\times 1\frac{1}{2}$) about $\frac{3}{4}$ in. long, on spreading stalks, 1-nerved; seeds (F, $\times 4$) numerous and very small, rounded, smooth, brownish (synonym *Sisymbrium thalianum* (L.) Gay) (family *Cruciferae*).

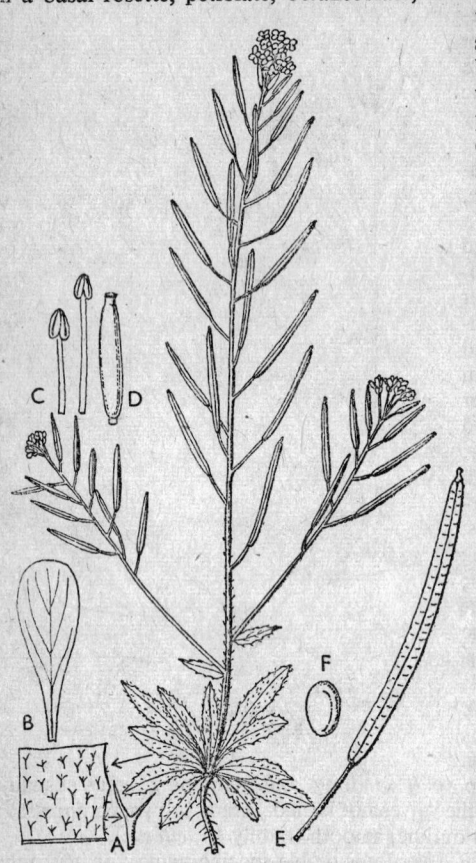

This species is locally abundant, and is found in light sandy fields, on walls and rocks. It is widely distributed.

HEDGE MUSTARD, *Sisymbrium officinale* (L.) Scop.

273. Hedge Mustard, *Sisymbrium officinale* (L.) Scop. ($\times \frac{1}{2}$); erect tough annual up to about 1½ ft. high, with green stems sometimes tinged with crimson, clothed with very short hairs, becoming rather zig-zag with age; lower leaves deeply and very irregularly pinnately lobed, the lobes rather unequally toothed or lobulate, thinly and very shortly bristly hairy on both surfaces; flowers very small, yellow, in short racemes terminating the branches, which elongate greatly in fruit, forming a leafy panicle; pedicels very short; sepals (A, $\times$ 6) 4, oblong, thinly hairy; petals (B, $\times$ 6) spoon-shaped, with a long slender claw; stamens (C, $\times$ 8) 6, 4 long and 2 shorter; anthers attached in the middle; ovary (D, $\times$ 10) very narrow, pubescent, the stigma nearly sessile, and bilobed; fruits (E, $\times$ 2) remaining parallel with and close to the elongated axis of the inflorescence, about ½ in. long, sharply pointed, pubescent or at length glabrous; valves with a prominent keel-like midrib; seeds (F, $\times$ 8) rounded but with a flat top (family *Cruciferae*).

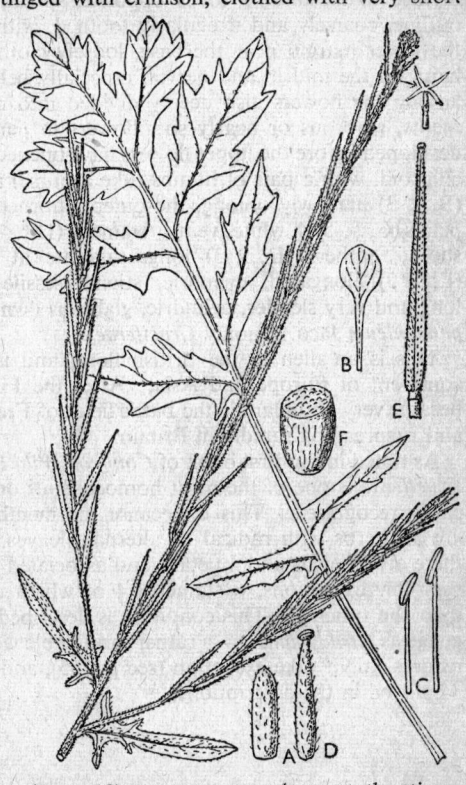

A weed in waste places and by the roadside, widely distributed into Russian Asia; flowers in summer; readily recognised by its elongated spreading branches.

TUMBLING MUSTARD, *Sisymbrium altissimum* L.

274. Tumbling Mustard, *Sisymbrium altissimum* L. (× ½); erect annual, up to about 1½–2 ft. high; basal leaves pinnately divided to the midrib, lobes opposite, spreading, lanceolate in outline, coarsely and irregularly toothed, with a larger lobe on the lower margin near the base, loosely clothed with long stiff hairs on the midrib and nerves, especially below; upper leaves among the flowers also deeply divided into narrow entire segments, glabrous or nearly so; flowers in panicles, fruits being developed before the upper flowers have opened; buds (A, × 1½) ellipsoid, with a pair of humps (like a purse) at the top; sepals (B, × 3) narrowly oblong, the outer 2 horned below the apex; petals (C, × 3) 4, white, veiny; stamens (D, × 3) 6, 4 long and 2 short; anthers (D, × 3) long, sagittate at the base; ovary (E, × 3) elongated, cylindric, stigma sessile; fruits (F, × ½) long and very slender, cylindric, glabrous (synonym *Sisymbrium pannonicum* Jacq.) (family *Cruciferae*).

This is an alien in the British flora, and is a native of the continent of Europe and Asia. After the First World War it became very abundant in the battle fields of France and Belgium, and is spreading rapidly in Britain.

As noted in our first book of *Common Wild Flowers*, the family *Cruciferae* is one of the most homogeneous or natural and very easily recognised. This is because the members of the family are all herbs with radical or alternate leaves, without stipules, there are 4 sepals and 4 petals, and associated with them, with a very few exceptions, 6 stamens, 4 of which are always longer than the other 2. This condition is described in botanical language as *tetradynamous*—a rather formidable word to which some readers might take exception (see p. 265), and which I have not employed in the descriptions.

109

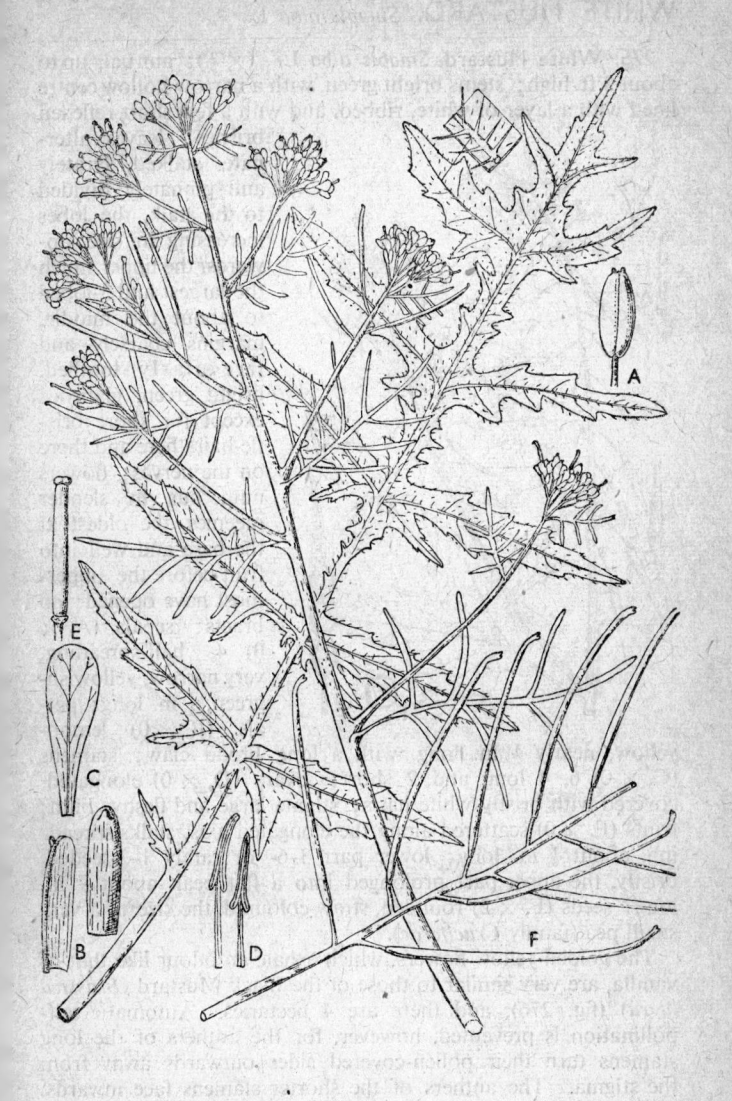

WHITE MUSTARD, *Sinapis alba* L.

275. White Mustard, *Sinapis alba* L. ($\times \frac{1}{3}$); annual, up to about 3 ft. high; stems bright green, with a narrow hollow centre lined with a layer of white, ribbed, and with a few short reflexed bristles; leaves alternate, stalked, lyrately and pinnately divided to the stalk, the lobes increasing in size upwards, the upper much the largest and 3-lobed to about the middle, margins coarsely and irregularly toothed, bright green, glabrous except for short bristle-hairs here and there on the nerves; flowers numerous in slender racemes, the oldest at the base and well into fruit before the uppermost have opened; no bracts; sepals (A, $\times$ 0) 4, half-spreading, very narrow, yellowish-green, $\frac{1}{4}$ in. long; petals (B, $\times$ 0) lemon-yellow, nearly $\frac{1}{2}$ in. long, with a long broad claw; stamens (C, $\times$ 0) 6, 4 long and 2 short; ovary (D, $\times$ 0) elongated, covered with bristly white hairs; stigma large and fleshy, bifid; fruits (E, $\times$ 0) scattered along the elongated axis, stalks spreading, about $\frac{1}{3}$ in. long; lower part 3–6- or rarely 1–2-seeded, bristly, the upper part prolonged into a flat beak about $\frac{3}{4}$ in. long; seeds (F, $\times$ 2) rounded, straw-coloured, the size of a very small pea (family *Cruciferae*).

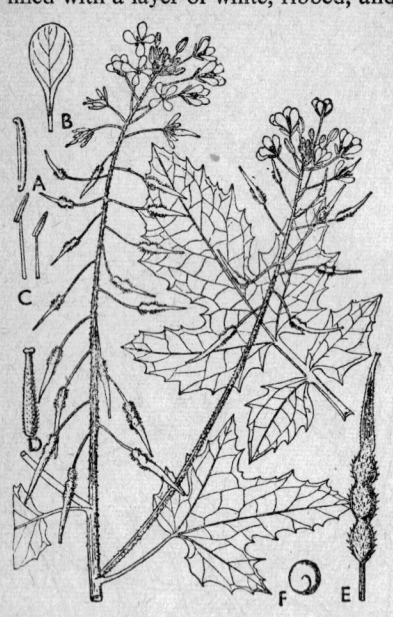

The golden-yellow flowers, which exhale an odour like that of vanilla, are very similar to those of the Black Mustard (*Brassica nigra*) (fig. 276), and there are 4 nectaries. Automatic self-pollination is prevented, however, for the anthers of the long stamens turn their pollen-covered sides outwards away from the stigma. The anthers of the shorter stamens face inwards. Honey-bees and hover-flies visit the flowers.

BLACK MUSTARD, *Brassica nigra* (L.) Koch.

276. Black Mustard, *Brassica nigra* (L.) Koch. ($\times \frac{1}{3}$); annual up to about 4 ft. high, glaucous-green all over, especially the branches, not hairy (glabrous); leaves alternate, lower stalked, more or less obovate or broadly elliptic, with one or two much smaller or very small extra lobes on the edge of the deeply channelled stalk, wavy-toothed on the margin, paler below; leaves smaller upwards and entire as they become bracts at the base of the branches bearing the flowers; these few in racemes; buds (A, $\times$ 0) 4-humped at the top; sepals (B, $\times 1\frac{1}{3}$) spreading in flower, a little longer than the claws of the lemon-yellow petals (C, $\times$ 0); stamens (D, $\times 1\frac{1}{3}$) 6, 4 long and 2 short; anthers becoming curved, arrow-shaped at the base; ovary (E, $\times 1\frac{1}{3}$) narrow, containing several ovules inserted on the walls; fruits (F, $\times$ 0) parallel with the flower axis, about $\frac{1}{2}$ in. long, beaked by the persistent style, 4-angled by the 4 ribs, a rib up the middle of each valve; seeds (G, $\times$ 4) dark brown, closely and minutely pitted (family *Cruciferae*).

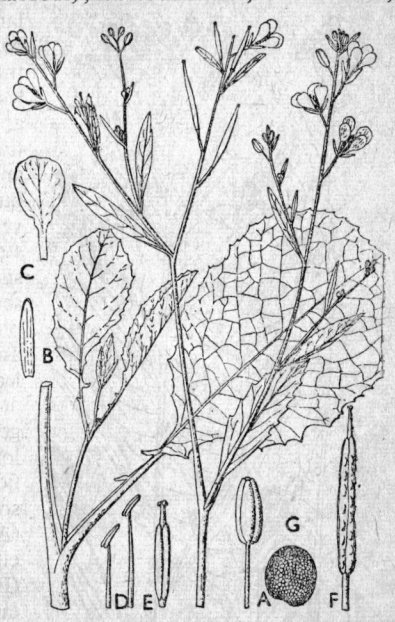

To be found in hedges and waste places, sometimes on sea-cliffs; frequently an escape from cultivation; it has the appearance of a maritime plant because of the clean glaucous-green colour of the stems. The bright-yellow flowers of this species have a strong odour of coumarin. There are 4 green nectaries, of which 2 are on the inner side of the short stamens, and the others between the insertions of the long stamens. Insects effect cross-pollination. Self-pollination may also be brought about when the flowers are bent by the wind, as the anthers of the long stamens are at the same level and close to the stigma.

HORSE RADISH, *Amoracia lapathifolia* Gilib.

277. Horse Radish, *Armoracia lapathifolia* Gilib. (× ½); perennial with a stout parsnip-like root-stock, very sharp to the taste; basal (radical) leaves large, on long stalks, the base of the stalk embracing the stem; blade more or less elliptic, rounded at the apex, some decurrent at the base, usually bluntly and irregularly crenate, but sometimes deeply and very irregularly divided; stem leaves gradually sessile, linear and only obscurely toothed; racemes on long axillary peduncles and all forming an oblong leafy panicle, the flowers at first closely bunched together, the lower stalks long and very slender; flower-buds broadly ellipsoid, glabrous; sepals 4 (A, × 5) unequal, ovate-elliptic, green; petals 4 (B, × 2½) white, ovate-lanceolate; stamens 6 (C, × 5), 4 long and 2 short; anthers ovoid; ovary (D, × 6) ellipsoid, crowned by a fat sessile stigma; fruits (E, × ½) not ripening in Britain (synonym *Cochlearia armoracia* L). (family *Cruciferae*).

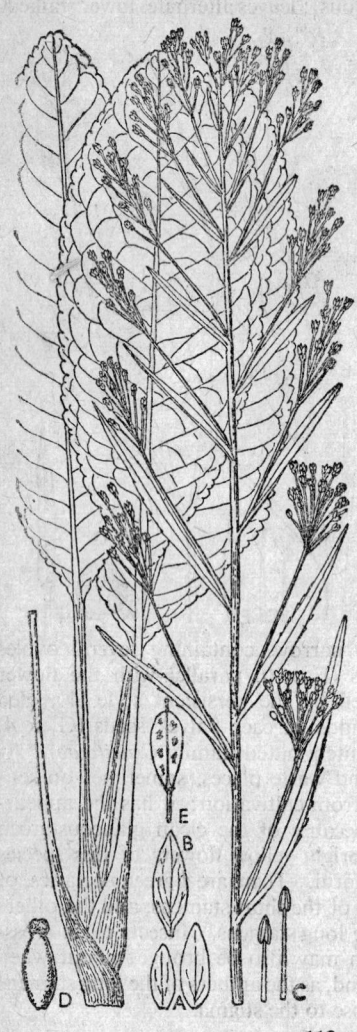

Horse Radish is always associated with the roast beef of Old England, and its roots find a place in nearly every kitchen garden. It is also naturalised in many places.

ICELAND WATERCRESS. *Rorippa islandica* (Geder) Borbás

278. Iceland Watercress, *Rorippa islandica* (Geder) Borbás ($\times \frac{1}{2}$); perennial growing in muddy places by ditches, etc.; basal leaves withering as the plant develops; stem-leaves auriculate at the base, lyrately-pinnately lobed almost to the midrib, lobes rather unequal, the top 3 more or less merged together into one, all the lobes coarsely toothed, glabrous; flowers numerous on axillary and terminal leafy shoots, very soon producing fruits whilst a few at the top are still in bloom; stalks slender, as long as the fruit; sepals (A, $\times$ 6), elliptic, rounded at the apex; petals (B, $\times$ 6) 4, white, narrowly obovate, clawed; stamens (C, $\times$ 6) 6, 4 long and 2 short; anthers elliptic; ovary (D, $\times$ 4) ellipsoid, with a short style and 2-lobed stigma; fruit (E, $\times 1\frac{1}{2}$) narrowly oblong, almost round in section, containing numerous small pale brown closely beaded seeds (F, $\times$ 6) (synonym *Nasturtium palustre* (Leyss.) DC.) (family *Cruciferae*).

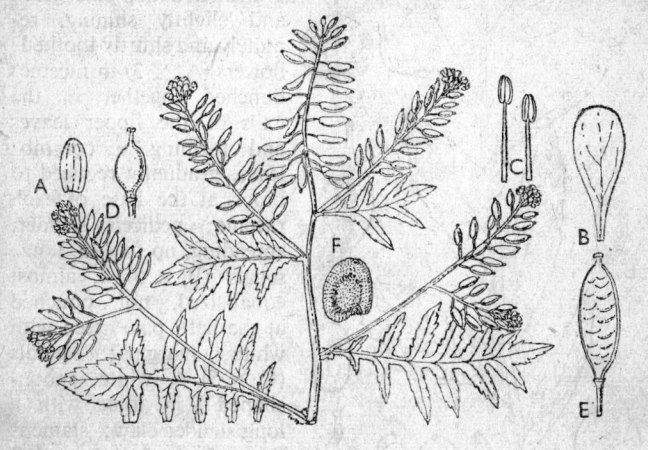

This is quite a common plant which is described in most Floras and lists under the name *Nasturtium palustre* DC. The latest classification, however, assigns it to a separate genus, *Rorippa*. It has also been called *Radicula*, and if it could speak it might modify this word a little to abuse the botanists who have changed its name so often.

HOARY CRESS, *Cardaria draba* (L.) Desv.

279. Hoary Cress, *Cardaria draba* (L.) Desv. ($\times \frac{1}{2}$); perennial; stems simple, up to about 1 ft. high or more, with prominent angles, not hairy (glabrous), or very slightly so; leaves alternate, sessile, oblong or oblong-elliptic, deeply eared (auriculate) at the base, rather rounded to the subacute apex, very minutely hairy on both surfaces, with short unbranched hairs, pale green and slightly shining, remotely and shortly toothed; flowers (A, $\times$ 3) in racemes bunched together in the axils of the upper leaves and forming a corymb; leaves gradually reduced to bracts at the base of each raceme; pedicels slender, spreading, up to $\frac{1}{2}$ in. long; sepals (B, $\times$ 5) 4, almost equal-sized, not pouched at the base, pale green with white margins; petals (C, $\times$ 5) 4, white, spoon-shaped $\frac{1}{8}$ in. long, with a long slender claw; stamens (D, $\times$ 5) 6, 4 long and 2 short; anthers ellipsoid; ovary (E, $\times$ 5) narrowly ovate, compressed, with 1 ovule in each loculus (F, $\times$ 5); style short, stigma head-like; fruit (G, $\times$ 2) compressed at right angles to the partition, broadly ovate, reticulate, not winged; seed (H, $\times$ 3) solitary in each loculus, flattened, elliptic, smooth, brown (synonym *Lepidium draba* L.) (family *Cruciferae*).

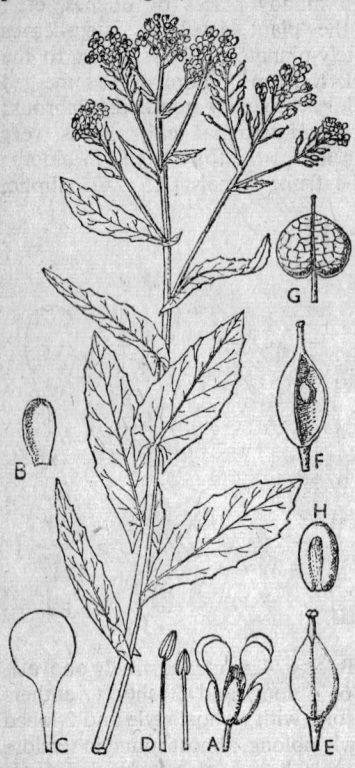

Grows in waste places and by roadsides, and widely distributed in Central and South Europe and into Russian Asia; it flowers during spring and early summer.

SCURVY GRASS, *Cochlearia officinalis* L.

280. Scurvy Grass, *Cochlearia officinalis* L. ($\times \frac{1}{2}$); a fleshy annual or biennial up to about 1 ft. high; lower leaves on long stalks, rounded-ovate, widely cordate at the base, about 2 in. wide, sometimes larger and more or less pentagonal, 3–5 nerved from the base, with undulate or crenate margins; stem-leaves sessile and eared (auriculate) at the base; flowers (K, $\times 2$) in short corymb-like racemes collected into a leafy panicle; sepals (A, $\times 2$) 4, oblong-elliptic; petals (B, $\times 4$) white, oblong, broadly clawed; stamens (C, $\times 5$) 6, 4 long and 2 shorter; anthers (D, E, $\times 7$) attached at the back above the base; ovary (F, $\times 3$) broadly ovoid, with a short thick style and capitate stigma; fruit (G, H, long-section, $\times 2$) broadly ellipsoid, $\frac{1}{4}$ in. long, openly reticulate, beaked by the short persistent style, the valves falling away and leaving the white membrane-like false septum; seeds (J, $\times 8$) few, much curved, with a caruncle, and closely pitted all over (family *Cruciferae*).

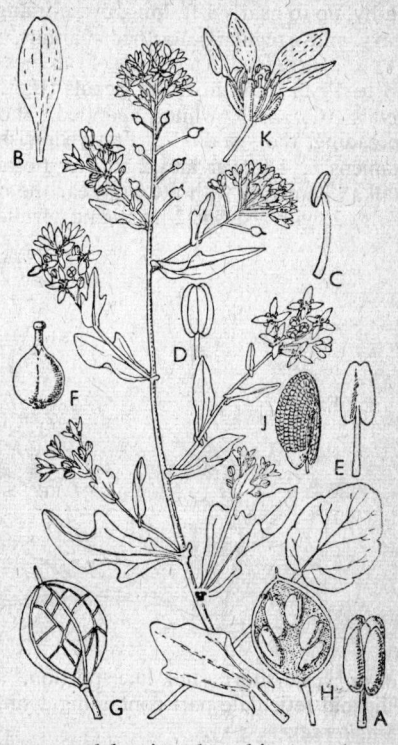

Scurvy Grass is common on many muddy seashores and on damp maritime cliffs, especially where water trickles down. The flowers open from May to July, and are followed by the short, nearly globular fruits. The common name is derived from its former antiscorbutic use, and it was well known to the early voyagers as a remedy for the disease which in olden days decimated ship's crews on long voyages.

SEA KALE, *Crambe maritima* L.

281. Sea Kale, *Crambe maritima* L. ($\times \frac{1}{3}$); a maritime plant on sandy and shingly coasts; perennial, with fleshy rootstock; branches spreading from the root; leaves few, large and fleshy, up to nearly 1 ft. long, ovate-triangular in outline but with wavy and irregularly toothed margins, very glaucous; flowers (A, $\times$ 2) arranged in a panicle of racemes; flower-stalks (pedicels) up to $1\frac{1}{2}$ in. long in fruit; sepals (B, $\times$ 2) 4, soon falling off; petals (C, $\times 1\frac{1}{3}$) white, rounded, shortly stalked (clawed), spreading, the "stalk" at first yellowish-green, then violet-red, stamens 6, 4 longer and 2 shorter (tetradynamous), the longer stalks (filaments) with a tooth near the middle (D, $\times$ 2); ovary (E, $\times$ 2) with a sessile 2-fid stigma; fruit (F, $\times$ 0) composed of a lower very short stalk-like portion, and an upper broadly ellipsoid reticulate part containing a single globose seed (family *Cruciferae*).

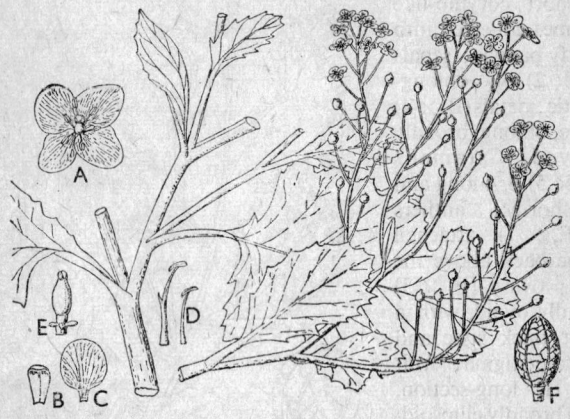

Well known to gardeners, who force it in the dark in greenhouses in early spring; the etiolated growths are eaten as a delicacy. It was at one time an object of special regard in the dwellings of South Coast fishermen, who climbed the cliffs or hung by means of ropes in order to collect the tender shoots as they emerged from the sand and shingle in spring.

The flowers smell like honey, and at the base of each pair of longer stamens is a large green nectary, to which a drop of nectar clings. The stigma is already mature in the bud before the anthers open, and occupies the middle of the newly opened flower.

PEPPERWORT, FIELD CRESS. *Lepidium campestre* (L.) R. Br.

282. Pepperwort, Field Cress, *Lepidium campestre* (L.) R. Br. ($\times \frac{1}{2}$); annual or biennial up to about 15 in. high, with a long slender tap-root, softly and very shortly hairy all over; lower leaves forming a loose rosette, withering away in fruit, spathulate-oblanceolate, entire to pinnatifid; stem-leaves narrowly oblong-lanceolate, sessile and eared (auriculate) at the base; racemes few, forming a panicle at the top of the plant, at first short and dense, soon elongating, with the fruits maturing in the lower part whilst the top is still in flower; pedicels spreading; sepals (A, $\times 5$) oblong, rounded at the top; petals absent; anthers (B, $\times 6$) yellow; ovary (C, $\times 6$) broadly elliptic, notched at the top and with a very short style; fruits (D, $\times 2$) numerous, somewhat compressed, ovate in outline, with a wing on each side from near the base upwards, minutely flaky; seeds (E, $\times 3$) oblong-ellipsoid (family *Cruciferae*).

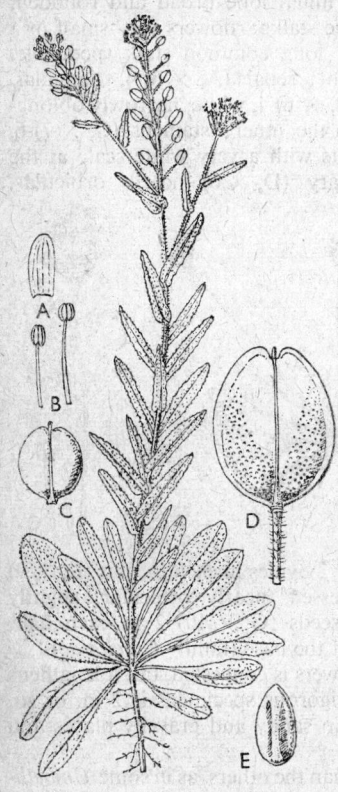

The fruits are very characteristic, and with their stalks resemble a small ladle-spoon.

In some books this plant is called "Mithridate Pepperwort". In old pharmacy the term mithridate was used for a composition of many ingredients which were regarded as a universal antidote or preservative against poison and infectious disease. It grows in hilly fields and in cultivated and waste ground.

SHEPHERD'S CRESS, *Teesdalia nudicaulis* (L.) R. Br.

283. Shepherd's Cress, *Teesdalia nudicaulis* (L.) R. Br. (× ½); usually a tiny and neat annual with a rather long taproot, but sometimes up to 1½ ft.; leaves spreading in a rosette forming a circle 2–3 in. diam., deeply pinnately lobed, the largest lobes towards the end, the terminal lobe broad and rounded, glabrous or nearly so except the stalks; flowers very small in a dense cluster at the end of a long common stalk (peduncle) from one to several to each plant; sepals (A, × 6) 4, triangular, green with white tips; petals (B, × 6) 4, white, narrowly oblong-oblanceolate, outer longer than the inner; stamens (C, × 7) 6, 4 long and 2 shorter; filaments with a very white scale at the base; anthers ellipsoid; ovary (D, × 6) nearly orbicular, glabrous, with a sessile stigma; 2 ovules in each loculus (E, × 9) fruits (F, × 3) rather compressed, nearly orbicular, slightly winged, about ⅛ in. diam.; seeds (G, × 10) 2 in each half, rounded, with a narrow crest at the base (family *Cruciferae*).

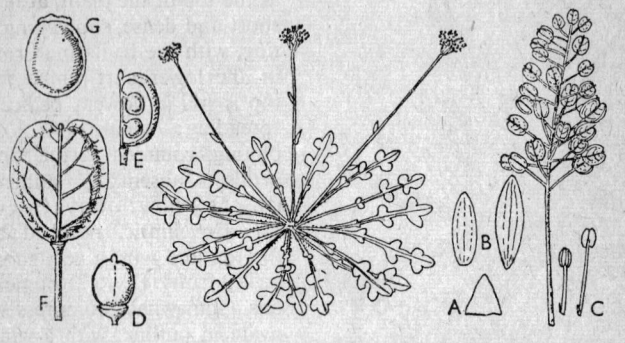

At first the raceme of tiny flowers is congested, but it lengthens as the fruits develop, and in vigorous specimens is 2 in. or so, excluding the stalk; it grows in sandy and gravelly places and flowers from April to June.

The outer petals are larger than the others, as in some *Umbelliferae*, and the inflorescence at first resembles that of the same family. As the outer flowers fade in turn, however, the axis of the inflorescence lengthens out into a raceme. There are 4 nectaries, and failing cross-pollination, self-pollination is effected by the long stamens.

SPURRY, *Spergula arvensis* L.

284. Spurry, *Spergula arvensis* L. ($\times \frac{2}{5}$); a slender annual weed, branching from the base into erect or ascending stems, the latter glabrous or very slightly hairy; leaves in clusters at the nodes and appearing in whorls, almost needle-like, i.e. very narrow, like those of a pine-tree, up to about 1 in. long, very slightly hairy; stipules very small and dry; flowers numerous in terminal forked cymes, the slender stalks turning downwards as the flowers mature; sepals 5, ovate-elliptic, slightly pubescent outside; petals (A, $\times$ 2) 5, white, broadly oblong-elliptic, shortly contracted at the base, usually shorter than the sepals, not divided; stamens (B, $\times$ 3) 10 or 5 on the same plant; anthers rounded; ovary rounded, 1-locular; styles 5; capsule (C, $\times$ 3) ellipsoid, opening from the top into 5 entire parts; seeds (D, $\times$ 4) flattened, orbicular, papillous, and with a narrow membranous margin (family *Caryophyllaceae*).

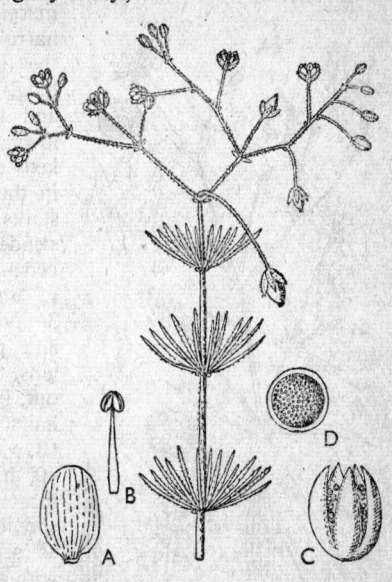

Spurry is a common weed in moist fields on light soils, but in some parts of Europe it is grown for fodder. Sheep are very fond of it, and cows fed on it are said to give good milk. The leaves and seeds are also eaten by poultry. Formerly in Scandinavia a kind of bread was made of the seeds in times of scarcity.

Though a favourite plant with farmers on the Continent, it is usually regarded as a troublesome weed in this country. On this account in Norfolk it is called "Pickpurse", and is considered by farmers to merit the name.

HEATH STITCHWORT, *Stellaria graminea* L.

285. **Heath Stitchwort,** *Stellaria graminea* L. ($\times \frac{1}{2}$); perennial; stems very slender and straggling, sharply 4-angled, not hairy; leaves opposite, united and slightly hairy on the margin at the base, very narrowly lanceolate, acute at the tip, up to about $1\frac{1}{2}$ in. long, with a strong midrib and faint parallel nerves below; flowers many, but very laxly arranged, with the oldest in the forks, $\frac{1}{2}$-$\frac{2}{3}$ in. diam.; stalks up to $1\frac{1}{2}$ in. long, slender; buds acute and ribbed; sepals (A, $\times$ 0) 5, slightly united at the base, with 3 prominent green nerves and pale membranous margins, the outermost one without, but the others with short hairs on the margin; petals (B, $\times$ 2) 5, but appearing like 10, being deeply divided almost to the base, white, spreading, not twice as long as sepals; stamens (C, $\times$ 2) with small brown anthers attached in the middle; ovary (D, $\times$ 2) 1-locular with several ovules attached to the central axis (E, $\times$ 4); styles 3, with slightly swollen tips; fruit (F, $\times$ 0) a capsule, a little longer than the sepals; seeds (G, $\times$ 4) orbicular, verrucose (family *Caryophyllaceae*).

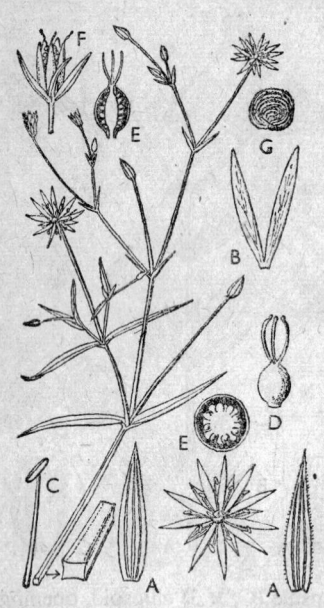

Grows in dry pastures, hedgebanks, and at the base of crumbling walls, flowering from May to August. It is not always easy to distinguish this from the very similar *S. palustris* Ehrh., which grows in wetter places; the latter is glaucous (more greyish), and has petals very much longer than the sepals, and its sepals are not hairy on the margin. In *S. graminea* the petals are usually not much longer than the sepals.

There is a nectary at the base of each of the outer stamens. When the flower opens these bend inwards and open, the 5 inner ones not yet being ripe and curved outwards, and the stigmas are not receptive.

FIELD CHICKWEED, *Cerastium arvense* L.

286. **Field Chickweed,** *Cerastium arvense* L. ($\times \frac{2}{3}$); perennial herb much branched from the base, often much matted together and prostrate, the flowering branches ascending to about 6 in. high, leafy to the top and covered all around with deflexed hairs; leaves opposite, linear, entire, the bases touching round the stem, obtuse or only half acute at the apex, $\frac{1}{2}-\frac{3}{4}$ in. long, more or less hairy all over, but especially on the margin; no stipules; flowers about 3–5 (rarely more) together in a cyme at the end of each shoot, rather large and conspicuous; sepals 5, $\frac{1}{4}$ in. long, oblong-elliptic, green with a narrow membranous margin, softly pubescent; petals twice as long as the sepals, deeply 2-lobed; stamens (A, $\times$ 4, B, $\times$ 8) usually 10; ovary (C, $\times$ 4) globose, 1-locular, with numerous ovules on a free central placenta (D, $\times$ 6); styles 5, free; capsule (E, $\times$ 2) oblique; a little longer than the sepals, opening at the top by 10 teeth; seeds rounded-obovoid, warted all over (F, $\times$ 3) (family *Caryophyllaceae*).

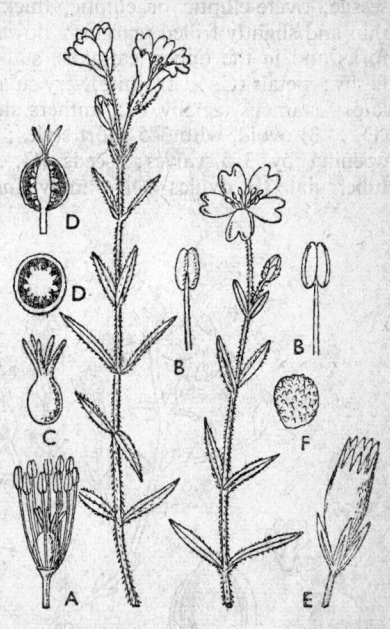

Grows in sandy fields and waste ground, flowering from spring to early summer, and found in many parts of the world.

SEA PURSLANE, *Arenaria peploides* L.

287. Sea Purslane, *Arenaria peploides* L. ($\times \frac{1}{2}$); perennial with creeping root-stock; stems usually much branched, rather fleshy, glabrous; leaves (A, $\times 0$) opposite, in four rows, sessile, ovate-elliptic or elliptic, thick and fleshy, green, with thin and slightly frilled margins; flowers (B, $\times 2$) solitary in the forks and in the upper leaf-axils, stalked; sepals 5, green and fleshy; petals (C, $\times 2$) white, very small, spoon-shaped (spathulate); stamens usually 10; anthers short and rounded; ovary (D, $\times 3$) ovoid, with 3–5 short styles; fruit (F, $\times 1\frac{1}{2}$) a capsule opening by 3–5 valves; seeds (G, $\times 2\frac{1}{2}$) obovoid, minutely tuberculate (E, ovules $\times 4$) (family *Caryophyllaceae*).

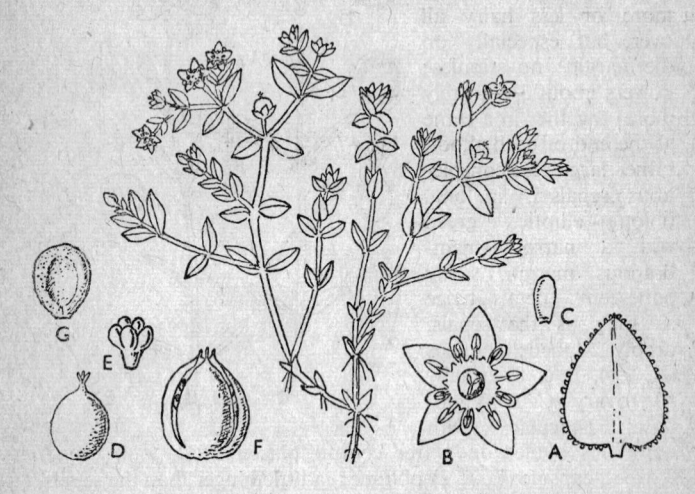

A very widely spread maritime plant growing in sandy places and sometimes amongst shingle; rather outstanding, and different in general appearance from other species of *Arenaria*; the petals are very small. In habit it somewhat resembles the Sea Milkwort (*Glaux maritima* L.) (see fig. 305), but the latter grows on muddy shores. The root-stock is long and slender and creeps in the sand or amongst the pebbles. In Yorkshire the plant was formerly much used as a pickle and accredited with a pleasant pungent taste.

The species is sometimes regarded as representing a genus distinct from *Arenaria*, and is then called *Honkenya peploides* (L.) Ehrh.

APETALOUS or ANNUAL PEARLWORT, *Sagina apetala* Ard.

288. Apetalous or Annual Pearlwort, *Sagina apetala* Ard. ($\times \frac{4}{5}$); a tiny annual with numerous branches from the base, forming a flat tuft; branches almost thread-like (filiform), glabrous; leaves opposite, awl-shaped (subulate), very acute, with membranous margins united at the base and fringed with hairs like a comb; flowers (A, B, $\times 6$) usually 2 or 3 at the top of each shoot, on very slender thread-like stalks; sepals 4, free, green, ovate-elliptic; petals none or very minute; stamens (C, $\times 12$) 4, opposite the sepals; anthers rounded, the loculi separate; ovary (D, $\times 10$) sessile, ovoid, glabrous, crowned by 4 short stigmas, 1-locular, with numerous ovules on a central placenta (F, $\times 20$); seeds (G, $\times 16$) minute, closely warted (family *Caryophyllaceae*).

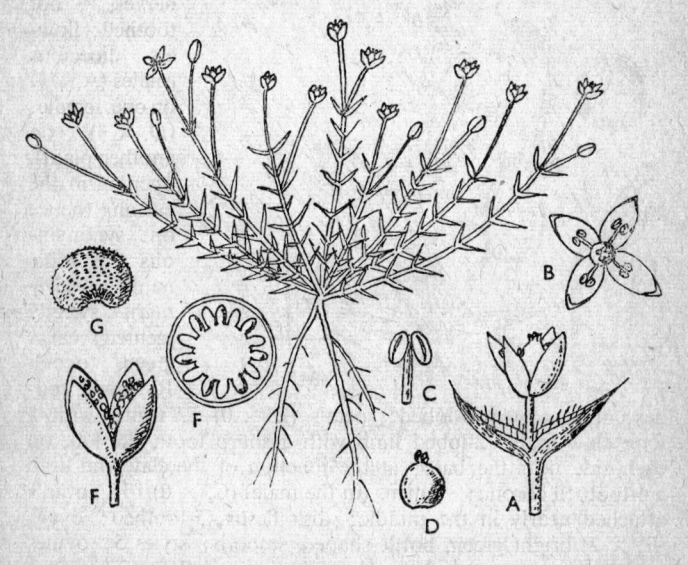

It needs a strong lens to examine the very small flowers of this tiny plant, which might be mistaken for *Linum catharticum* L. or *Radiola linoides* Roth., both of which have petals, however, and belong to quite another family, *Linaceae*; in *Radiola* the sepals are also 4, but they are united in the lower half.

WHITE CAMPION, *Lychnis alba* Mill.

289. White Campion, *Lychnis alba* Mill. ($\times \frac{1}{3}$); strong-growing biennial up to 3 ft. high; stem hollow, branches loosely covered with long pale several-celled hairs; leaves opposite, bases connected by a narrow hairy rim, oblanceolate, narrowed to the apex, softly hairy on the nerves, not toothed; flowers dioecious (males (A, $\times \frac{2}{3}$) on one, females (D, $\times \frac{2}{3}$) on another plant), opening in the evening (hence one synonymous specific name, *vespertina*), sweetly scented; calyx green, ovoid, 10-ribbed, pubescent, narrowly 5-lobed; petals (B, $\times$ 0) 5, white, with a long claw and a 2-lobed limb with a sharp tooth-like lobe on each side near the base; at the junction of the claw and limb a 4-toothed corona; stamens (in the male) (C, $\times$ 0) 10; anthers attached nearly in the middle; disk fleshy, 5-toothed; ovary (E, $\times$ 2) bright green, bottle-shaped, smooth; styles 5; ovules numerous on a central pentagonal placenta (F, $\times 2\frac{1}{4}$); fruit (G, $\times$ 0) ovoid, opening by 10 teeth; seeds (H, $\times$ 4) kidney-shaped, closely warted (synonym *Melandrium album* (Mill.) Garcke) (family *Caryophyllaceae*).

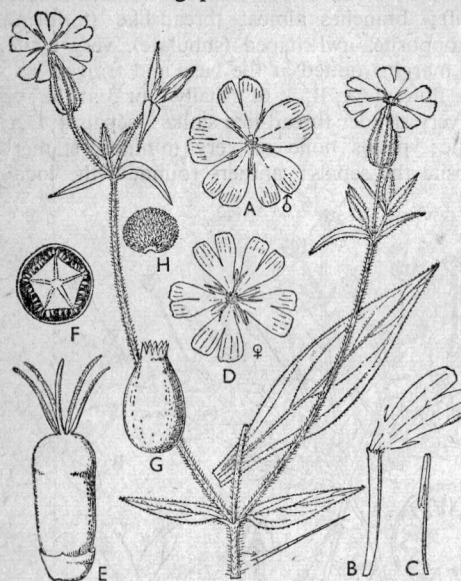

Flowers in the early summer in fields and hedgerows, the blooms opening in the evening and giving off a sweet scent. When females are found growing remote from the males, the flowers, not being pollinated, drop off very readily.

SEA CAMPION, *Silene maritima* (Hornem.) With.

290. Sea Campion, *Silene maritima* (Hornem.) With. (× ½); perennial with numerous radiating and horizontally spreading glabrous stems, often tinged with dull purple up one side; leaves (A, × 0) opposite, sessile, lanceolate to ovate-lanceolate, rather acute and thick, bright glaucous-green, slightly joined at the base, not distinctly nerved; flowers few to each stem, terminal, on slender stalks; calyx (B, × ¾) about ¾ in. long, inflated, green or tinged with crimson, distinctly veined, shortly 5-lobed; petals (C, × 0) 5, white, deeply 2-lobed, long-clawed, the claw with a bifid scale at the top; stamens 10; anthers (D, × 3) versatile (attached in the middle); ovary (E, × 0) 4-locular at the base, with numerous ovules on axile placentas (F, × 2½); styles 3–4, free to the base; fruit campanulate, nerved and reticulate; seeds (G, × 4) kidney-shaped, transversely striolate (family *Caryophyllaceae*).

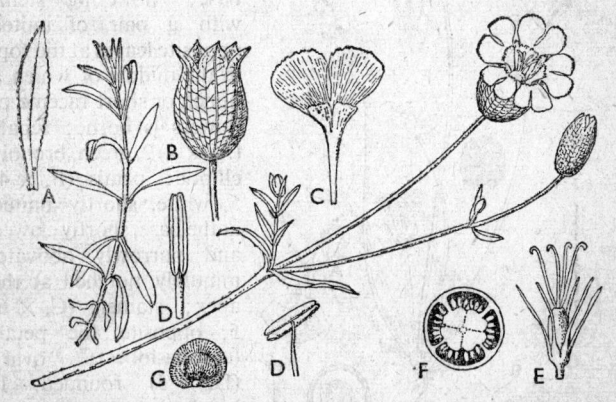

In some Floras this is treated as a maritime variety of *Silene cucubalus* Wibel (Pelican, *Common Wild Flowers*, fig. 103); It is very distinct in habit, however, the stems being prostrate and spreading. It grows in shingle by the sea or on the shores of maritime lochs.

PERFOLIATE MONTIA, *Montia perfoliata* (Don) Howell

291. **Perfoliate Montia,** *Montia perfoliata* (Don) Howell (× ⅓); annual in cultivated or waste ground; leaf-stalks and blades thick and fleshy, glabrous; basal leaves on long stalks, ovate or almost rhomboid, more or less wedge-shaped at the base, entire, up to about 1 in. long and broad, faintly 3-nerved from above the base; flowering stems with a pair of united opposite leaves at the top, in the middle of which a bunch or short raceme of flowers is borne; sepals (A, × 2) 2, green, broadly elliptic; petals (B, × 4) 5, white, shortly united at the base, shortly clawed and narrowly obovate, minutely notched at the apex; stamens (C, × 6) 5, opposite the petals (corolla-lobes); ovary (D, × 5) rounded, 1-locular, composed of 3 united carpels; style white, columnar, divided into three curved papillous stigmas; fruit (F, × 1½) splitting to the base into 3 valves; seeds (G, × 3) black and shining, in vertical section (H, × 4) showing the much curved embryo around the endosperm (E, flower bud, × 1½) (synonym *Claytonia perfoliata* Willd.) (family *Portulacaceae*).

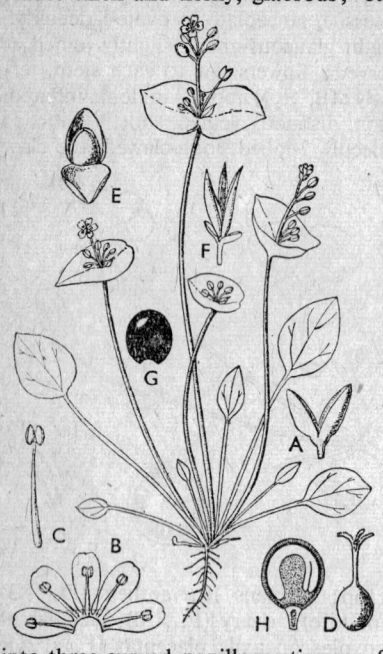

In the latest classification of the genera of this family, this species is referred to the genus *Montia*, of which there is a second native species in Britain, *Montia fontana*, a tiny plant with spoon-shaped leaves, a zygomorphic corolla and only two stamens. The species of the genus *Claytonia*, in which *M. perfoliata* has usually been placed, are perennials, whilst most species of *Montia* are annuals. *M. perfoliata* has also been placed in a third genus *Limnia*. It is a native of North America and naturalised in Britain.

MOUNTAIN WILLOW-HERB, *Epilobium montanum* L

292. Mountain Willow-Herb, *Epilobium montanum* L. ($\times \frac{1}{3}$); perennial; stems up to about 2 ft. high, with a few withered leaves towards the base, rounded, minutely hairy; leaves alternate or opposite or both on the same stem, very shortly stalked, spreading horizontally, rather narrowly ovate, only half acute, rounded at the base, rather sharply and irregularly toothed (doubly dentate), 2–3 in. long, apparently smooth, but really very minutely hairy (pubescent); flowers stalked; sepals 4, at the top of the very long inferior ovary, shortly united at the base, oblong, acute, $\frac{1}{4}$ inch long, 1-nerved; petals (A, $\times 1\frac{1}{4}$) 4 spirally arranged in bud, pink, and veiny obovate, deeply 2-lobed; stamens (B, $\times 2$) 8, alternately long and short; anthers attached at the back; style (C, $\times 2$) white, with 4 thick spreading lobes; ovary (D, $\times 4$) 4-locular and 4-angled, very shortly hairy; ovules numerous, in 2 rows in each compartment; fruit (E, $\times \frac{1}{2}$) a capsule 2–$3\frac{1}{2}$ in. long; seeds (F, $\times 3$) tipped with a brush of long fine hairs (family *Onagraceae*).

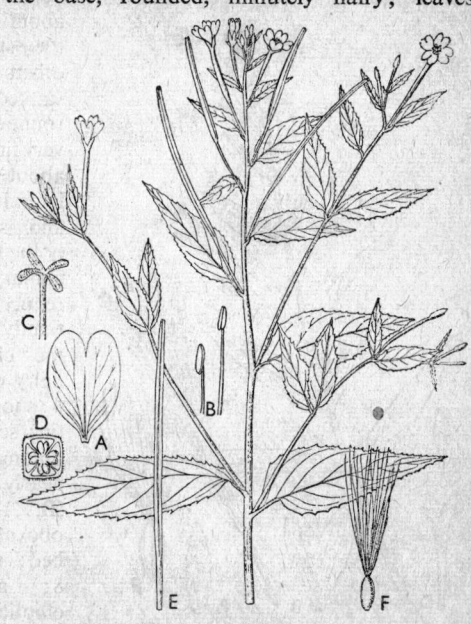

On shady banks, old walls and on roofs, and often a weed in shady garden borders; in autumn stolons covered with a rosette of scales; widely distributed into North and western Asia and as far south as the Himalayas. Insect visitors are very few, and self-pollination takes place through the anthers of the long stamens maturing at the same time as the stigmas. The anthers of the shorter stamens open later, and may effect cross-pollination.

HOARY WILLOW HERB, *Epilobium parviflorum* Schreb.

293. Hoary Willow Herb, *Epilobium parviflorum* Schreb. ($\times \frac{2}{5}$); perennial up to 1½ ft. high; stems reddish, covered with soft white hairs; leaves opposite or the upper alternate, those about the middle of the stem sessile, the others very shortly stalked, lanceolate, rounded at the base, very finely toothed, with about 5-6 pairs of lateral nerves, shortly and softly hairy on both surfaces; flowers axillary in the upper reduced leaves, distinctly stalked below the elongated slightly hairy ovary; buds with 4 short knobs at the tip; sepals (A, $\times 1\frac{1}{2}$) 4, oblong-elliptic, reddish, nearly glabrous; petals (B, $\times 1\frac{1}{2}$) 4, rosy, broadly obovate, deeply bilobed; stamens (C, $\times 4$) 8; anthers broadly elliptic in outline; style (D, $\times 2$) club-shaped when young, but opening out into 4 lobes; ovary inferior and resembling a thickened stalk; fruit (E, $\times 2$) elongated, splitting into 4 narrow recurved parts and releasing the numerous tiny seeds (F, $\times 8$) with a tuft of silky hairs at the top; flowers in summer (family *Onagraceae*).

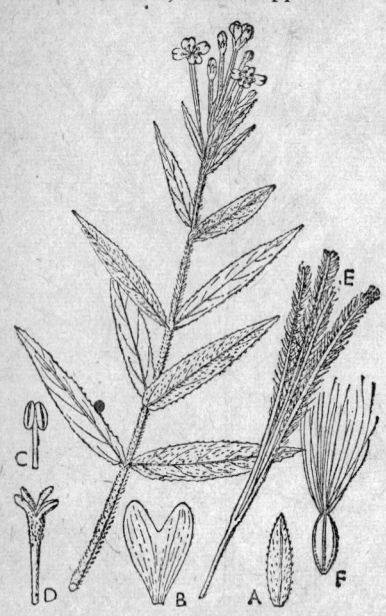

Grows in ditches and on river-banks, flowering in July and August; stolons are produced in the autumn, and have a bunch of nearly sessile leaves. It is widely distributed into North Africa and as far east as the Himalayas.

MARSH WILLOW HERB, *Epilobium palustre* L.

294. Marsh Willow Herb, *Epilobium palustre* L. ($\times \frac{1}{2}$); perennial with slender subterranean scaly stolons bearing in autumn scaly buds; stems slender, erect, rounded, more or less equally hairy all around, the hairs soft and short; leaves sessile, opposite, but the upper becoming alternate and bract-like, lanceolate to almost linear, apex obtuse, finely hairy, especially on the midrib below, lateral nerves few, ascending; flowers (A, $\times 1\frac{1}{2}$) few to solitary at the top of the stems, each subtended by a leafy bract, distinctly stalked, nodding in bud; ovary (inferior) resembling a thickened stalk and densely and softly pubescent; calyx shortly tubular 4-lobed, lobes oblong, hairy, margined with red; petals (B, $\times 2$) 4, rosy-lilac, $\frac{1}{4}$ in. long, deeply notched; stamens (C, $\times 2$) 8; anthers broadly ellipsoid; style (D, $\times 2$) with a club-shaped, entire stigma; capsule (E, $\times 2$) up to about 3 in. long, slender, splitting from the top downwards and releasing rows of superposed seeds (F, $\times 2\frac{1}{2}$), the latter smooth but crowned by a tuft of long silky hairs like the pappus of a thistle (family *Onagraceae*).

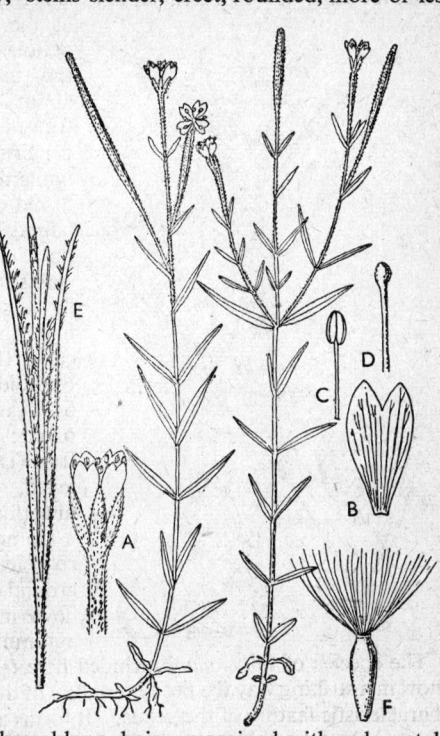

This is found in wet boggy places, and flowers in summer. It is widely distributed as far as Asiatic Russia and even into the Arctic regions.

PEACHWORT, RED-SHANKS, *Polygonum persicaria* L.

295. Peachwort, Red-Shanks, *Polygonum persicaria* L. ($\times \frac{2}{5}$); annual, erect or spreading, with leggy branches from the base, reddish; leaves alternate, lanceolate, half acute, narrowed at the base into a short petiole to which is adnate the thin tubular stipule about ½ in. long; stipules fringed at the top with slender bristles; lateral nerves numerous; flowers (A, × 5) red or greenish, in often paired spike-like racemes up to 1½ in. long; flower-stalks very short, subtended by a small fringed bract like a miniature stipule; calyx (B, × 5) 5-lobed to the middle; stamens 5 or 6; ovary (C, × 5) broadly ovoid; styles 2, recurved; fruit (D, × 4) slightly flattened, nearly black, shining (family *Polygonaceae*).

Common in ditches, by roadsides, and on waste ground and rubbish-heaps, flowering in summer and autumn.

The species of *Polygonum* included here (see also figs. 296–8) show in a striking way the peculiar nature of the stipule, which is a characteristic feature of the genus. It forms a sheath, sometimes of considerable size, within the leaf-stalk, and is called an *ochrea*. Usually this is fringed with long hairs or bristles.

There are no petals in the flowers of the family *Polygonaceae*, but the sepals often make up for this deficiency by being coloured. It is closely related to the Pink family, *Caryophyllaceae*.

WATERPEPPER, *Polygonum hydropiper* L.

296. Waterpepper, *Polygonum hydropiper* L. ($\times \frac{1}{2}$); a slender annual, common in wet places, stream and pond-sides, and in damp gullies in woods; stems decumbent and rooting at the base, usually reddish or green and tinged with red, glabrous; leaves alternate, very shortly stalked, the base of the stalk encircling the stem and prolonged upwards into a large sheathing stipule (ochrea), which is truncate at the top and fringed with slender bristles; blade lanceolate, fringed with very short hairs, otherwise glabrous; flowers in slender racemes in the axils of the leaves and at the top of each shoot, the short stalks jointed at the top; bract (A, $\times$ 2) like the stipule in shape, but much shorter, and not fringed with bristles; sepals (B, $\times 2\frac{1}{2}$) 3, green and pink, pustulate; no petals; stamens (C, $\times 2\frac{1}{2}$) usually 6, opposite the sepals; ovary (D, $\times 2\frac{1}{2}$) flattened, with 2–3 short styles; fruit (E, $\times 2\frac{1}{2}$) black, 3-angled, pitted when ripe (family *Polygonaceae*).

Polygonum hydropiper is called " Smart-weed " in Canada, and is listed among the " Pesky plants " of that country. The juice of the leaves and stems contains an irritant substance that produces burning and itching of the skin, especially between the fingers or on the back of the hand. When chewed, the leaves taste as hot as pepper.

The species has a wide range over the whole of Europe and most of Asiatic Russia, and Russian peasants use the fresh plant and other species of the genus as a poultice, gargle, etc.

FLOATING POLYGONUM, *Polygonum amphibium* L.

297. Floating Polygonum, *Polygonum amphibium* L. ($\times \frac{1}{3}$); perennial with slender woody root-stock; stem erect or ascending, often in water; leaves stalked, with a large intrapetiolar sheath (ochrea) at the base, lanceolate, gradually and rather broadly pointed, rounded at the base, up to about 4 or 5 in. long, minutely and closely toothed on the margin, lateral nerves numerous, repeatedly looped towards the margin; flowers numerous in rather thick spike-like racemes which are single or paired at the top of the stem; calyx (A, $\times$ 2) petaloid, pink to purple-red 5-lobed; stamens (B, $\times$ 5) 5, anthers broadly ellipsoid, attached near the middle; ovary (C, $\times$ 2) 1-locular, with 1 basal ovule; style deeply divided, with head-like stigmas; nut flattened (family *Polygonaceae*).

In ditches and ponds, flowering during summer; when growing away from the water, in dried up places, etc., stems creeping at the base, and the leaves often hairy.

Notes on the remarkable stipules accompanying fig. 295 apply also to this species. Two species of the genus grow in or near the water—that described above, and *P. hydropiper* L., shown in fig. 296.

The flowers smell like honey, nectar being secreted around the base of the ovary by 5 orange-yellow glands. The land form (var. *terrestre* Leers) possesses short hairs on the stalks secreting a viscid fluid which affords protection from creeping insects. The typical form is glabrous, the surrounding water giving access to none but flying insects.

BLACK BINDWEED, *Polygonum convolvulus* L.

298. Black Bindweed, *Polygonum convolvulus* L. ($\times \frac{1}{2}$); an annual with a twining glabrous ribbed stem; leaves stipulate, alternate, stalked, rounded-ovate, very widely sagittate-heart-shaped (cordate) at the base, rather long-pointed, glabrous but minutely rugose, especially when dried in a plant-press; nerves looped and branched well within the entire margin; stipules encircling the stem, $\frac{1}{4}$ in. long, nerved longitudinally; flowers

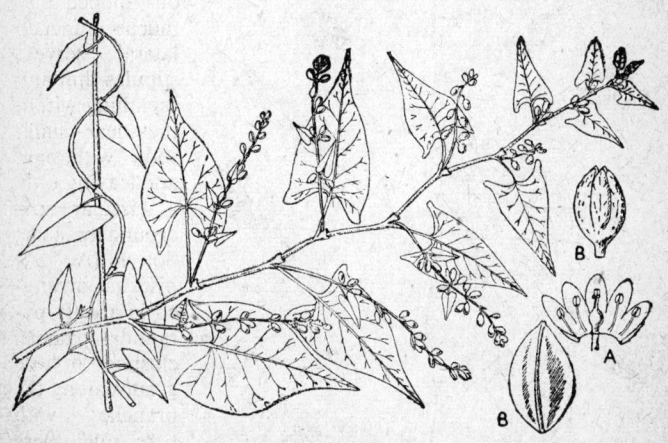

(A, $\times 2\frac{1}{2}$) shortly stalked in axillary clusters, obovate in bud; sepals 5, glabrous, green with white margins, the outer 3 remaining around the fruit and narrowly keeled; no petals; stamens 5, opposite the sepals; ovary with 3 styles; fruit (B, $\times$ 3) enclosed by the sepals, triangular, black and shining, the stalk jointed above the middle (family *Polygonaceae*).

This plant may prove injurious to stock fed on grain amongst which the fruits ("seeds") are very often mixed. Oats which contain too many of them may, by prolonged use, cause enteritis, with sometimes fatal results.

SHARP DOCK, *Rumex conglomeratus* Murray

299. Sharp Dock, *Rumex conglomeratus* Murray ($\times \frac{1}{3}$); perennial; stems 2-3 ft. high, zig-zag, ribbed; leaves alternate, stalked, lanceolate, rounded at the base, broadly pointed at the apex, entire or very faintly crenulate on the margin, with numerous looped and much - branched lateral nerves; stipules thin and sheathing within the leaf - stalk, soon withering, and leaving only a circular scar around the stem; flowers (A, $\times \frac{2}{5}$) bisexual, arranged in a leafy pyramidal panicle, clustered in little groups along the branches with here and there a leafy bract; stalks jointed between the middle and the base, the basal part persisting like little pegs; sepals 6, not toothed, the 3 outer very small, the 3 inner larger and erect around the fruit, in the latter state each with a large elliptic swelling (tubercle) in the lower half (C, $\times 3$); fruit (B, $\times 3$) a glossy triangular nut (family *Polygonaceae*).

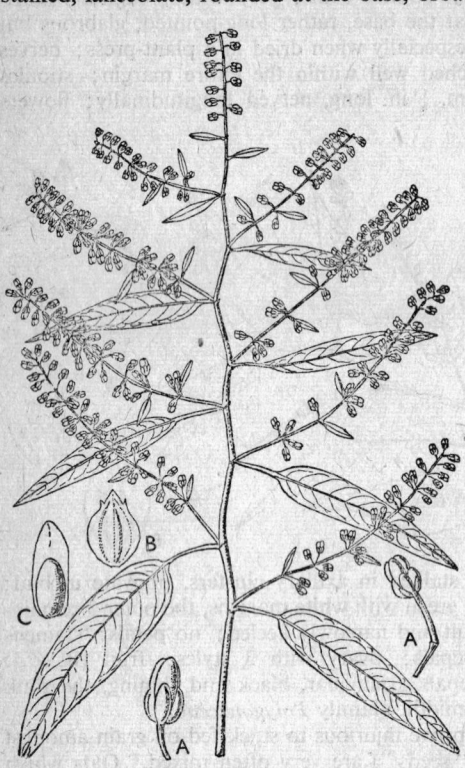

This species may be recognised by the leaves never being arrow-shaped at the base, by the entire (not toothed) sepals, which are not cordate (heart-shaped) at the base, and by the swelling on the back of all three, and not only on one, as in *R. sanguineus* L.

BROAD-LEAVED DOCK, *Rumex obtusifolius* L.

300. **Broad-leaved Dock**, *Rumex obtusifolius* L. ($\times \frac{1}{3}$); perennial; stems 2–3 ft. high, nearly straight, ribbed; lower leaves (A, $\times \frac{1}{3}$) stalked, rather large, elliptic or elliptic-lanceolate, rounded to acute at the base, gradually and broadly pointed, distinctly crenulate on the margin, with numerous looped and branched lateral nerves; stipules membranous, sheathing within the petiole (intrapetiolar); flowers very numerous in a stiff erect panicle, the main axis and branches of which bear narrow lanceolate leaves here and there; flower-stalks (B, $\times 2\frac{1}{2}$) jointed just below the middle, the lower part persisting like little pegs; inner sepals broadly ovate, coarsely toothed, some of the teeth ending in a fine point; in fruit these 3 inner sepals (C, $\times 2$) closely appressed to the 3-sided shining nut (D, $\times 2\frac{1}{2}$), and with an ellipsoid swelling (tubercle) in the lower half, also coarsely reticulate (family *Polygonaceae*).

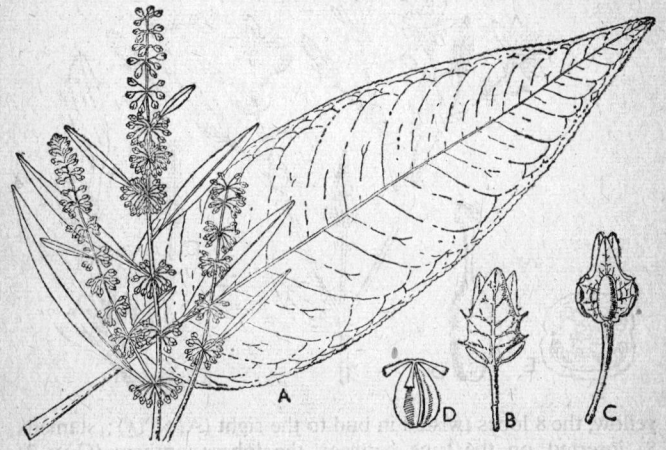

On roadsides, in ditches, fields and waste places, and widely distributed in many parts of the world; flowers during summer.

The two species of Dock described in the present book belong to different groups, one set of species, to which *R. obtusifolius* belongs, having the inner sepals toothed on the margin, whilst in the other, to which *R. conglomeratus* (see fig. 299) belongs, the sepals are not toothed, and all three of them have a swelling (tubercle) in the lower part.

YELLOW-WORT, *Blackstonia perfoliata* (L.) Huds.

301. Yellow-wort, *Blackstonia perfoliata* (L.) Huds. ($\times \frac{1}{2}$); erect annual up to 1½ ft. high, glaucous (like the bloom on a grape) all over and without hairs (glabrous); leaves opposite, united at the base (perfoliate), each half broadly ovate and somewhat acute at the apex, the largest up to about 2½ in. from tip to tip, each leaf 3-nerved; flowers in a dichotomous cyme (see drawing for this), the oldest flower in the first fork and subsequent forks; bracts becoming smaller upwards, like miniature leaves; calyx (A, $\times 1\frac{1}{2}$) divided to the base into 8 linear-subulate parts longer than the corolla-tube; corolla (B, $\times 0$) bright cream-yellow, the 8 lobes twisted in bud to the right (A, $\times 1\frac{1}{2}$); stamens 8, inserted on the tube between the lobes; anthers (C, $\times 2$) linear; ovary (D, $\times 2\frac{1}{2}$) 1-locular, with numerous ovules on the 2 bilobed parietal (on the walls) placentas (E, $\times 5$); fruit a capsule with persistent style; seeds minute (synonym *Chlora perfoliata* L.) (family *Gentianaceae*).

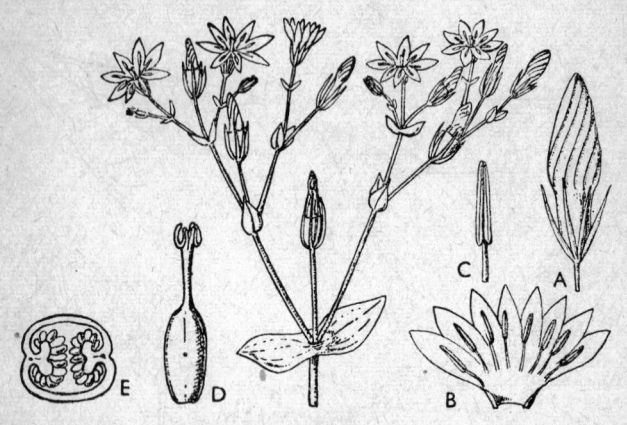

In some seasons this is plentiful on the chalk downs and banks by the sea, and is a very pretty sight, often growing in the company of another member of the same family, *Centaurium umbellatum* (*Common Wild Flowers*, fig. 117). It is only locally common, but is fairly widely distributed in England. It extends eastwards as far as the Caucasus.

This very attractive plant seems to be quite independent of insect visitors, for the flowers secrete no nectar. They close at night, and the two thick bilobed stigmas are self-pollinated.

WOOD ANEMONE

Anemone nemorosa

ANGELICA
Angelica sylvestris

SNOWDROPS *Galanthus nivalis*

BUGLE *Ajuga reptans*

STITCHWORT
Stellaria holostea

COLTSFOOT
Tussilago farfara

LADY'S MANTLE *Alchemilla vulgaris*

WOODRUFF *Asperula odorata*

GLOBE
FLOWER
Trollius europaeus

COWSLIPS
Primula veris

MONKEY FLOWER
Mimulus guttatus

WOOD SANICLE
Sanicula europaea

ENCHANTER'S NIGHTSHADE
Circaea lutetiana

HAREBELL, SCOTCH BLUEBELL
Campanula rotundifolia

HEATH RUSH *Juncus squarrosus*

WOOD SAGE
Teucrium scorodonia

DAFFODILS   *Narcissus pseudonarcissus*

FULLER'S TEASEL
Dipsacus sylvestris

SEA THRIFT   *Armeria maritima*

PURPLE LOOSESTRIFE
Lythrum salicaria

WHITE BRYONY

Bryonia dioica

TOOTHWORT

Lathraea squamaria

CREEPING JENNY, MONEYWORT, *Lysimachia nummularia* L.

302. Creeping Jenny, Moneywort, *Lysimachia nummularia* L. ($\times \frac{1}{3}$); perennial; stems prostrate, rooting at the lower nodes, with a broad groove alternately above and at the side between; leaves opposite, all spreading in the same plane, shortly stalked, very broadly ovate-rounded, not toothed (entire), with about 5 pairs of rather faint nerves, bright green, not hairy (glabrous); no stipules; flowers (A (bud), B, $\times \frac{3}{4}$) axillary, or rarely 2 in one of the leaf-axils; stalks erect, up to 1½ in. long, smooth; sepals broadly ovate-triangular, eared (auriculate), at the base, pale green; corolla of 5 nearly separate petals, rich buttercup-yellow, about 1 in. diam. when fully expanded, the lobes twisted (contorted) in bud (A, $\times \frac{3}{4}$); stamens (C, $\times 2$) 5, opposite to the corolla-lobes; stalks (filaments) shortly united at the base, densely covered with short blunt hairs; anthers rounded to a short tip (mucronate) (D, $\times 3$); ovary (E, $\times 2$) free within the stamens, 1-locular (F, $\times 4$) with numerous ovules around the central axis, the latter not reaching to the top of the chamber; fruit a capsule opening by 5 valves; seeds attached in the middle (G, floral diagram) (family *Primulaceae*).

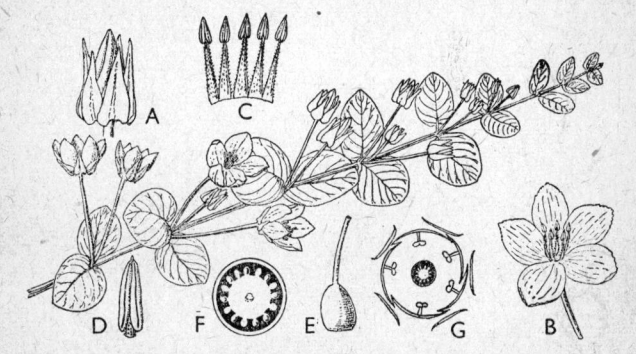

Beginners may not see much in common between this plant and the common Primrose, though they both belong to the same family, *Primulaceae*. The best spotting feature of this family is that the stamens are inserted on and opposite to the more or less united petals.

WOOD or YELLOW PIMPERNEL, *Lysimachia nemorum* L.

303. Wood or Yellow Pimpernel, *Lysimachia nemorum* L. ($\times \frac{1}{2}$); perennial with procumbent stems rooting at the lower nodes; leaves opposite, stalked, ovate, entire, up to $1\frac{1}{2}$ in. long and nearly as much broad, 3-nerved from the base; no stipules; flowers solitary in the upper leaf-axils, on long slender stalks; sepals (A, $\times$ 2) 5, linear-lanceolate, acute; corolla (B, $\times 1\frac{1}{2}$) yellow, with a short tube and 5 spreading lobes twisted (contorted) in bud; stamens (C, $\times$ 3) 5, inserted towards the base and opposite to the lobes; anthers linear, attached near the base, opening by slits lengthwise; ovary (D, G, $\times$ 3) above the calyx, rounded, 1-locular, with numerous ovules on a central basal placenta (E, $\times$ 4); fruit (F, $\times 1\frac{1}{2}$) a capsule shorter than the sepals, and curling around on its stalk when ripe; seeds few on a fleshy placenta (family *Primulaceae*).

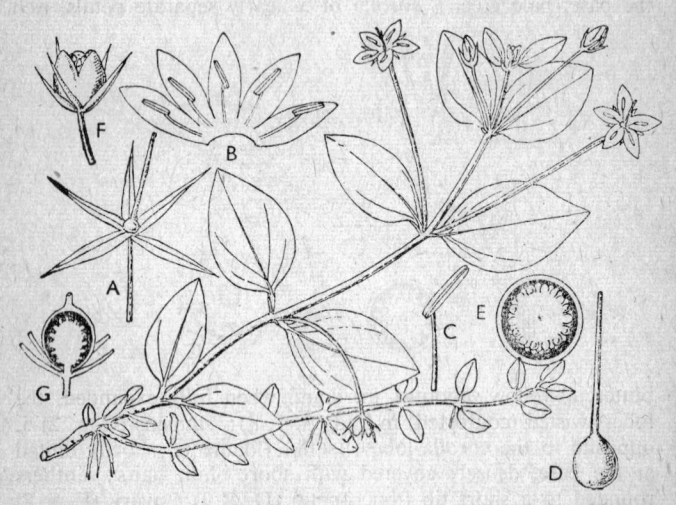

Grows in woods and shady places, sometimes forming a loose carpet amongst grasses, etc., flowering most of the summer, and in the south during late spring.

In the egg-yellow flowers of this species the diverging stamens are of equal length, and remote from the stigma, which is situated at a somewhat lower level, preventing self-pollination for some time.

BOG PIMPERNEL, *Anagallis tenella* (L.) Murr.

304. Bog Pimpernel, *Anagallis tenella* (L.) Murr. ($\times \frac{1}{2}$); a tiny creeping perennial growing in bogs and wet places chiefly beside brooks; stems rooting at the nodes; leaves opposite, shortly stalked, ovate-orbicular, entire, minutely speckled with brown (showing more when dried), glabrous; no stipules; flowers axillary, often together in the leaf-pairs, on slender stalks up to 1 in. long; sepals (A, $\times 2\frac{1}{2}$) 5, very narrowly lanceolate, acute; corolla 5-lobed, pale pink, tube short, the lobes twisted in bud; stamens (B, $\times 4$) 5, erect in the middle of the flower and held together by the very hairy filaments (C, $\times 12$); hairs on these jointed; ovary above the calyx, 1-locular, with several

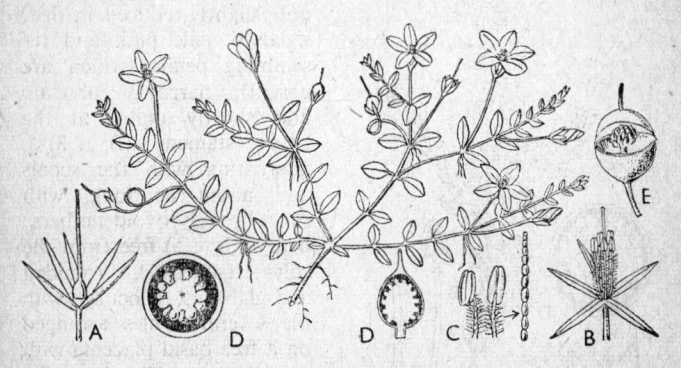

ovules on a free central placenta, which does not reach the top of the loculus (D, $\times 12$); style slender, undivided; fruit (E, $\times 2$) a capsule opening by a transverse slit (family *Primulaceae*).

Found mainly in the western counties of Britain and in Eire, flowering during summer. The hairs on the filaments of the stamens make a pretty microscopical object, with the cells forming a little chain. The interlacing of these peculiar hairs loosely holds together the stamens.

If these drawings of plants belonging to the Primula family, *Primulaceae*, be examined, it will be noticed that in the cross-section of the ovary (fig. E) no lines are shown dividing it up into separate compartments, or loculi, as botanists now call them. This is a good spotting feature for the family, the ovary being 1-locular, with the ovules arranged on what is called a *free basal placenta* (fig. D), which does not extend to the top of the ovary as in the related Pink family, *Caryophyllaceae* (compare figs. 284–290).

SEA MILKWORT, *Glaux maritima* L.

305. Sea Milkwort, *Glaux maritima* L. (× ⅔); small perennial with short decumbent branches often slightly fleshy, up to about 6 in. high; root-stock creeping, rooting at the nodes, which bear the remains of old leaves; lower leaves opposite, the upper alternate, ovate to oblong or even nearly linear, entire, glabrous; flowers (A, × 3) axillary, nearly sessile, forming a leafy spike-like raceme, the upper leaves only slightly reduced in size; sepals 5, pale pink and resembling petals (which are absent), narrowly obovate and shortly united at the base; stamens (B, × 3) 5, alternating with the sepals and about as long, with short broadly ovoid anthers; ovary (C, × 5) free from the calyx (superior), rounded and glabrous, 1-locular, with the several ovules arranged on a free basal placenta with no dividing walls (D, × 7); fruit a globose capsule opening by valves; seeds attached in the middle (peltate) (family *Primulaceae*).

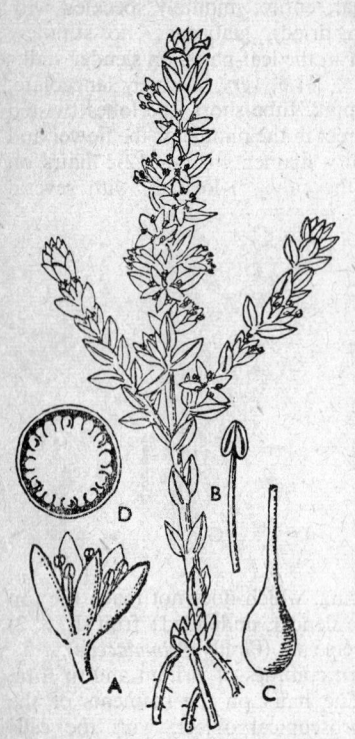

At first one would scarcely think this could be associated with the *Primula* family, as it bears little resemblance to either the Primrose or Cowslip. In most other families the stamens, when equal in number to the calyx-lobes, are placed opposite to them, and are therefore alternate with the petals. In other *Primulaceae*, however, they are opposite the petals, and in this genus without petals they stand in their place.

The pink flowers, with their coloured calyx, rather resemble those of some species of *Polygonum*, but then the absence of stipules at once distinguishes the plant from the latter, in which they are sheathing and very prominent (see figs. 295–298).

BROOKWEED, *Samolus valerandi* L.

306. Brookweed, *Samolus valerandi* L. ($\times \frac{1}{2}$); perennial often flowering in the seedling stage; basal leaves (A, $\times$ 0) with longish and broad flat stalks, obovate-oblanceolate, slightly fleshy, glabrous, with about 3–4 pairs of obscure looped lateral nerves; stem-leaves becoming less stalked and finally sessile, at the base of the inflorescence carried up on the stalk and becoming a leafy bracteole (see notes below); flowers (B, $\times 1\frac{1}{2}$) in terminal racemes and terminating the upper branches; stalks bearing a leafy bracteole near the top; calyx 5-lobed, gland-dotted, shortly joined to the lower part of the ovary; corolla (C, $\times$ 2) white, of 5 partly united petals; stamens 5, in the corolla tube and opposite the lobes, with small, white subulate staminodes between the lobes; ovary (D, $\times 1\frac{1}{2}$) half-inferior, flat on top, with a short slender style; ovules numerous on a basal placenta, which is not carried to the top of the ovary (E, $\times$ 3); fruit girt by the persistent calyx-lobes, opening by 5 valves (F, cross section of ovary, $\times$ 6) (family *Primulaceae*).

This is an exceptional genus in the *Primulaceae* because the ovary is partly united with the calyx, causing the former to be semi-inferior. In appearance the plant is rather like some species of *Myosotis* in *Boraginaceae*. As the leaves become bracts they are carried up some distance on the flower-bearing branchlets.

The corolla-tube is extremely short, and there is no nectar secretion. Insect visits are very rare. As the anthers are at the same level in the corolla-tube as the stigma, and mature at the same time, automatic self-pollination takes place, and is effective.

SEA PLANTAIN, *Plantago maritima* L.

307. Sea Plantain, *Plantago maritima* L. ($\times \frac{1}{2}$); perennial with a woody root-stock and woolly hairs amongst the leaves at the base; leaves up to 1 ft. long, linear and flat, 3-nerved, or shorter and almost needle-like and resembling those of Sea-thrift (*Armeria*), glabrous and entire; flowers in dense slender spikes overtopping the leaves, the common stalk (peduncle) slightly hairy; sepals (A, $\times 4$) 4, ovate; corolla (B, $\times 4$) short, 4-lobed, dry and membranous, lobes spreading; stamens (C, $\times 3$) 4, alternate with the lobes of the corolla and scarcely exserted; anthers (D, $\times 8$) with a produced tip; ovary 2-locular, with 2 ovules; capsule (E, $\times 3$) opening by a circular transverse slit, with 2 seeds (family *Plantaginaceae*).

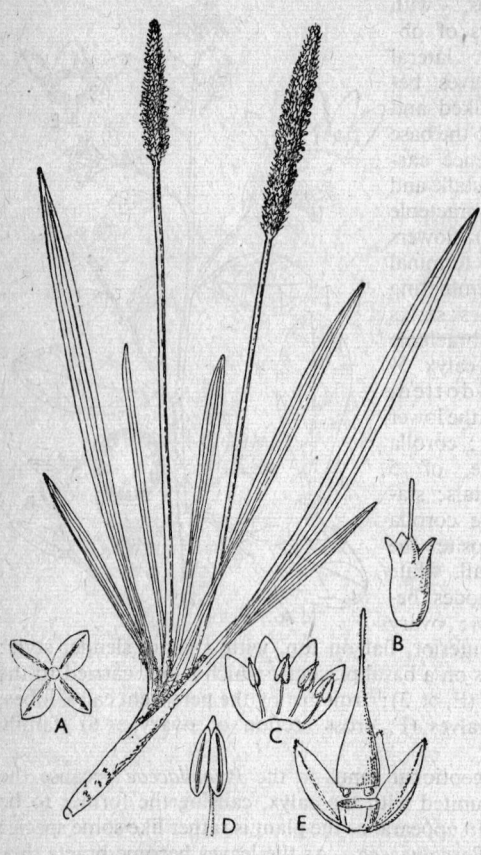

Found mainly near the sea on muddy shores and in salt marshes, but widely distributed in various parts of the world, sometimes on mountains inland.

BUCKSHORN PLANTAIN, *Plantago coronopus* L.

308. Buckshorn Plantain, *Plantago coronopus* L. ($\times \frac{2}{5}$); perennial with short thick upright root-stock; leaves spreading in a rosette, numerous, pilose, spoon-shaped or oblanceolate in outline, deeply and pinnately divided into narrow acute lobes; common stalks of spikes densely villous when young, and the spike bristly with sharp-pointed bracts; spikes on slender stalks longer than the leaves; peduncles closely hairy; bracts (A, $\times$ 3) obovate, sharply and rather long-acuminate, shortly hairy on the margin; sepals (B, $\times$ 3) 4, with a broad darker midrib and thin hairy margins; corolla (C, $\times$ 3) bottle-shaped, 4-lobed, thin and membranous; stamens (D, $\times$ 4) 4, long-exserted from the corolla; ovary (E, $\times$ 4) bottle-shaped, with a long hairy style, 4-locular, each with 1 ovule; fruit (F, $\times$ 2½) splitting by a circular transverse slit; seeds (G, $\times$ 4) surrounded by a narrow white margin (family *Plantaginaceae*).

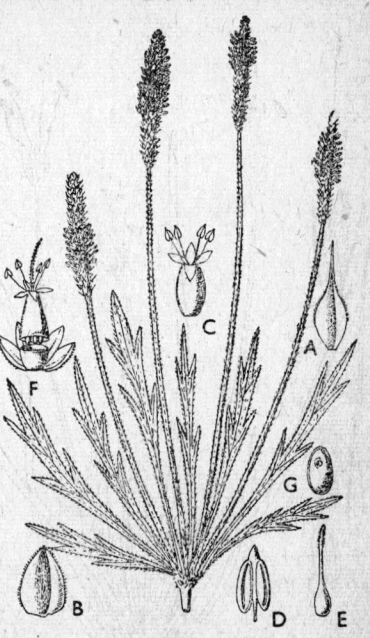

This is also a maritime species growing in dry, stony or sandy places, flowering in summer and autumn.

The mode of opening of the fruits in order to set free the seeds is an interesting departure from the usual type found in flowering plants, and it is common also in the *Primula* family, to which the *Plantago* family is now considered to be related. This is by a transverse slit, a type described in botanical language as *circumscissile*.

SHOREWEED, *Littorella uniflora* (L.) Ascherson

309. Shoreweed, *Littorella uniflora* (L.) Ascherson ($\times \frac{1}{4}$); perennial with a bunch of rather numerous stout roots; leaves all radical, narrowly linear, bright green, entire, up to $3\frac{1}{2}$ in. long; flowers of one sex, the males (A, $\times 3$) on slender stalks up to 4 in. long, the females (C, $\times 3$) at the base of the male flower-stalks, sessile and hidden amongst the bases of the leaves; male sepals 4, oblong-elliptic, with thin margins; corolla with 4 narrow lobes just above the sepals; stamens (B, $\times 1\frac{1}{2}$) 4, with slender thread-like filaments up to $\frac{3}{4}$ in. long; anthers large and conspicuous; female flower with 3–4 unequal sepals, an urn-shaped corolla, and a small ovary (D, $\times 3$) with a thread-like style; fruit a hard nut with one erect seed (family *Plantaginaceae*) (synonym *Littorella lacustris* L.).

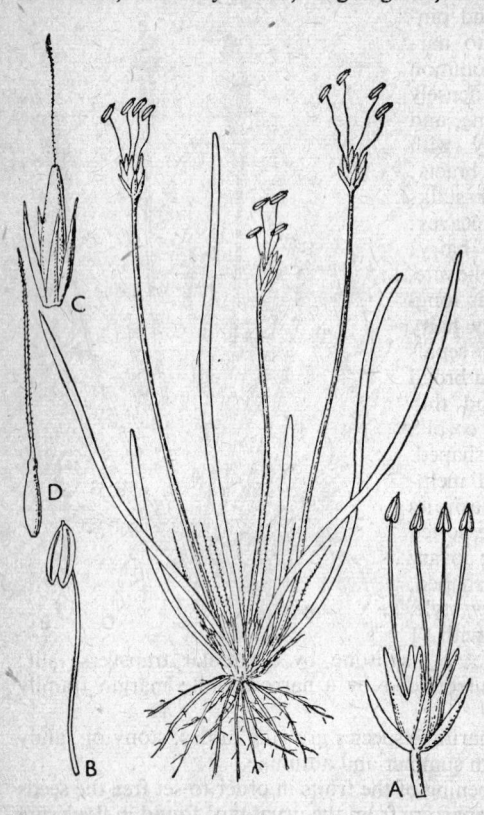

There are two kinds of flowers, those on slender stalks being male, the others hidden at the base being female and revealed by their long thread-like styles. It grows in mud and wet sand on the margins of pools, sometimes completely submerged, flowering during summer; widely distributed in Europe and in the Arctic.

RUE-LEAVED SAXIFRAGE, *Saxifraga tridactylites* L.

310. **Rue-Leaved Saxifrage, *Saxifraga tridactylites* L.** ($\times \frac{1}{2}$); erect annual, covered all over with short gland-tipped hairs; leaves alternate or very rarely opposite here and there, broadly stalked, spoon-shaped in outline, deeply 3–5-lobed, lobes obovate to oblanceolate, rather blunt, entire; upper leaves becoming entire and gradually diminishing into bracts; pedicel opposite the leaf or terminal, very slender, glandular; calyx-tube (A, $\times 3$) united high up with the ovary, lobes 5, erect, ovate; petals (B, $\times 4$) 5, white, small, obovate, 3-nerved; stamens (C, $\times 5$) 10; anthers rounded; ovary inferior, 2-locular; styles 2; ovules numerous on the axis; fruit (D, $\times 3$) a capsule, with 2 short spreading beaks; seeds (E, $\times 15$) minute, brown, obovoid, slightly tubercled (family *Saxifragaceae*).

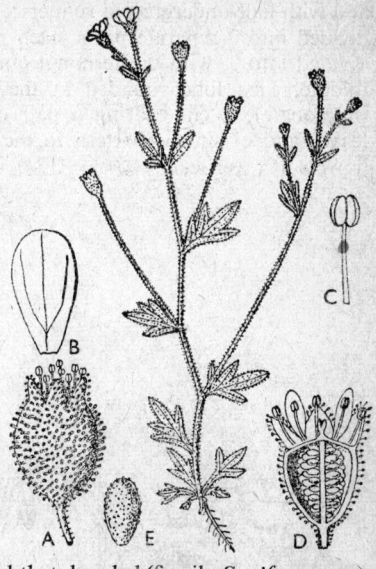

Distinguished among the British species in being an annual, growing on walls and rocks, and flowering during spring and early summer. It is widely distributed from the Arctic Circle to North Africa.

The flowers close in dull weather, but in the sunshine during the midday hours the nectary surrounding the style in the form of a yellow fleshy ring produces glistening drops. Besides the normally bisexual flowers there are often some of indeterminate sex, half male or half female. When the flowers open the stigmas are already mature, and the anthers then open one after another, first those of the outer whorl, then of the inner. Self-pollination is effective.

MOSCHATEL, *Adoxa moschatellina* L.

311. **Moschatel**, *Adoxa moschatellina* L. ($\times \frac{1}{2}$); a small weak pale-green perennial herb growing in moist shady places; root-stock short, covered with the remains of the old leaf-stalks and with half-underground runners; basal leaves on long stalks, divided into 3 separate parts, each part long-stalked and again divided into 3, with the terminal portion 3-parted to below the middle, each lobe rounded at the top, but with a little tip (mucronate); stem bearing a pair of opposite smaller stalked leaves and of similar pattern to the basal leaves, all glabrous; flowers (C, vertical section, $\times 2\frac{1}{2}$) in a small globose stalked cluster at the top of the stem, usually 5 together, 1 terminal, the others facing outwards in 4 directions; calyx 2–3-lobed; corolla spreading, 4–6-lobed; no disk; stamens (A, $\times 8$) double the number of the corolla-lobes (due to splitting of the filaments) with 1-locular anthers; ovary (D, cross-section, $\times 6$) semi-inferior, 3–5-locular; style (B, $\times 4$) 3–5-lobed; fruits (E, $\times \frac{1}{2}$) pendulous on the bent stalk, rimmed by the persistent calyx (family *Adoxaceae*).

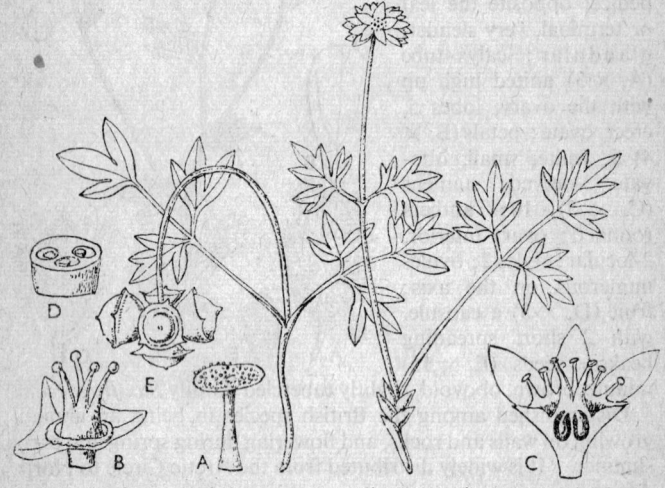

This interesting little plant has been the subject of considerable discussion as to its relationship with other families. It was formerly included in the Honeysuckle family, *Caprifoliaceae*, but it is here as a separate family, more closely related to the *Saxifragaceae*. The arrangement of the flowers has been aptly compared with a town-hall clock, four of the flowers facing in different directions.

SUNDEW, *Drosera rotundifolia* L.

312. Sundew, *Drosera rotundifolia* L. ($\times$ 0); herb growing in boggy acid soil often amongst Sphagnum moss; leaves in a rosette, on long stalks, spoon-shaped or orbicular, the stalks clothed with a few fine hairs, the upper surface of the blade, and especially the margin, covered with viscid-tipped reddish processes which entrap small insects; flowering stems 1–3 from the rosette, leafless, slender, simple or divided into 2 branches, the flowers to one side of the axis, the lowest opening first; each flower (A, $\times$ 3) subtended by a threadlike bract; calyx deeply 5-lobed, glabrous; petals 5, free, white; stamens (B, $\times$ 6) 5, free; anthers broadly ellipsoid, 2-locular; ovary (C, $\times$ 7) free from the calyx, 1-locular, with usually 4 divided styles, and with the numerous ovules borne on 4 marginal (parietal) placentas (D, $\times$ 7); fruit a capsule; seeds spindle-shaped, pointed at both ends (family *Droseraceae*).

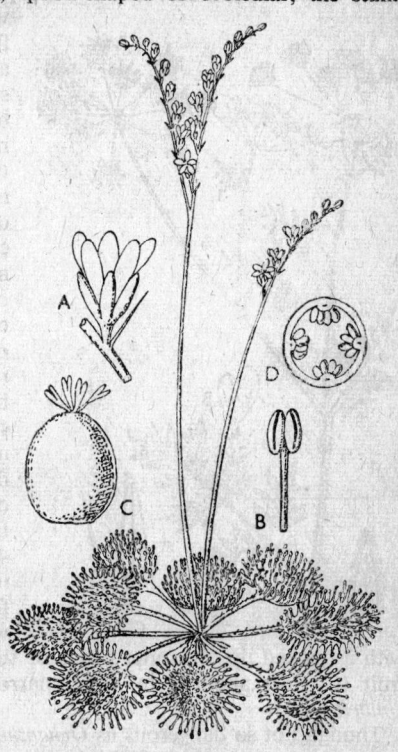

This is Britain's best example of an insectivorous plant, the sticky hairs on the rounded leaves attracting and imprisoning small flies. The juices secreted in the hollow of the leaf are capable of digesting the flies, just as food in the stomach is digested by gastric juices. It is such plants as these that give rise to the belief in the lay mind that there are "man-eating plants".

ROUGH CHERVIL, *Chaerophyllum temulum* L.

313. Rough Chervil, *Chaerophyllum temulum* L. ($\times \frac{2}{5}$); erect biennial up to about 3 ft. high, usually growing on shady banksides, often under trees; stems often purplish, loosely clothed with rather bristly deflexed hairs; leaves alternate, stalked, the stalks sheathing at the base and with pale thinner margins, the blade twice pinnate (bipinnate), with the ultimate divisions deeply lobed or coarsely toothed and mucronate, bristly hairy on both surfaces; umbels compound, the primary one with about a dozen rays, but without any bracts at the base of the stalks, the ultimate umbels with about 20–25 flowers with an involucre of bracts at the base fringed with hairs (A, $\times$ 4); flower-stalks elongating as they develop into fruits; petals (B, $\times$ 5) white, obovate, bilobed with a hooked tip, the outer petals of the umbel rather larger; fruit (C, $\times$ 2) about $\frac{1}{3}$ in. long, narrow and turgid (family *Umbelliferae*).

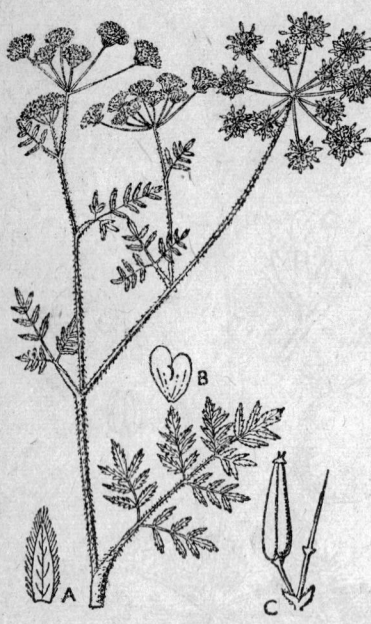

Though not so dangerous as *Oenanthe crocata* (fig. 316), this species is also poisonous, and is known to have caused the death of pigs and cows in Germany. The plant has a strong odour and acrid taste. It is widely distributed in Britain, but only locally common. Like so many other of our common species, it extends east to beyond the Caucasus Mountains.

MARSH WORT, *Apium nodiflorum* (L.) Lag.

314. Marsh Wort, *Apium nodiflorum* (L.) Lag. (× ½); perennial with decumbent stems; annual flowering shoots more erect and sometimes several feet high; leaves with a long thin-margined sheath at the base, pinnate, with up to about 10 pairs of opposite elliptic or ovate-elliptic toothed sessile leaflets; terminal leaflet stalked and sometimes unequally lobed; umbels on a very short common stalk, appearing to be axillary, but really opposite the leaf (leaf-opposed); no common involucre, or rarely 1 or 2 bracts; partial involucres of a few leafy bracts (B, × 2½) becoming reflexed; flowers (A, × 5) very small, shortly stalked; petals (C, × 4) white; ovary inferior; styles 2; stigmas capitate; fruit small, ovoid, each carpel with 5 slender ribs and a single vitta (resin channel) between each (family *Umbelliferae*).

This genus is easily recognised amongst British *Umbelliferae* by the umbels being nearly sessile on the opposite side of the stem from the leaves. It grows in marshy meadows and wet ditches, flowering in summer. There is thus a danger of the plant being mistaken for Watercress, though it is not known to be poisonous, and is unpalatable. In consequence it is often called "Fool's Watercress". It is widely distributed as far east as Persia and into northern Africa.

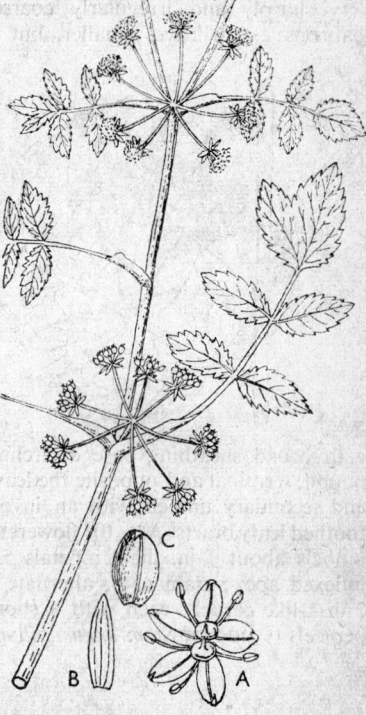

LESSER SIUM, *Sium erectum* Huds.

315. Lesser Sium, *Sium erectum* Huds. (× ½) perennial; stems bent and ascending, up to 3 ft. high, leafy; lower leaves up to about 1 ft. or more, pinnate with about 10 pairs of sessile leaflets, these ovate to oblong-lanceolate, rounded at the base, very sharply and irregularly coarsely toothed and lobulate, glabrous; stem leaves smaller, but much in the same pattern, with broad sheathing base encircling the stem; umbels compound, terminal and opposite the leaves (leaf-opposed); primary and secondary umbels with an involucre of several divided or toothed leafy bracts (A, × 0); flowers (B, × 2) white, the secondary umbels about ¾ in. diam.; petals 5, obovate, with an oblique inflexed apex; stamens 5, alternate with the petals; ovary of 2 disk-like carpels, each with a short stigma; fruits on slender pedicels (synonym *Sium angustifolium* L.) (family *Umbelliferae*).

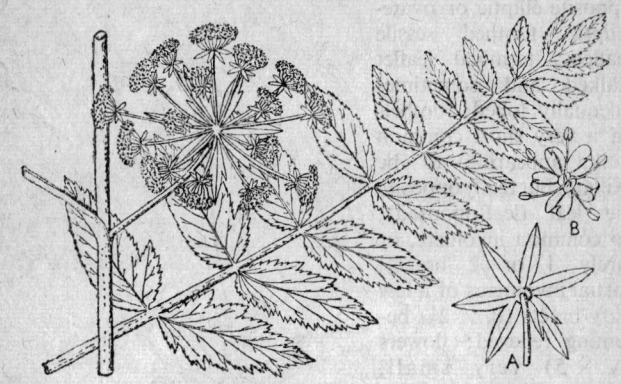

WATER DROP-WORT, HEMLOCK-WORT
Oenanthe crocata L.

316. Water Drop-Wort, Hemlock-Wort, *Oenanthe crocata* L. (× ¼); perennial up to about 5 ft. high; roots tuberous, like a bunch of small narrow carrots, and with numerous fine fibrous roots (A, × ½); stems thickened at the nodes, juice becoming yellow when exposed to the air; leaves bipinnate, the segments broadly cuneate and coarsely toothed or pinnately lobed, glabrous or nearly so; umbels numerous on long terminal peduncles; primary umbel usually without bracts, but sometimes with modified leaves, smaller umbels with a few bracts, and these sometimes quite leafy (foliaceous); outer flowers in each umbel stalked and mostly infertile (male), the middle ones sessile or nearly so and fertile; petals white; ovary inferior, with 2 distinct styles; fruit (B, × 5) narrow, oblong-cylindric, with a solitary vitta (resin channel) between each pair of ribs (family *Umbelliferae*).

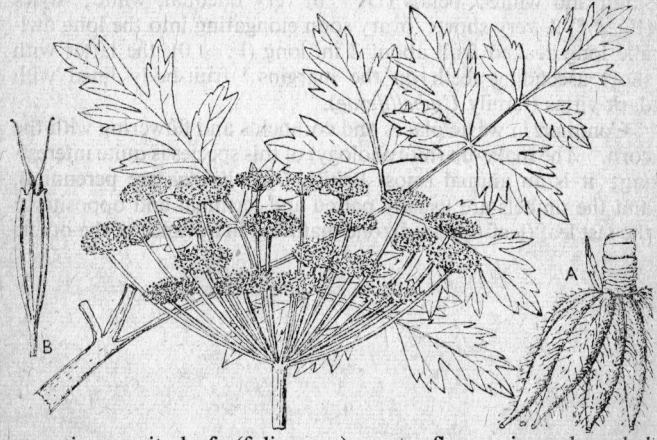

This species is very poisonous in all its parts, and may be mistaken for celery and the root-stock for parsnips. It is liable to be collected amongst other herbs for rabbit food. The root is the most toxic, and drying does not destroy the poisonous property. In cases of poisoning the symptoms usually appear very quickly, and death may take place within an hour or two. It grows in marshes and ditches and along the banks of tidal rivers such as the Thames, flowering in summer.

SHEPHERD'S NEEDLE, VENUS' COMB, *Scandix pecten-veneris* L.

317. Shepherd's Needle, Venus' Comb, *Scandix pecten-veneris* L. ($\times \frac{1}{2}$); annual up to about 1 ft. high, sometimes much branched and spreading from the base; stems with short stiff spreading hairs; leaves sheathing at the base, on slender stalks, twice to thrice pinnate and dissected into fine narrow acute segments, glabrous or with short stiff hairs; umbels usually 2 together, terminal and leaf-opposed, on short peduncles; bracts leafy, deeply divided into 2 acute lobes (A, $\times$ 3); flowers (C, $\times 2\frac{1}{2}$) very shortly stalked, few (5–8) in each umbel (B, $\times 1\frac{1}{2}$) small and white; petals (D, $\times$ 6) very unequal, white; styles (E, $\times$ 5) 2, very short; ovary soon elongating into the long awl-like long-beaked fruit about 2 in. long (F, $\times$ 0), the latter with short ascending teeth on the margins; fruit-body lined with dark vittas (family *Umbelliferae*).

Common in waste places and cornfields and flowering with the corn. The make-up (morphology) of this species is quite interesting; it is an annual (most British *Umbelliferae* are perennial), and the umbels are usually paired and terminal and opposite to the last leaf (leaf-opposed), one maturing in advance of the other.

153

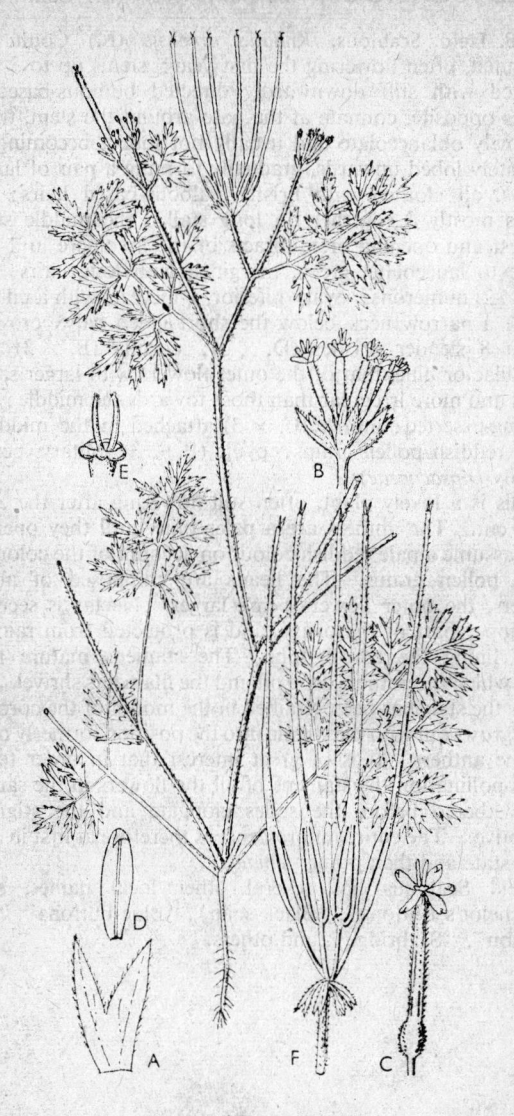

FIELD SCABIOUS, *Knautia arvensis* (L.) Coult.

318. Field Scabious, *Knautia arvensis* (L.) Coult. ($\times \frac{3}{5}$); perennial, often flowering the first year; stems up to 5 ft. high, clothed with stiff downwardly directed bulbous-based hairs; leaves opposite, connate at the base around the stem, the lower narrowly oblanceolate and usually not lobed, becoming deeply pinnately lobed upwards, gradually forming a pair of lanceolate bracts, all clothed with bristly bulbous-based hairs; flower-heads mostly 3 together on long stalks, the middle stalk the longest and opening first; bracts of the involucre in 2–3 rows, ovate to lanceolate, green, margined with long hairs; flowers (A, $\times$ 2) numerous; ovary inferior, 1-locular, with a ciliate rim, above a narrow neck below the short green calyx crowned by about 8 slender bristles (D, $\times$ 3); corolla (B, $\times$ 3) tubular, pale lilac or blue, that of the outer flowers with larger spreading lobes and more irregular than those towards the middle; stamens 4, long-exserted; anther (C, $\times$ 3) attached in the middle, with large reddish pollen grains; ovule (E, $\times$ 3) solitary, pendulous (family *Dipsacaceae*).

This is a lovely plant, often still flowering after the corn has been cut. The anthers are a paler blue until they open, when they assume a pale reddish colour on account of the colour of the large pollen grains. The heads are composed of about 50 flowers, the outer flowers being larger. Nectar is secreted on the upper part of the ovary, and is protected from rain by the hairs lining the corolla-tube. The stamens mature in turn, after which the anthers drop off and the filaments shrivel. Meanwhile the style has been retained in the mouth of the corolla, and now grows out with the stigma into the position formerly occupied by the anthers. It is of great interest that in order to ensure cross-pollination the stamens of all the flowers in the same head are withered before the styles elongate and the stigmas are receptive. The entire inflorescence is therefore at first in a purely *male* state and then purely *female*.

Field Scabious has several other local names, such as "Bachelor's Buttons", "Black-soap", "Blue-buttons", "Lady's-cushion", "Scabridge", and others.

155

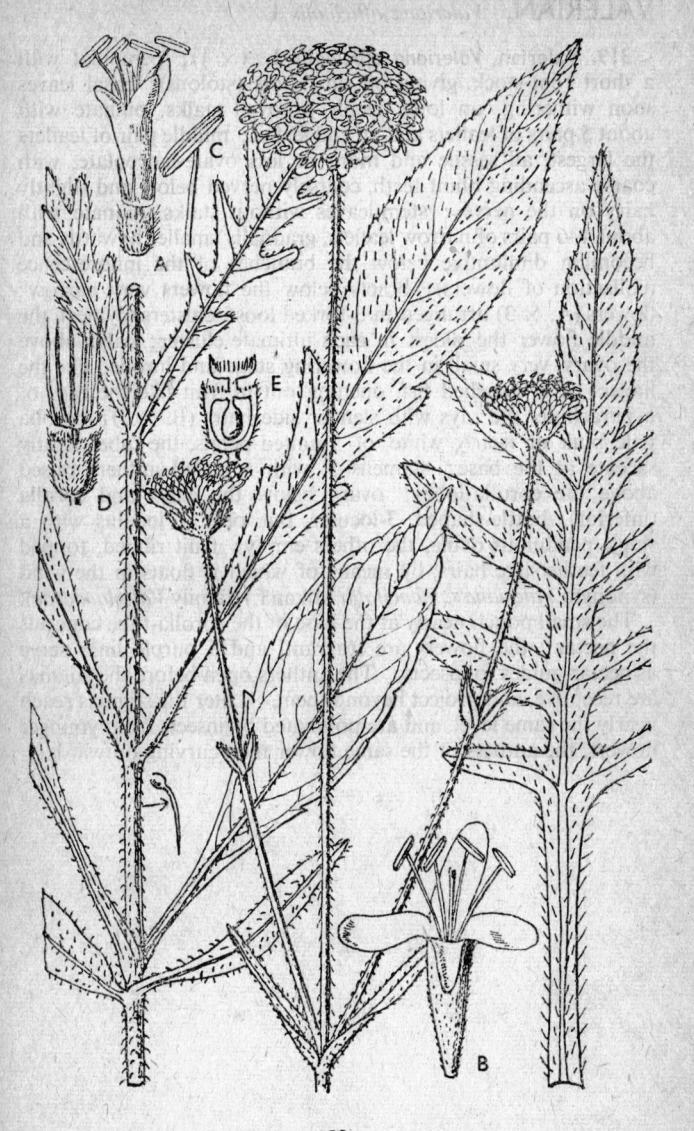

VALERIAN, *Valeriana officinalis* L.

319. Valerian, *Valeriana officinalis* L. ($\times \frac{1}{2}$); perennial with a short root-stock, giving off off-shoots (stolons); basal leaves soon withering, on long deeply grooved stalks, pinnate with about 5 pairs of leaflets and an end leaflet; middle pair of leaflets the largest, all sessile and more or less ovate-lanceolate, with coarse ascending blunt teeth, coarsely nerved below and slightly hairy on the nerves; stem-leaves without stalks, pinnate with about 4–6 pairs of narrow leaflets, gradually smaller upwards and becoming diminutive below the branches of the inflorescence (collection of flowers); bracts below the flowers very narrow; flowers (A, $\times$ 3) arranged in 3-forked loose clusters (cymes), the middle flower the oldest in each ultimate cluster; calyx above the ovary, very small in the flowering stage and inrolled like the fingers of a clenched fist, opening out in fruit like the rays of a parachute, the rays with slender side hairs (B, $\times$ 3); corolla pale pink or nearly white, of 5 united petals, the tube slightly saccate at the base; stamens 3, with rounded anthers raised above the corolla-lobes; ovary below the calyx and corolla (inferior), bottle-shaped, 3-locular, but only 1 loculus with a single pendulous ovule, the others empty; fruit ribbed, topped with feather-like hairs, by means of which it floats in the wind (synonym *Valeriana sambucifolia* Mikan f.) (family *Valerianaceae*).

The small pouch nearly at the base of the corolla-tube conceals the nectar; the flowers are fragrant, and 5 purple lines serve as nectar-guides to insects. The anthers open before the stigmas are receptive, and project beyond them. Later the stigmas reach nearly the same level, and are pollinated by insects from younger flowers, the anthers of the same flower then curving outwards.

157

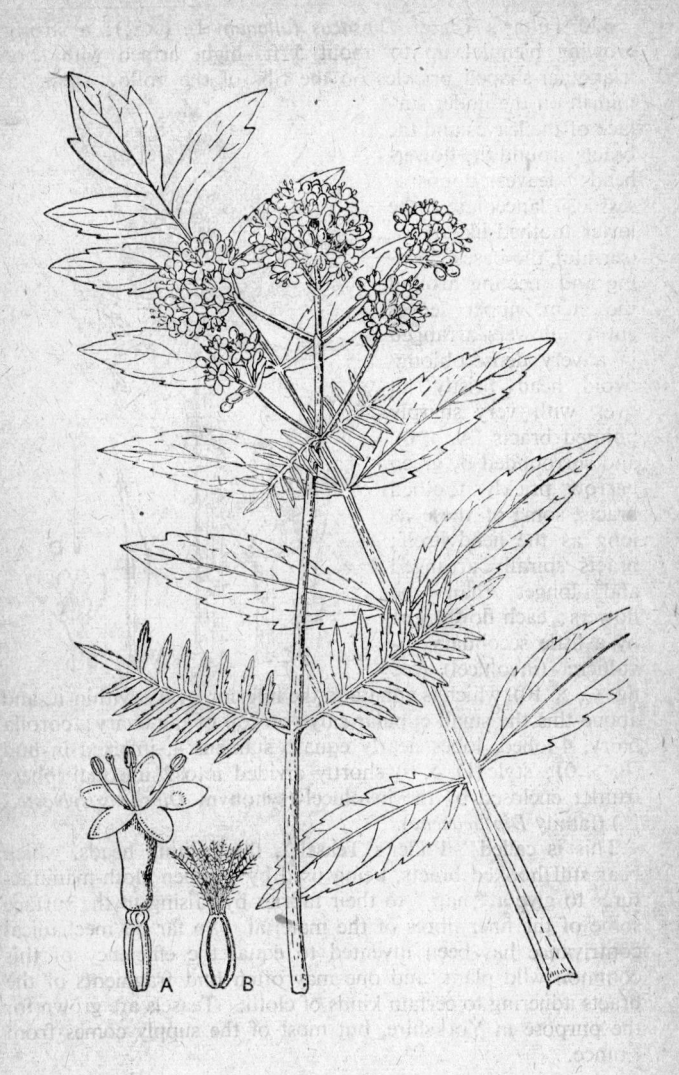

FULLER'S TEASEL, *Dipsacus fullonum* L.

320. Fuller's Teasel, *Dipsacus fullonum* L. ($\times \frac{1}{3}$); a strong-growing biennial up to about 5 ft. high, armed with short triangular-shaped prickles on the ribs of the hollow stem, the midrib on the under surface of the leaves and the bracts around the flower-head; leaves opposite, sessile, lanceolate, the lower toothed like a saw (serrate), the bases clasping and meeting around the stem, upper leaves entire; flowers arranged in a very dense oblong-ovoid head bristly all over with very sharply pointed bracts (A, $\times 0$), and surrounded by green narrow prickly toothed bracts, some of these as long as the head itself; bracts spirally arranged and longer than the flowers; each flower girt by a little secondary involucre (involucel) (see fig. C, $\times 10$), which is adnate to the inferior ovary within it, and above this the small cupular calyx on top of the ovary; corolla hairy, 4-lobed, lobes nearly equal; stamens 4, inflexed in bud (B, $\times 0$); style (D, $\times 0$) shortly divided into 2 unequal lobes; fruitlet enclosed by the involucel (synonym *Dipsacus sylvestris* L.) (family *Dipsacaceae*).

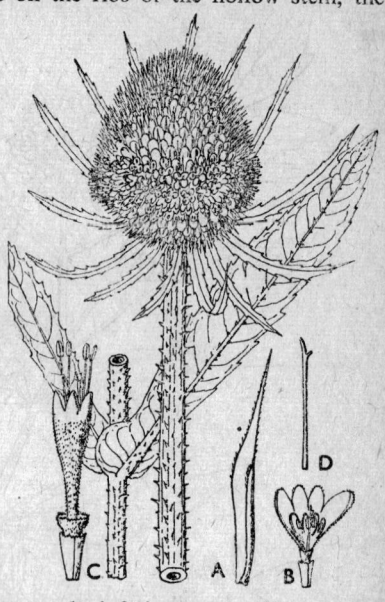

This is called "Fuller's Teasel", the fruiting heads, which bear stiff hooked bracts, being used by woollen cloth-manufactures to give a "nap" to their fabrics by raising to the surface some of the finer fibres of the material. So far no mechanical contrivance has been invented to equal the efficiency of this common wild plant, and one may often find fragments of the bracts adhering to certain kinds of cloth. Teasels are grown for the purpose in Yorkshire, but most of the supply comes from France.

CREEPING BELL-FLOWER, *Campanula rapunculoides* L.

321. Creeping Bell-Flower, *Campanula rapunculoides* L. ($\times \frac{1}{2}$); root-stock creeping, with underground stolons; stems usually unbranched, up to 2½ ft. high, slightly ribbed and with very short deflexed hairs; leaves (A, $\times \frac{1}{2}$) alternate, broadly lanceolate, apex acute, base rounded into the broad petiole, irregularly serrate, nearly glabrous, the lower on long petioles, gradually becoming sessile upwards and merging into bracts; flowers pendulous in a slender leafy raceme, very shortly stalked, spreading or pendulous; bracts gradually decreasing upwards, becoming linear; calyx-lobes (B, $\times 3$) linear, recurved, ½ in. long; corolla bright blue, 1 in. long, lobes margined with long white hairs; stamens (C, $\times 6$) 5, anthers opening before the stigmas are receptive; style (B, $\times 3$) very hairy outside, and covered with pollen, with 3 recurved stigmas (D, $\times 3$); ovary inferior (below the calyx-lobes), 3-locular, with numerous ovules in each chamber (E, $\times 4$); fruit opening by pores at the base (family *Campanulaceae*).

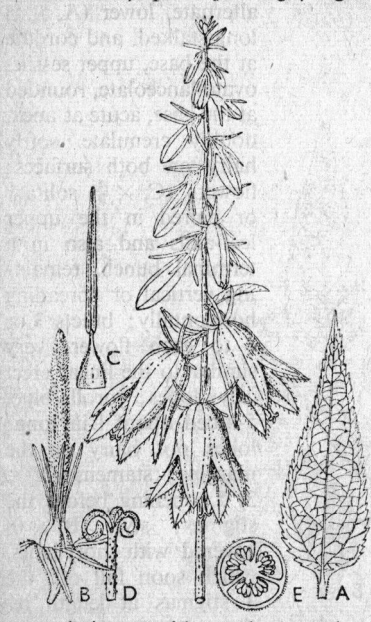

This species is doubtfully native, as it is usually found in cultivated fields, on railway banks, and in waste land. It is widely distributed as far east as the Caucasus.

The densely hairy style of the pendulous flowers pushes out the pollen from the anther " cylinder ", after which the stamens shrivel and the stigmas spread out and become recurved. The little drops of nectar on top of the inferior ovary are covered by the expanded bases of the filaments, which are fringed with hairs.

CLUSTERED BELL-FLOWER, *Campanula glomerata* L.

322. Clustered Bell-Flower, *Campanula glomerata* L. ($\times \frac{2}{5}$); perennial with short creeping root-stock; stems erect, up to 15 in. high, flushed with crimson, very slightly hairy; leaves alternate, lower (A, $\times \frac{2}{5}$) long-stalked, and cordate at the base, upper sessile, ovate-lanceolate, rounded at the base, acute at apex, doubly crenulate, softly hairy on both surfaces; flowers (C, $\times \frac{4}{5}$) solitary or paired in the upper leaf-axils and also in a terminal bunch, remaining vertical or spreading horizontally; bracts 3 or 4 to each flower, very similar to the linear erect calyx-lobes; corolla blue, 5-lobed, about 1 in. long; lobes not hairy on the margins; stamens (D, $\times$ 3) 5, opening before the stigmas; style (B, $\times$ 0) covered with short hairs, which soon fall off, the 3 stigmas at length recurved; ovary (E, $\times$ 5) 3-locular, with numerous ovules on axile placentas; fruit (F, $\times$ 3) opening by pores near the base (family *Campanulaceae*).

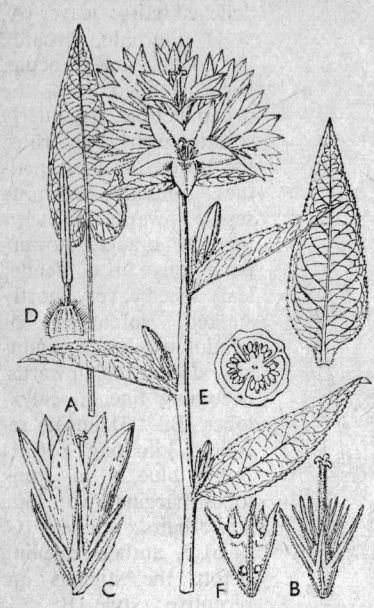

In the young flower the very hairy style is closely embraced by the long anthers, which open on the inside (introrse). When the flower opens the pollen is carried upwards by the hairs as the style elongates. Eventually the hairs fall away from the style, leaving it quite smooth, and the stigmas become receptive to pollen carried by insects from younger flowers.

This species shows in a striking manner how readily a head of flowers may be evolved by the crowding together of the upper leaves. In a similar way the dense head of flowers surrounded by crowded bracts has, no doubt, been brought about in the related and more advanced Daisy family, *Compositae*.

SHEEP'S BIT, *Jasione montana* L.

323. Sheep's Bit, *Jasione montana* L. ($\times \frac{1}{2}$); annual or biennial, up to about 1 ft. high; stems branched from the base, loosely clothed with white bristly hairs; leaves alternate, sessile, narrowly oblong, lanceolate, with wavy margins, loosely covered with long bristly hairs on both surfaces; flowers (B, $\times 4$) on short stalks and collected into a small rounded head on a long peduncle, surrounded by 2 or 3 rows of broadly ovate-triangular bracts (A, $\times 2$), toothed on the margin and clothed with a few bristly hairs; calyx-tube united with the ovary, divided into 5 narrow lobes; corolla pale blue, deeply divided into 5 very narrow segments; stamens (C, $\times 4$) 5; anthers united at the base into a ring, with very broad filaments fringed with hairs; ovary below the calyx (inferior); style slender; fruit a capsule opening at the top by 2 valves; seeds very small, shining (family *Campanulaceae*).

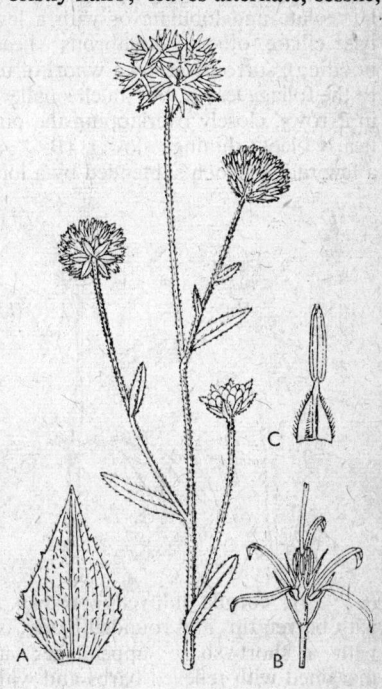

In heathy pastures mainly in light soils, flowering from June to September; widely distributed in Europe and as far east as the Caucasus.

In well-grown specimens a head contains 100–200 blue flowers, the corollas of which are divided nearly to their base into 5 narrow lobes, so that the nectar secreted on the top of the ovary is accessible to insects of the most varied kind. In a young stage the end of the style is covered with closely set erect hairs as in *Campanula*, and these receive the pollen, which is released in the bud-stage and pushed out by the growing style. After that the stigmas open out and become receptive to pollen.

THREE-LOBED BUR MARIGOLD, *Bidens tripartita* L.

324. Three-Lobed Bur Marigold, *Bidens tripartita* L. ($\times \frac{1}{2}$); annual with purplish nearly glabrous stems; leaves opposite, with a broad sheathing base, divided into 3 main segments, these lanceolate and lobulate or with a few sharp teeth; broadened base ciliate, otherwise glabrous; heads more or less erect (not nodding), surrounded by a whorl of unequal-sized bracts similar to the foliage leaves, but much smaller; smaller involucral bracts in 2 rows, closely overlapping the outer (A, $\times$ 2), broader and nearly black, shining; flowers (B, $\times$ 4) all tubular, or sometimes a few radiate, each subtended by a long membranous bract-scale

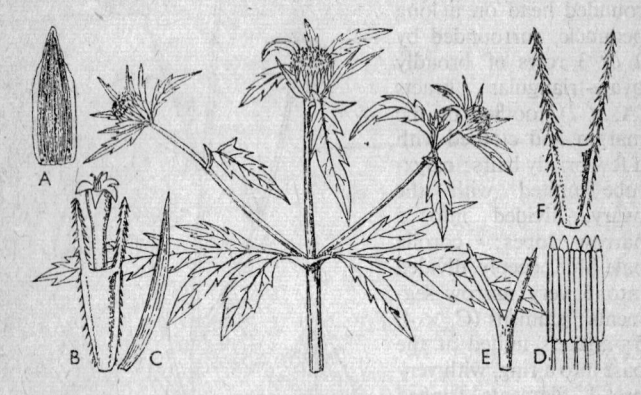

(C, $\times$ 4); corolla dull yellow-brown, 5-lobed; anthers (D, $\times$ 6) with barren tips and rounded bases; stigmas (E, $\times$ 6) blunt and with a short sharp appendage; achene (F, $\times$ 4) flattened, margined with reflexed barbs and with 2 bristles at the top also with reflexed barbs (family *Compositae*).

There are 2 species of Bidens in Britain, the one shown in the drawing and *B. cernua* L. In the latter the leaves are lanceolate and toothed, but not divided as they are in *B. tripartita*. Both species grow in wet ditches and marshy places and flower during summer and autumn. The achenes attach themselves to animals by means of the barbed bristles which represent the calyx.

MARSH CUDWEED, *Gnaphalium uliginosum* L.

325. Marsh Cudweed, *Gnaphalium uliginosum* L. ($\times \frac{1}{2}$); annual much branched from the base, covered all over with woolly hairs, the leaves at length becoming less hairy on the upper surface; leaves alternate, linear or slightly spoon-shaped, often bearing in their axils a short leafy shoot; flower-heads in terminal leafy clusters, sessile; involucral bracts brownish and shining; receptacle without scales between the flowers; outer flowers thread-like and female (A, $\times$ 5), inner flowers tubular and bisexual (B, $\times$ 10); anthers tailed at the base and with barren tips (C, $\times$ 20); style-branches very blunt at the tip (D, $\times$ 30); achenes very small, glabrous, crowned with a pappus of shining white bristles (E $\times$ 20) which soon fall off (family Compositae).

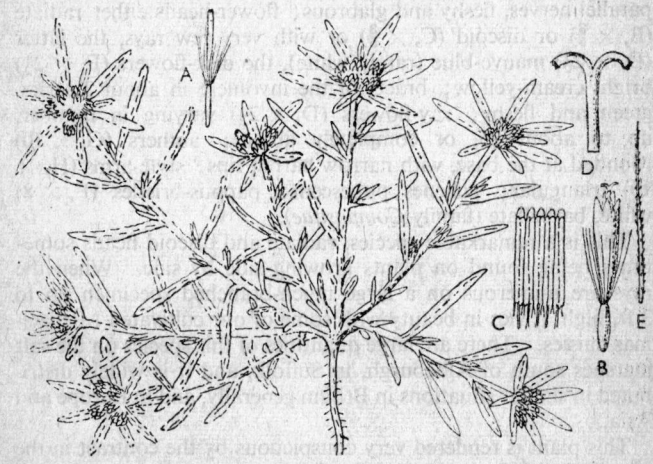

Grows in wet sandy places by roads, in waste land, and on heaths, flowering in summer and autumn. It is common throughout the British Isles, though shy of limestone soils.

SEA ASTER, *Aster tripolium* L.

326. Sea Aster, *Aster tripolium* L. ($\times \frac{3}{5}$); perennial only found in low salt marshes, often lining the gulleys or forming pure stands; stems from 1–3 ft. high, from little- to much-branched, fleshy, glabrous, with 3 grooves below each leaf, 1 representing the midrib, the other 2 the lateral nerves, these lines continued down to the next leaf; leaves (A, $\times \frac{3}{5}$) half clasping the stem, broadly linear, with a wide midrib and 2 fainter parallel nerves, fleshy and glabrous; flower-heads either radiate (B, $\times \frac{3}{5}$) or discoid (C, $\times \frac{3}{5}$) or with very few rays, the latter (D, $\times 2\frac{1}{2}$) mauve-blue (rarely white), the disk-flowers (E, $\times 2\frac{1}{2}$) bright cream-yellow; bracts of the involucre in about 3 series, green and fleshy; ray-flowers (D, $\times 2\frac{1}{2}$) varying in number, up to about 25, or completely absent; anthers (G, $\times 10$) rounded at the base, with narrow barren tips; style-arms (H, $\times 10$) triangular; achenes pubescent; pappus-bristles (F, $\times 8$) white, barbellate (family *Compositae*).

This is a remarkable species, radiate and discoid heads sometimes being found on plants growing side by side. When the rays are numerous on a large much-branched specimen up to 3 ft. high, it vies in beauty with some of our cultivated Michaelmas daisies. There are large quantities of this species on the salt marshes south of Aldeburgh, in Suffolk, and it is widely distributed in similar situations in Britain generally, and in Europe and Asia.

This plant is rendered very conspicuous by the contrast in the ray- and disk-flowers when the former are present, and by the crowding together of the heads. The ray-flowers are female and the disk-flowers bisexual. The pollen is swept out of the latter by the rhombic tips of the style branches, which are provided with sweeping hairs directed obliquely upwards. The pollen is thus exposed to visiting insects and is carried to older flowers in which the stigmas have become receptive. After fertilisation the disk-flowers fade to a discoloured orange, and at last become brown.

165

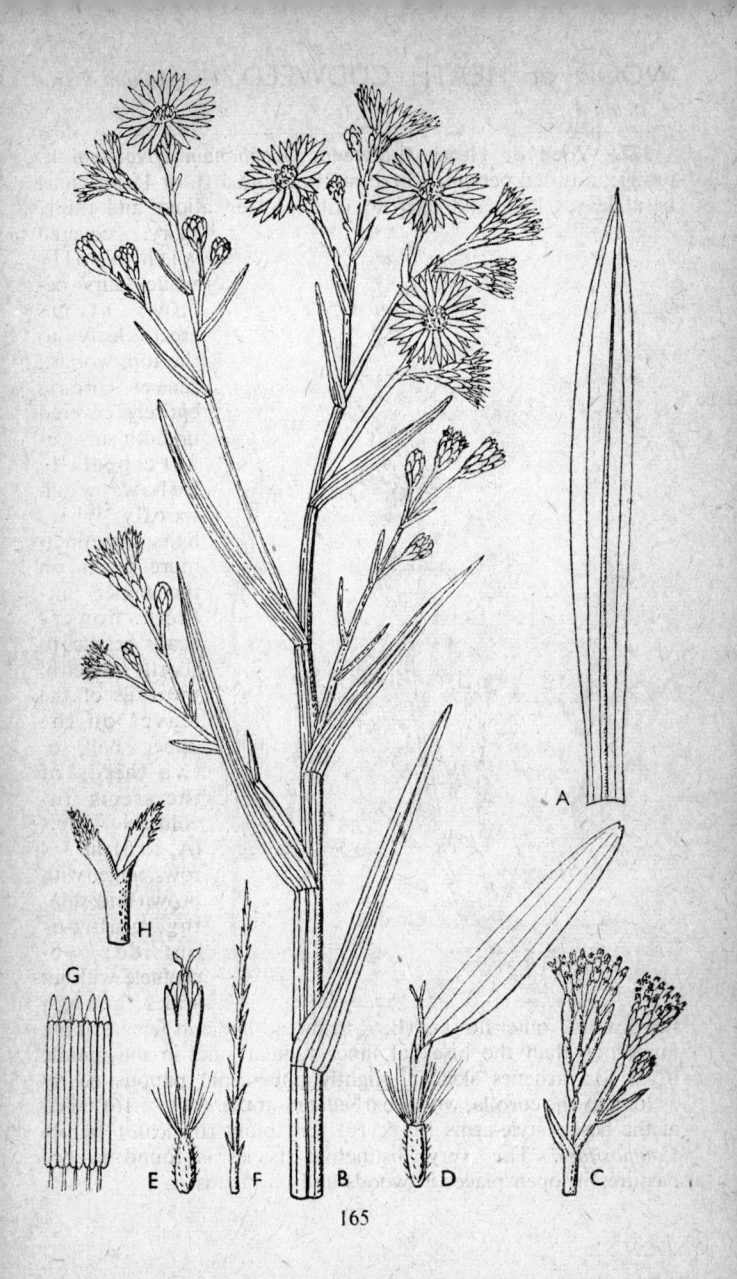

WOOD or HEATH CUDWEED, *Gnaphalium sylvaticum* L.

327. Wood or Heath Cudweed, *Gnaphalium sylvaticum* L. ($\times \frac{1}{2}$); a tufted perennial herb, up to about 1 ft. or 15 in. high; basal leaves long and narrow, entire, green above and thinly hairy, covered with woolly white hairs below; stems erect, leafy to the top, woolly; leaves linear, entirely covered on both surfaces but especially below with woolly white hairs, sometimes more green on the upper surface; flower-heads sessile to shortly stalked in the axils of the leaves on the upper half or two-thirds of the stem; involucral bracts (A, $\times$ 3) in 3-4 rows, tinged with brown and shining, glabrous outside; receptacle without scales amongst the flowers; outer flowers (B, $\times$ 8) thread-like and female, more numerous than the bisexual inner tubular ones in the middle (C, $\times$ 8); achenes slender, slightly pubescent; pappus nearly as long as the corolla, white, barbellate; anthers (D, $\times$ 16) tailed at the base; style-arms (E, $\times$ 16) very blunt (truncate) (family *Compositae*). This very distinctive species is found in dry pastures in open places in woods and on heaths.

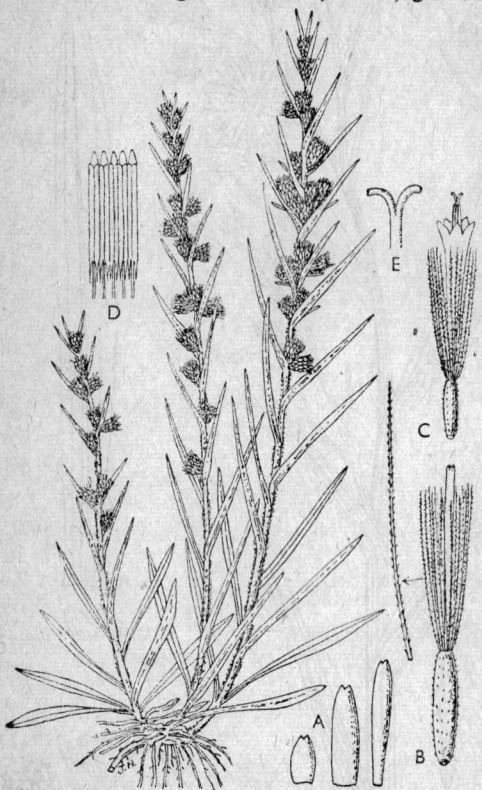

CUDWEED, *Filago germanica* L.

328. Cudweed, *Filago germanica* L. ($\times \frac{2}{5}$); slender annual cottony herb, with fibrous roots; stems up to about 1½ ft. high, forking here and there into 2 divergent branches with bunches of sessile flower-heads in the forks and at the ends; leaves shortly linear, with a hardened tip, covered with white cotton-wool-like hairs; bracts of the involucre (A, $\times 4$) woolly in the lower part, glabrous upwards, membranous and shining, the outer one with a green spot towards the top; very sharply pointed; receptacle with a row of scales only within the outer flowers; flowers in the middle (B, $\times 3$), bisexual, though sometimes infertile, those on the outside (C, $\times 3$) female and with a narrow thread-like corolla; anthers (D, $\times 8$) tailed at the base; style-arms (E, $\times 6$) club-shaped; achenes slightly hairy; pappus (F, $\times 8$) of white slightly rough bristles (family *Compositae*).

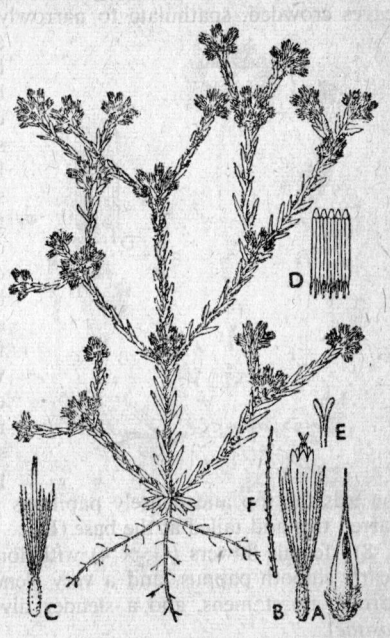

Grows in dry fields and stony and waste places, flowering in summer; widely distributed in Europe and western Asia, North Africa and the Atlantic islands.

It has some curious local names, such as Clod-weed, Down-weed, Herb Impious, Old Owl, Quidwort, Son-before-the-father, and several others.

MOUNTAIN EVERLASTING, CAT'S EAR, *Antennaria dioica* (L.) Gaertn.

329. Mountain Everlasting, Cat's Ear, *Antennaria dioica* (L.) Gaertn. ($\times \frac{2}{5}$); densely tufted perennial; stems up to 9 in. high; leaves crowded, spathulate to narrowly oblanceolate, glabrous above, densely covered below with white woolly hairs; flowering-stems densely woolly with scattered linear leaves, bearing a cluster of shortly stalked heads at the top; flower-heads dioecious (unisexual and on different plants); male bracts (A, $\times 1\frac{1}{2}$) shorter and broader than the female (F, $\times 1\frac{1}{2}$), all white and glabrous except the woolly base; male flowers (B, $\times 4$) with short infertile ovaries and pappus hairs swollen towards the top and densely papillous (C, $\times 6$); anthers with barren tips and tailed at the base (D, $\times 15$); style undivided (E, $\times 8$); female flowers (G, $\times 4$) with longer ovaries and longer nearly smooth pappus, and a very slender (almost thread-like) corolla, no stamens, and a slender divided style (family *Compositae*).

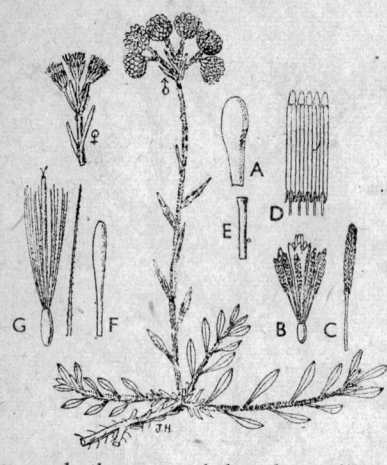

The flower-heads are of one sex, the males on one plant, the females on another; the heads of the two sexes look rather different, because the bracts of the male are much shorter than those of the female, which are white or rose-coloured, and the pappus of the two sexes is quite distinct.

The filaments of the male flowers are irritable, and curve when touched. In this way the anther-cylinder is retracted, so that pollen protrudes from its upper end and is exposed to insect visitors.

CORN MARIGOLD, *Chrysanthemum segetum* L.

330. Corn Marigold, *Chrysanthemum segetum* L. (× ⅓); annual with a tap root and very numerous fibrous rootlets; stem erect, glabrous, leafy; leaves alternate, sessile, oblong-oblanceolate in outline, coarsely toothed or pinnately lobed, lobes acute, glabrous and rather glaucous; flower-heads up to 2 in. diam., on long leafy peduncles; bracts (A, B, C, × 0) in 3–4 rows, with broad membranous margins and tops, glabrous; ray-flowers (D, × 1½) numerous, spreading, golden-yellow; corolla obovate-elliptic, 2-lobed at the top; disk-flowers (E, × 1½) tubular; anthers (F, × 4) with triangular tips and rounded bases; style of the disk-flower (G, × 6) with truncate papillous tips; achenes of the ray-flowers narrowly 2-winged, of the disk not winged; no pappus; receptacle nearly flat, without scales amongst the flowers (family *Compositae*).

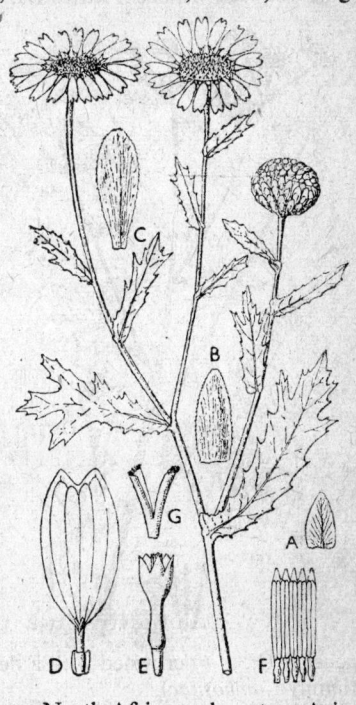

Widely distributed in Europe, North Africa and western Asia, and elsewhere as a weed of cultivation, often in cornfields. It is worth growing in a garden for its handsome flower-heads and glaucous foliage, though the farmer with a glut of it in his fields will scarcely appreciate its beauty, for it is a very troublesome weed. Its seeds have the power of lying dormant in the soil for several years, and coming to life again when turned up by the plough. Yellow Gowans, Gowlans, Gools and Yellow Bottle are names for it in different parts of the country. This and *Chrysanthemum parthenium* (fig. 331), together with *C. leucanthemum* (vol. 1, fig. 152), show all the species of this genus found in Britain.

FEVERFEW, *Chrysanthemum parthenium* (L.) Bernh.

331. Feverfew, *Chrysanthemum parthenium* (L.) Bernh. ($\times \frac{2}{5}$); perennial, stems branched up to about 1½ ft. high, leafy from the base, ribbed; leaves (A, $\times \frac{2}{5}$) deeply pinnately lobed, the lobes very coarsely toothed or lobulate, at most slightly hairy; flower-heads ½–¾ in. diam., about 3 or 4 at the end of each branch and forming a wide corymb; peduncles slender; bracts of the involucre in about 3 rows, each with a keeled midrib, slightly hairy; no scaly bracts below the disk-flowers; ray-flowers (B, $\times$ 3) about 15, white, spreading, broadly elliptic, 3-toothed at the apex; disk-flowers (C, $\times$ 3) numerous, yellow; corolla-tubes with a few scattered glands; anthers (D, $\times$ 6) rounded at the base; style arms (E, $\times$ 6) of the disk-flowers very short and blunt; achenes (F, $\times$ 6) crowned with a dentate pappus, with dark ribs (family *Compositae*).

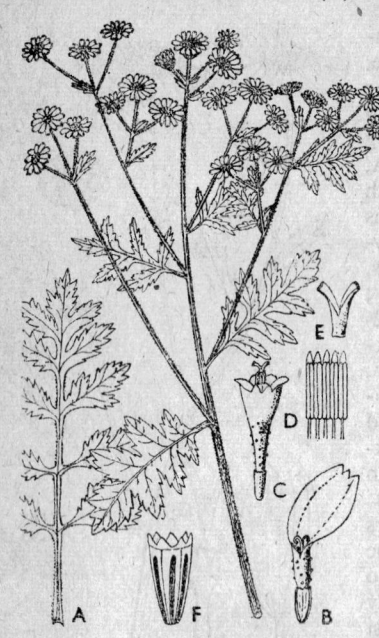

This rather handsome species grows by roadsides, near walls, and in waste places, and is doubtfully native, being usually an escape from gardens. It is distributed eastwards as far as the Caucasus.

Anthemis arvensis contd. from next page:—

and the achenes are smooth, whilst the receptacle (fig. A) is furnished with a bract below every one of the disk-flowers. In *A. cotula* (fig. 333) there is no style in the ray-flowers, the achenes are warted, and the receptacle bears bracts only amongst the upper flowers.

CORN CHAMOMILE, *Anthemis arvensis* L.

332. Corn Chamomile, *Anthemis arvensis* L. ($\times \frac{1}{2}$); erect or spreading much-branched annual, pubescent all over; leaves deeply pinnately divided into narrow acute segments; bracts of the involucre (B, $\times 2\frac{1}{2}$) in about 3 rows, gradually longer, the inner with membranous margins, hairy outside; ray-flowers (C, $\times 2$) white, numerous, about $\frac{1}{2}$ in. long, provided with a bilobed style; tip 3-toothed; disk-flowers (D, $\times 2$) yellow, numerous, each flower with a very narrow pointed scale at the base (A); anthers (E, $\times 10$) rounded at the base; style-arms (F, $\times 10$) truncate; achenes (G, $\times 6$) narrowed to the base, with rounded smooth ribs; no pappus (family *Compositae*).

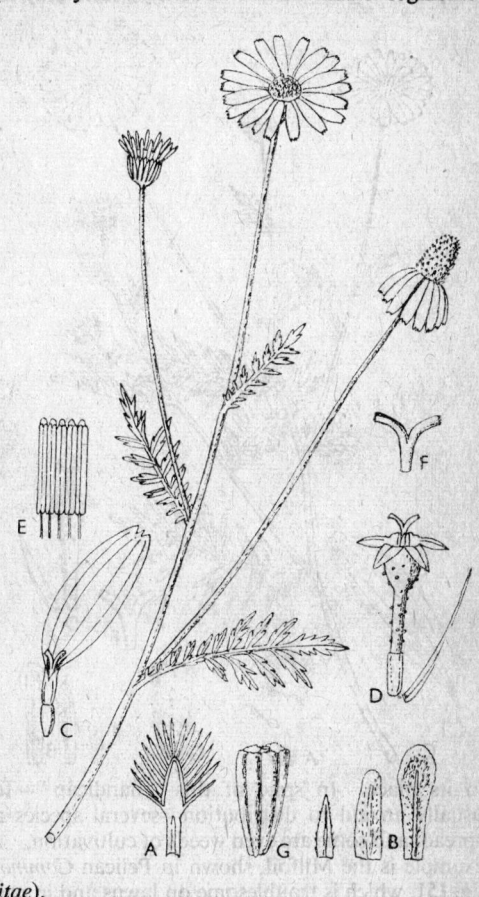

The genus *Anthemis* differs from *Matricaria* (Pelican Book, *Common Wild Flowers*, fig. 153) in that each of the upper disk-flowers, at any rate, is subtended by a narrow bract. In *A. arvensis* there is a style in the ray-flowers (see foot of p. 170),

171

FETID CHAMOMILE, *Anthemis cotula* L.

333. Fetid Chamomile, *Anthemis cotula* L. ($\times \frac{1}{2}$); a much-branched annual and very like *A. arvensis* (fig. 332), but the receptacle is furnished with bristly scales only in the upper half (fig. A) whereas in *A. arvensis* it is scaly-bracteate all over (i.e. one bract below every flower), the ray-flowers are barren and have no style, and the achenes (G, $\times$ 8) are prominently warted. For the difference between *Matricaria* and *Anthemis* see notes under fig. 332.

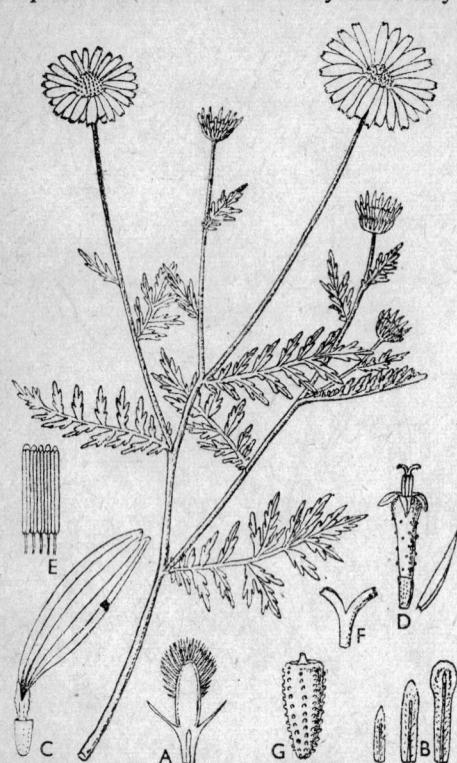

The tribe to which *Anthemis* belongs, tribe *Anthemideae*, is characterised by having no pappus (modified calyx), or merely a rim in its place. In spite of this "handicap"—for a pappus is usually an aid to distribution—several species are very widely spread, and some are even weeds of cultivation. A very common example is the Milfoil, shown in Pelican *Common Wild Flowers*, fig. 151, which is troublesome on lawns and in pastures.—B, $\times$ 2, bracts of involucre; C, $\times$ 2, ray-flower; D, $\times$ 2, disk-flower and subtending scale; E, $\times$ 6, anthers; F, $\times$ 6, style-arms of disk-flower; G, $\times$ 8, achene of disk-flower.

RAYLESS CHAMOMILE, *Matricaria matricarioides* (Less.) Porter

334. Rayless Chamomile, *Matricaria matricarioides* (Less.) Porter ($\times \frac{2}{5}$); annual, from very dwarf to about 9 in. high; stems green, often crimson towards the base, without hairs (glabrous), not hollow; leaves alternate, with a broad flat base (A, $\times$ 0), divided to the middle into very fine much-divided lobe, each leaf bearing in its axil a flowering branch, the oldest flower-head at the top; flower-heads (B, $\times$ 1) about 3 on each branch, shortly stalked; bracts of the involucre in 3-4 rows, pale green but with membranous tips and margins; no ray-flowers; disk-flowers (D, $\times$ 6) numerous, spirally arranged on a cone-like axis (C, $\times$ 1); corolla 4-lobed; stamens 4; anthers with barren tips and rounded base (E, $\times$ 12); ovary smooth, crowned by a slightly toothed rim at the top; style-arms very blunt, (F, $\times$ 12); achenes (G, $\times$ 4) marked with two or three resin-like lines (synonyms *Matricaria discoidea* DC. and *Matricaria suaveolens* (Pursh) Buchen. non L. (family *Compositae*).

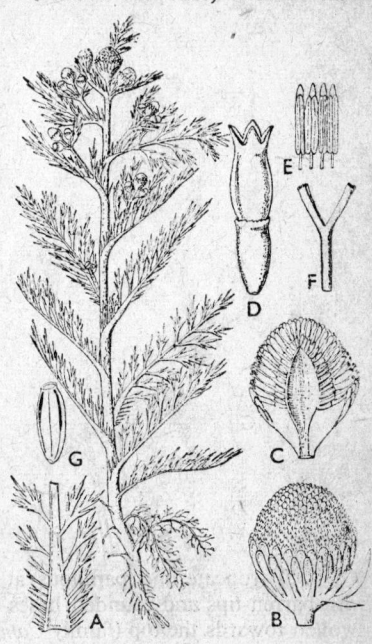

This species was mentioned under the name *Matricaria discoidea* DC. in our first book (see notes to fig. 153) as being an introduced weed and common on roadside and along pathways, often among cobbles in farmyards. The more it is trodden on the better it seems to thrive. It spreads rapidly because of the great number of fertile flowers, none of which is radiate, as in most other species of the genus. The tiny achenes are pretty microscopic objects. When ripe they will be seen to have two or three resin-like streaks running lengthwise, and recalling those so characteristic of the Hemlock family, *Umbelliferae*.

MARSH RAGWORT, *Senecio aquaticus* Hill

335. Marsh Ragwort, *Senecio aquaticus* Hill ($\times \frac{1}{3}$); erect perennial or biennial up to about 2 ft. high; basal leaves lobulate, soon withering; lower stem-leaves (A, $\times \frac{1}{3}$) lyrate-pinnatisect or lobed, the upper part of the blade sharply and coarsely toothed; upper leaves gradually becoming smaller and sessile, deeply cut, thinly woolly to nearly glabrous below; heads few in a loose corymb, about 1 in. diam.; outer bracts (B, $\times 1\frac{2}{3}$) few, awl-shaped (subulate), inner narrowly lanceolate, frilled on the margin and with hairy tips; ray-flowers (C, $\times 1\frac{2}{3}$) yellow, about 12–15; disk-flowers (D, $\times 1\frac{2}{3}$) numerous, yellow; achenes (E, $\times 4$) of both kinds of flowers ribbed, smooth and not hairy; pappus-hairs (F, $\times 5$) white, rough; style-arms (G, $\times 5$) truncate and papillous at the tip; anthers (H, $\times 7$) with barren tips and rounded bases without tails, the filaments swollen towards the top (family *Compositae*).

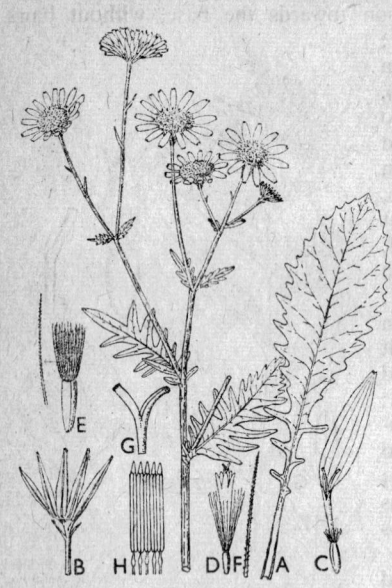

Very like the Common Ragwort (*Common Wild Flowers*, fig. 157), but the lower leaves less cut up, and the achenes of the disk-flowers not hairy (glabrous); it grows in wetter places than the Ragwort, by the sides of rivers, ditches and rills in meadows, especially in peaty soil.

WOOD SENECIO, *Senecio sylvaticus* L.

336. Wood Senecio, *Senecio sylvaticus* L. ($\times \frac{1}{2}$); annual much like the common Groundsel, but taller and more slender, the stems very minutely pubescent, and lined with several ribs; leaves deeply pinnate, divided into irregularly cut sharply angular lobes as shown in the drawing; flower-heads usually very numerous and forming a wide loose corymb, weaker specimens with fewer heads, as in the drawing; stalks slender and bearing 2 or 3 thread-like bracts; involucres bell-shaped, with about 12-15 narrow very shortly pubescent bracts in a single row and with darker tips; outer flowers (A, $\times 2\frac{1}{2}$) very small and inconspicuous, the corolla limb being rolled up in dry weather; achenes (E, $\times 4$) nearly black, ribbed when dry, and shortly and softly hairy, crowned with a pappus of soft white hair-like bristles; fruiting heads with sharply deflexed involucral bracts (F, $\times 1\frac{1}{4}$) (family Compositae) (B, disk-flower, $\times 3$; C, anthers; D, style-arms of disk-flowers).

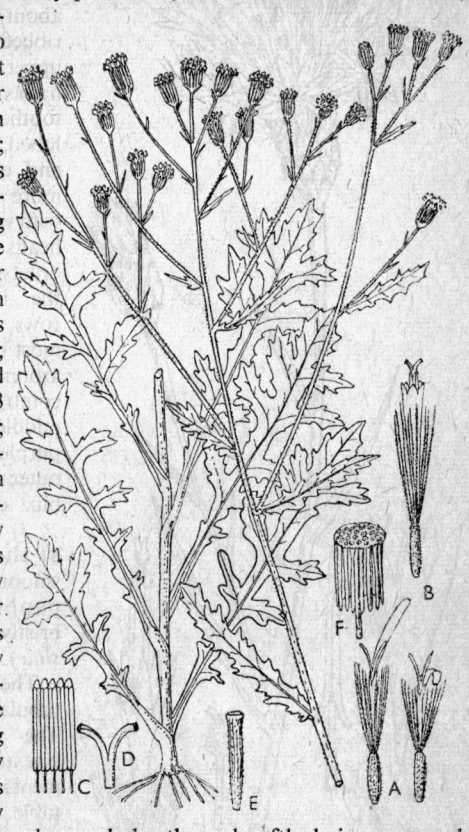

Rather like Groundsel (*Common Wild Flowers*, fig. 158), but usually much taller and with more numerous flower-heads.

BLUEBOTTLE, CORNFLOWER, *Centaurea cyanus* L.

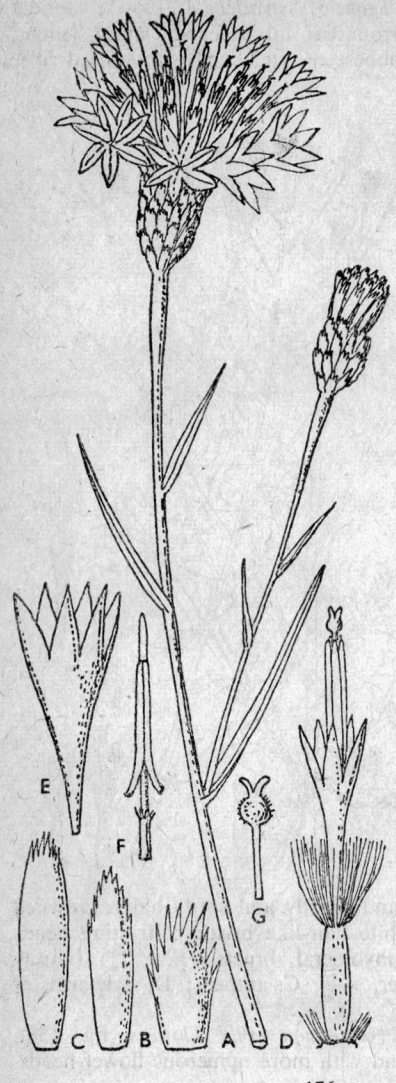

337. Bluebottle, Cornflower, *Centaurea cyanus* L. ($\times \frac{4}{5}$); annual about 2 ft. high; stems ribbed, clothed in the upper parts with woolly hairs; lower leaves toothed or pinnately lobed, the upper linear and entire, very acute, more or less woolly with white hairs; flower-heads on woolly stalks; bracts (A, B, C, $\times 2$) of the involucre in 4–5 rows, chaffy, the outermost quite short, all cut around the top like a comb; flowers in the middle (D, $\times 1\frac{1}{2}$) bluish-purple, smaller than the outer (E, $\times 1\frac{1}{2}$) bright-blue ones; anthers (F, $\times 3$) with blunt tails at the base; achene smooth, with a short pappus; receptacle bristly (family *Compositae*).

The outer flowers are tubular but not fertile. The disk-flowers are bisexual, and the filaments are highly irritable. When touched by an insect these are drawn downwards (retracted), and the pollen within the anther-cylinder is swept out by the ring of hairs below the style-branches.

SCOTCH or COTTON THISTLE, *Onopordon acanthium* L.

338. Scotch or Cotton Thistle, *Onopordon acanthium* L. ($\times \frac{1}{2}$); a vigorous biennial herb up to about 6 ft. high, very prickly and covered all over with loose woolly hairs; stem clothed by the decurrent leaf-bases from top to bottom; basal leaves (A, $\times \frac{1}{2}$) stalked, 1 ft. or more long, coarsely lobulate, the lobules with a few sharp prickle-like teeth; stem-leaves narrow and very prickly; flower-heads large and at the ends of the few branches; bracts of the involucre very numerous in several series, awl-shaped from a broader base, matted together with woolly hairs; receptacle (B, $\times 1\frac{1}{2}$) honeycombed into cavities with jagged margins; flowers (C, $\times 1\frac{1}{2}$) pale purple, all of one kind, tubular, 5-lobed; anthers (D, $\times 4$) with narrow barren tips and arrow-shaped at the base; style (E, $\times 4$) very shortly split at the tip; achenes (F, $\times 2$) slightly compressed, ribbed lengthwise and transversely rugose when ripe (G, $\times 2$) pappus bristles (H, $\times 5$) rough, a few longer than the others (family *Compositae*).

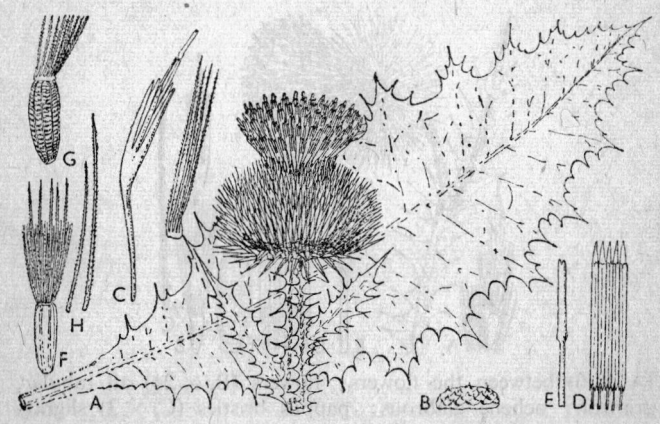

A widely spread and handsome species, and representing the Scotch heraldic thistle; common in the Mediterranean region.

This is an imposing plant, and well worth a place in the garden. The stems are broadly winged and more or less function as leaves, the latter becoming reduced to very small proportions towards the top of the plant. It prefers rather dry sandy soil, and flowers in July and August. Besides the names given above it is also called "Argentine", "Oat", "Queen Mary's" and "Silver Thistle".

MUSK THISTLE, *Carduus nutans* L.

339. Musk Thistle, *Carduus nutans* L. (× ½); biennial herb up to about 3 ft. high, usually covered very slightly with cottony hairs but not conspicuously so; stems winged with the very narrow prickly extensions of the leaf-bases; basal leaves pinnately lobed and with very prickly margins; stem-leaves narrow and sessile, very prickly on the lobulate margin and thinly hairy; flower-heads nodding, about 1¼–1½ in. diam., solitary on simple stems or these with a few branches at the top, each ending in a flower-head; bracts of the involucre in about 6 or 7 rows, narrowly lanceolate, with a long sharp point, interlaced with woolly hairs; receptacle with long smooth bristles

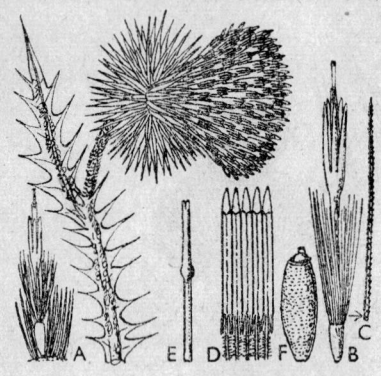

(A, × 0) between the flowers; flowers (B, × 2½) all tubular, crimson; achene glabrous; pappus bristles (C, × 3) slightly rough; corolla slender, deeply 5-lobed; anthers (D, × 3) with long tails at the base, and very hairy filaments; style (E, × 3) smooth, slightly 2-lobed at the apex; ripe achenes (F, × 2½) straw-coloured, very minutely wrinkled (family *Compositae*).

The Musk Thistle is often conspicuous on waste ground and rubbish-heaps, and seems to follow man wherever he goes, though it shows a definite preference for light and sandy soils, especially in chalky districts. The seeds are used for feeding cage-birds. Other common names for the plant are Queen Ann's thrissel, and Bank, Buck, and Dog Thistle.

It is widely distributed to North Africa, and eastwards to the Himalayas and Siberia.

LESSER BURDOCK, *Arctium minus* (Hill) Bernh.

340. Lesser Burdock, *Arctium minus* (Hill) Bernh. ($\times \frac{1}{3}$); strong-growing biennial herbs with rather large almost rhubarb-like leaves; lower leaves ovate, widely cordate at the base, triangular at the apex, up to 1 ft. or more long and little less broad, rather undulate-denticulate, thinly cottony below, but becoming glabrous or nearly so; upper leaves becoming much smaller and entire or almost entire, and not cordate at the base; heads ovoid, forming a leafy one-sided raceme, the lateral shortly stalked; involucral bracts numerous (A, $\times$ 0), hooked at the apex, inner purple, not or only slightly connected with cottony hairs; receptacle covered with bristles of unequal length (B, $\times$ 0); flowers (C, $\times 1\frac{1}{4}$) all tubular; corolla purple; anthers (D, $\times$ 2) tailed; style (E, $\times$ 2) swollen and hairy below the arms; achene (C, $\times 1\frac{1}{4}$) angular, closely warted between the ribs; pappus-bristles in several whorls, short, scabrid (family *Compositae*).

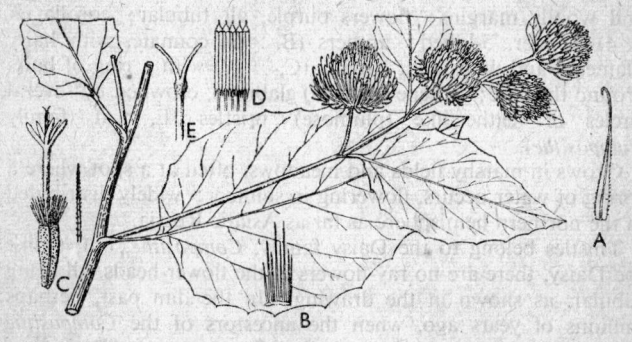

A weed of waste places, rubbish-dumps, and on roadsides, flowering from July to August.

The hooks of the involucral bracts surrounding the flower-head catch on the clothing and to the coats of animals, and assist in distributing the seed. It is little more than a small edition of the larger and less widely spread Greater Burdock, in which the size of the flower-heads varies considerably.

# MARSH THISTLE, *Cirsium palustre* (L.) Scop.

341. Marsh Thistle, *Cirsium palustre* (L.) Scop. ($\times \frac{1}{2}$); a stiff-growing annual or biennial, variable in height up to about $4\frac{1}{2}$ ft.; stems mostly unbranched except at the top, closely ribbed and beset with prickles; leaves narrowly lanceolate in outline to linear, pinnately lobed, the lobes ending in very sharp prickles, thinly cobwebby below; flower-heads usually 3 or more in the axils of the leaves and crowded towards the top and making the plant appear top-heavy; heads almost sessile on the common short stalk, about 1 in. long and as much in diam.; bracts of the involucre very numerous, narrow, with sharp tips and woolly margins; flowers purple, all tubular; corolla (A $\times$ 4) slender, 5-lobed; anthers (B, $\times$ 3) connate, with hairy filaments and with tails; stigma (C, $\times$ 10) with a ring of hairs around the base; achene (D, $\times$ 5) glabrous, crowned by several circles of feather-like (plumose) bristles (E, $\times$ 6) (family *Compositae*).

Grows in marshy fields and meadows, often at a spot where a spring of water occurs, flowering in summer; widely distributed in the northern hemisphere as far as Asiatic Russia.

Thistles belong to the Daisy family, *Compositae*, but, unlike the Daisy, there are no ray-flowers in the flower-heads, all being tubular, as shown in the drawing. In the dim past, perhaps millions of years ago, when the ancestors of the *Compositae* were beginning to change their inflorescence (collection of flowers) into their flower-head as we know it to-day, the flowers were probably arranged in a loose elongated spike, each with a bract below, and the calyx was not much modified, certainly not into the bristly, feathery thing shown in the drawing. As more crowding took place on the shortening of the axis, the outer flowers became modified into strap-shaped bodies in order to continue to attract insects.

181

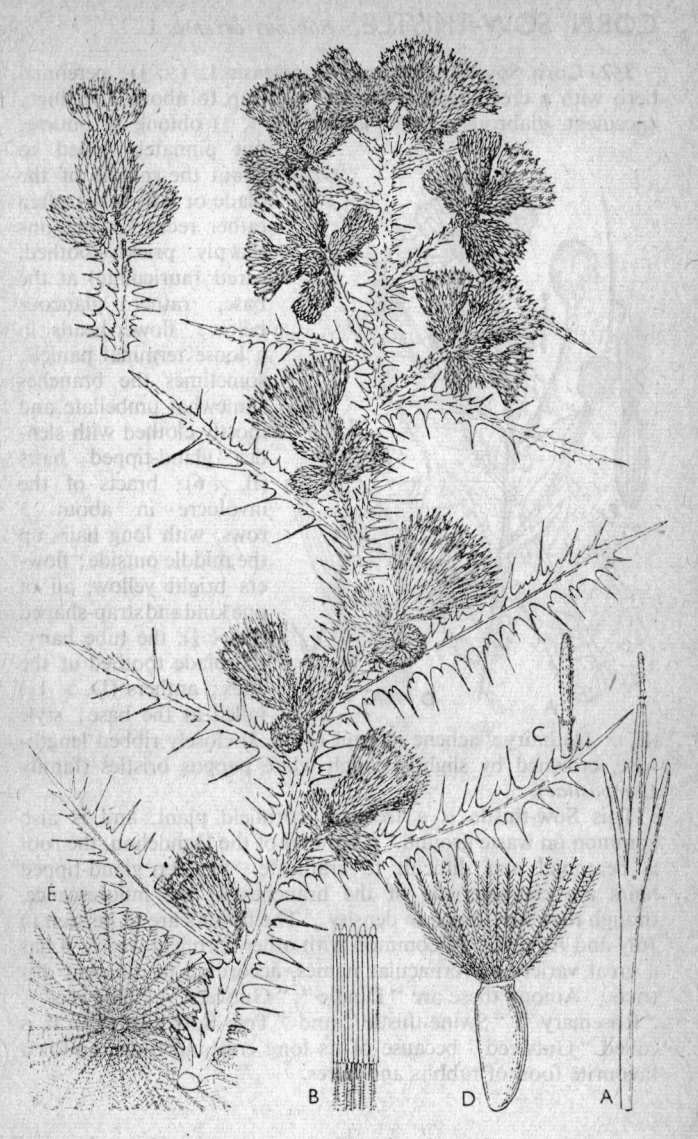

CORN SOW-THISTLE, *Sonchus arvensis* L.

342. Corn Sow-thistle, *Sonchus arvensis* L. ($\times \frac{1}{2}$); perennial herb with a creeping root-stock; stem up to about 3 ft. high, succulent, glabrous; lower leaves (A, $\times \frac{1}{2}$) oblong in outline, but pinnately lobed to about the middle of the blade or less, lobes often rather recurved, margins sharply prickly-toothed, eared (auriculate) at the base, rather glaucous below; flower-heads in a loose terminal panicle, sometimes the branches somewhat umbellate and mostly clothed with slender gland-tipped hairs (B, $\times 6$); bracts of the involucre in about 3 rows, with long hairs up the middle outside; flowers bright yellow, all of one kind and strap-shaped (C, $\times \frac{3}{4}$), the tube hairy, the blade toothed at the apex; anthers (D, $\times 1\frac{1}{2}$) tailed at the base; style (E, $\times 1\frac{1}{2}$) hairy; achene in fruit (F, $\times 3$) closely ribbed lengthwise, crowned by slightly rough white pappus bristles (family *Compositae*).

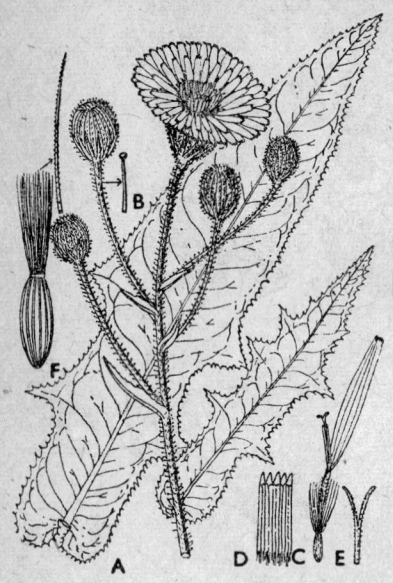

This Sow-thistle is a frequent cornfield plant, and is also common on waste ground. Like that of the Dandelion, the root is perennial and difficult to eradicate. Slender gland-tipped hairs are characteristic of the branches of the inflorescence, though they vary much in density. The flowers are to be seen in July and August. In common with other cornfield weeds, it has a great variety of vernacular names, according to different districts. Among these are "Dindle", "Gutweed", "Hogweed", "Rosemary", "Swine-thistle" and "Tree Sow-thistle". It is called "Gutweed" because of its long creeping roots, and is a favourite food of rabbits and hares.

WALL LETTUCE, *Lactuca muralis* (L.) Fresen.

343. Wall Lettuce, *Lactuca muralis* (L.) Fresen. ($\times \frac{1}{2}$); an annual or biennial up to about 2 ft. high, or taller in shady places; stems slender, branched at the top into a loose slender panicle, glabrous and sometimes covered with "bloom"; leaves, especially those up the stem, auriculate at the base, then narrowed into a winged part like a stalk, and in the upper half irregularly pinnately lobed, the lobes remotely denticulate, green or tinged with crimson and glaucous below; flower-heads (A, $\times \frac{2}{3}$) very narrow, about $\frac{1}{2}$ in. long, with a few short bracts at the base of the main involucre consisting of a few narrow bracts with broad thin margins; flowers (B, $\times 2$) few, all of one kind (ligulate), yellow; achenes glabrous, ellipsoid in flower; pappus hairs (D, $\times 5$) white, barbellate; anthers (E, $\times 5$) short-tailed at the base; achenes in fruit (C, $\times 2\frac{1}{2}$) with a short slender beak, closely ribbed lengthwise (family *Compositae*).

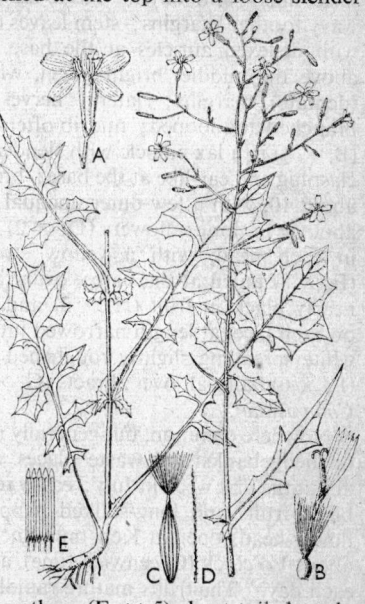

This is a very well marked species, which is usually found growing in shady places, and should not be difficult to identify with the aid of the drawing. It is distributed as far east as Asia Minor and the Caucasus, and it is also found in Algeria. The stem-leaves are markedly auricled at the base, and more deeply cut than those of *L. virosa* (see fig. 344), whilst the achenes are more shortly beaked.

WILD LETTUCE, *Lactuca virosa* L.

344. Wild Lettuce, *Lactuca virosa* L. ($\times \frac{1}{2}$); biennial, with erect stems up to 6 or 7 ft. high or shorter, according to soil; juice milky and bitter; basal leaves obovate to oblong, with wavy toothed margins; stem leaves (A, $\times \frac{1}{2}$) sessile and clasping, with deflexed auricles at the base, oblong or slightly broader above the middle, bright green, with wavy irregularly toothed (dentate) margins; lateral nerves numerous and spreading, branched and looped; midrib often prickly below; flower-heads (B, $\times \frac{1}{2}$) in a lax panicle with slender spreading branches; bracts clasping and ear-like at the base; bracts of the involucre (C, $\times 0$) about 10, with a few outer unequal sized, green, the whole head about $\frac{3}{4}$ in. long; flowers (D, $\times 2$) all of one kind, about 15–20 in each head, with a yellow strap-shaped corolla; anthers (E, $\times 8$) tailed at the base; ovary at first yellow, but becoming nearly black in fruit (H, $\times 3$) and flattened, with about 7 ribs on each face, at length narrowed into a slender beak, bearing the white spreading slightly roughened pappus-hairs (J, $\times 8$); style (F, $\times 6$) hairy all over; bracts (G, $\times 0$) spreading in fruit (family *Compositae*).

Nowhere common, but generally distributed, and found mostly on hedgebanks and waste places, and on cliffs, flowering from about the first week in July; easily recognised by its ribbed almost black fruits and long-stalked pappus of spreading hairs. The flower-heads open at Kew on a fine day about 9 and close again about 1 o'clock (Greenwich time), and only a few heads are open each day. The fruits mature rapidly, when the bracts surrounding them become reflexed and the pappus hairs spread out horizontally, by means of which the fruits ("seeds") float away in the wind; a few flowers remain sterile. In a related species, *Lactuca sativa* L., observations have shown that there is quite a considerable difference in the time of the opening of the flower-heads at different latitudes. For example, at Upsala, in Sweden, the flower-heads opened at 7 a.m. (Greenwich time) and closed at 10 a.m., whilst at Innsbruck, in Austria, they opened between 8 and 9 a.m., and closed between 1 and 2 p.m. This is probably due to the fact that during the flowering time of this species the sun rises about an hour and a half earlier at Upsala than at Innsbruck.

185

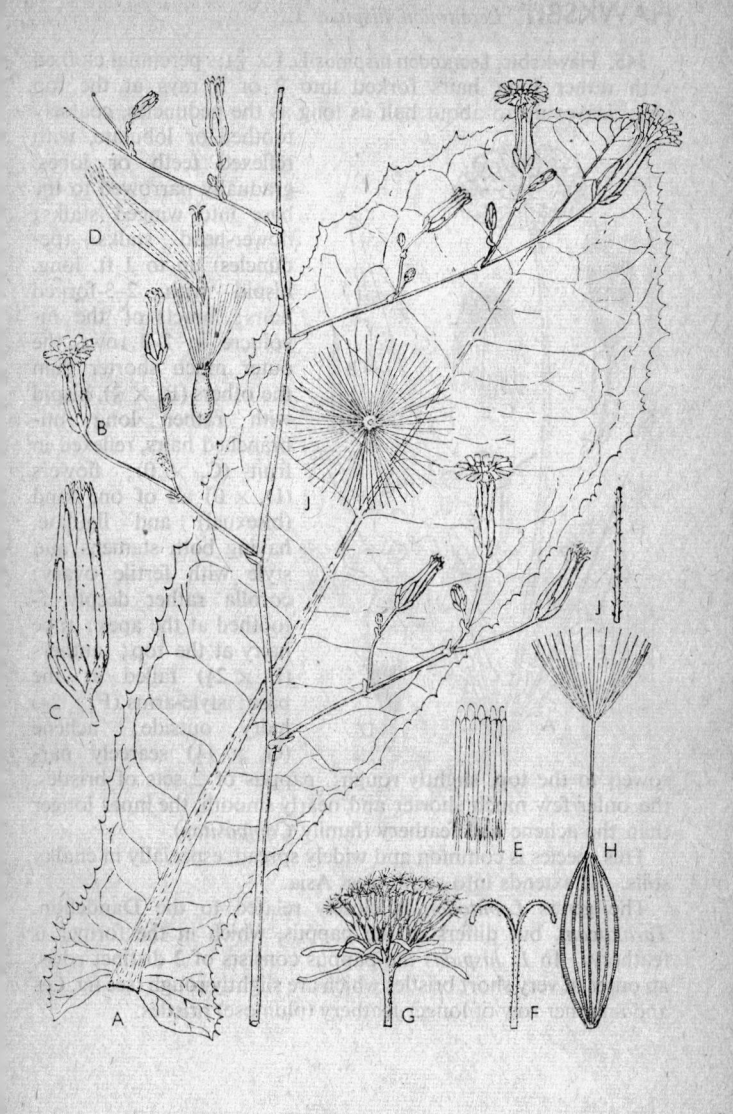

HAWKSBIT, *Leontodon hispidus* L.

345. Hawksbit, *Leontodon hispidus* L. ($\times \frac{2}{5}$); perennial clothed with rather long hairs forked into 2 or 3 rays at the top (A); leaves up to about half as long as the peduncles, coarsely toothed or lobulate, with reflexed teeth or lobes, gradually narrowed to the base into winged stalks; flower-head stalks (peduncles) up to 1 ft. long, hispid with 2–3-forked hairs; bracts of the involucre* in 2–3 rows, the outer much shorter than the others (B, $\times \frac{4}{5}$), hispid with rather long unbranched hairs, reflexed in fruit (C, $\times$ 0); flowers (D, $\times$ 0) all of one kind (bisexual) and ligulate, having both stamens and style with fertile ovary; corolla rather deeply 5-toothed at the apex; tube hairy at the top; anthers (E, $\times 2\frac{1}{2}$) tailed at the base; style-arms (F, $\times 2\frac{1}{2}$) hairy outside; achene (G, $\times 1\frac{1}{2}$) scarcely narrowed to the top, slightly rough; pappus of 2 sets of bristles, the outer few much shorter and nearly smooth, the inner longer than the achene and feathery (family *Compositae*).

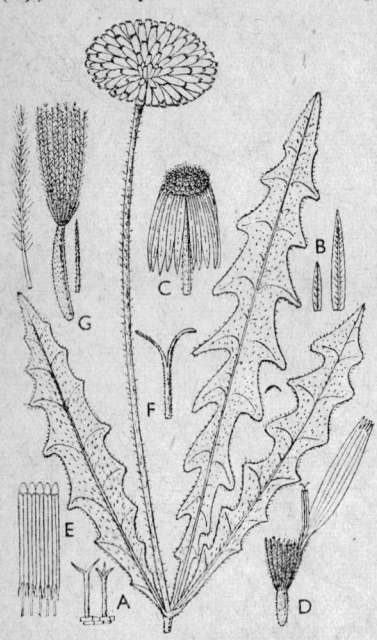

This species is common and widely spread, especially in chalky soils. It extends into south-west Asia.

The genus *Leontodon* is closely related to the Dandelion, *Taraxacum*, but differs in the pappus, which in the former is feathery. In *L. hispidus* the pappus consists of 2 distinct rows, an outer of very short bristles which are slightly rough (see fig. G), and an inner row of longer feathery (plumose) bristles.

TEA PLANT, *Lycium chinense* Mill.

346. Tea Plant, *Lycium chinense* Mill. ($\times \frac{1}{2}$); a slender shrub often growing on old walls, with long whip-like pendulous branches; bark greyish, angular; leaves alternate, oblanceolate, tapered to each end, pale glaucous-green, entire, glabrous, very obscurely nerved; flowers (A, $\times$ 10) 1–3 in the leaf axils; pedicels about $\frac{1}{2}$ in. long; calyx irregularly divided into 2 or 3 lobes; corolla deep lilac, tubular, with 5 spreading lobes with dark honey-guide markings at the base, minutely fringed with hairs; stamens (B, $\times 1\frac{1}{2}$) 5, inserted inside the corolla-tube; filaments with a tuft of hairs towards the base; anthers attached in the middle, sagittate at the base, opening by slits; ovary (C, $\times 1\frac{1}{2}$) 2-locular, with numerous ovules on axile placentas; fruit (D, $\times$ 0) an oblong berry (family *Solanaceae*).

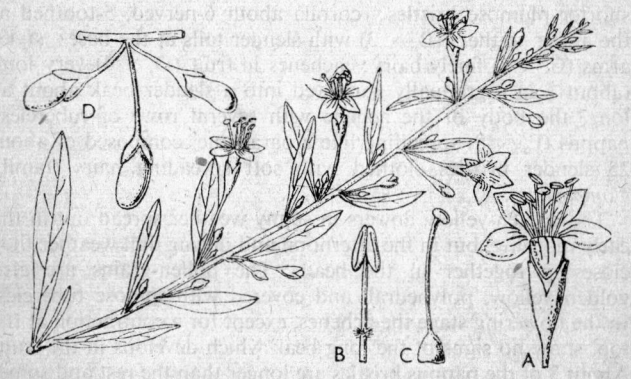

Naturalised on walls and in hedges around dwellings; in many British botanical books it is called *Lycium barbarum*.

Nectar is secreted by the ovary and stored in the base of the corolla-tube. The inside of the throat of the corolla is lined with thick woolly hairs, which protect the nectar from rain and unwelcome guests. The stigma and anthers mature at the same time, and the filaments and the style are about the same length, but the latter may be bent away from the anthers. Insect visitors may therefore bring about self- or cross-pollination.

GOAT'S BEARD SALSIFY, *Tragopogon pratensis* L.

347. Goat's Beard Salsify, *Tragopogon pratensis* L. ($\times \frac{1}{2}$); perennial up to 2 ft. high, with a tap root; juice milky; leaves alternate, grass-like, entire, linear and gradually broadened to the half-clasping base, with a few nerves parallel with the midrib, the tips curled, quite glabrous; peduncles elongated above the leaves, gradually thickened upwards; involucral bracts in 2-3 rows, about 20, tapered to a point, a little longer than the flowers, the latter numerous, yellow, and all ligulate (A, $\times$ 2); achenes in the flowering stage smooth, short and ovoid, contracted towards the top; pappus of about 3 longer, and numerous shorter plumose bristles; corolla about 6-nerved, 5-toothed at the apex; anthers (B, $\times$ 3) with slender tails at the base; style-arms (C, $\times$ 6) finely hairy; achenes in fruit (D, $\times$ 4) very long (about ¾ in.), gradually narrowed into a slender beak about as long, the body of the achene with several rows of tubercles; pappus (E, $\times$ 8) spreading like a parachute, composed of about 25 slender bristles clothed with soft spreading hairs (family *Compositae*).

The golden-yellow flowers in sunny weather spread out in the early morning, but in the afternoon and during dull weather they close up together in the head. The pollen-grains are also golden yellow, polyhedral, and covered with spinose tubercles. In the flowering stage the achenes, except for a contraction at the top, show no signs of the long beak which develops in the fruit. About 3 of the pappus bristles are longer than the rest and somewhat thicker, this character showing more in the flowering stage.

Goat's Beard grows in fields and meadows, especially in hilly pastures. It also flourishes by the side of pathways, and is often common on railway-embankments, where so many British wild flowers find sanctuary from man's operations and browsing animals. Its numerous native names nearly all refer to the habit of closing its flowers in the afternoon: " Shepherd's Clock ", " Go-to-bed-at-noon ", " Nap-at-noon ", " Noontide ", " Sleep-at-noon ". Others refer to the bearded fruiting head.

189

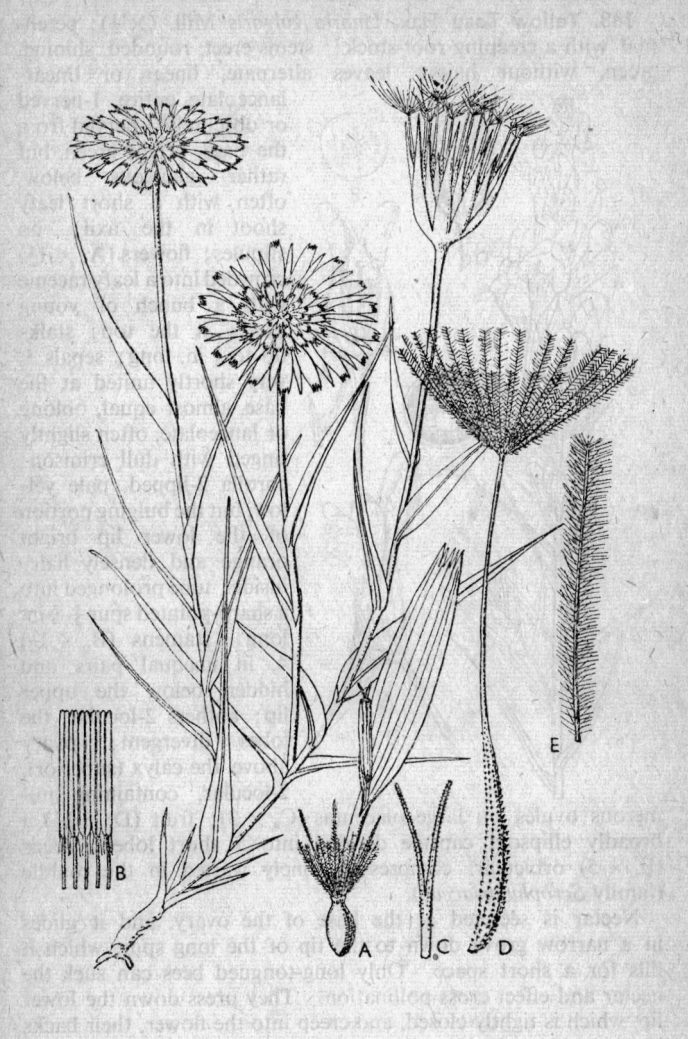

YELLOW TOAD FLAX, *Linaria vulgaris* Mill.

348. Yellow Toad Flax, *Linaria vulgaris* Mill. (× ½); perennial with a creeping root-stock; stems erect, rounded, shining, green, without hairs; leaves alternate, linear or linear-lanceolate, entire, 1-nerved or obscurely 3-nerved from the base, bright green, but rather glaucous below, often with a short leafy shoot in the axil; no stipules; flowers (A, × 1½) crowded into a leafy raceme with a bunch of young leaves at the top; stalks up to ⅓ in. long; sepals 5, very shortly united at the base, almost equal, oblong or lanceolate, often slightly tinged with dull crimson; corolla 2-lipped, pale yellow, but the bulging portion of the lower lip bright orange and densely hairy inside; tube prolonged into a sharp-pointed spur ½–¾ in. long; stamens (B, × 1½) 4, in unequal pairs and hidden below the upper lip; anthers 2-locular, the lobes divergent; ovary above the calyx (superior), 2-locular, containing numerous ovules on large placentas (C, × 3); fruit (D, × 1½) a broadly ellipsoid capsule divided into 5 short lobes; seeds (E, × 5) orbicular, compressed, finely warted in the middle (family *Scrophulariaceae*).

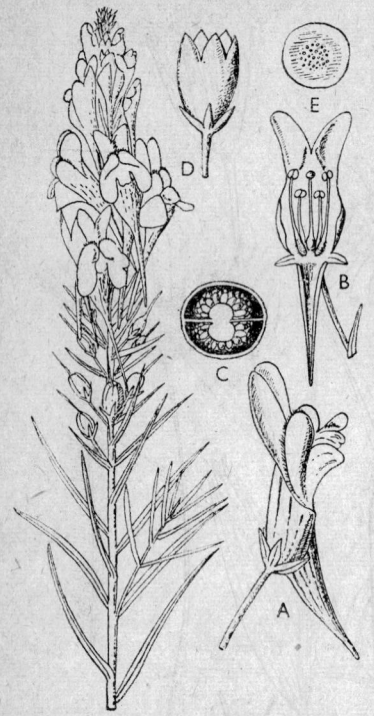

Nectar is secreted at the base of the ovary, and it glides in a narrow grove down to the tip of the long spur, which it fills for a short space. Only long-tongued bees can suck the nectar and effect cross-pollination. They press down the lower lip, which is tightly closed, and creep into the flower, their backs becoming dusted with pollen, which they transfer to the stigma of another flower.

BROOK-LIME SPEEDWELL, *Veronica beccabunga* L.

349. Brook-Lime Speedwell, *Veronica beccabunga* L. ($\times \frac{2}{5}$); perennial by the sides of brooks and ditches, the stems sometimes floating in the water, rooting at the nodes, thick, succulent and hollow, quite glabrous; leaves opposite, stalked, rounded-elliptic or obovate, rounded at the top, slightly toothed, glabrous and rather fleshy, with about 3 pairs of lateral nerves; a short rim across the stem between the leaf-stalks; flowers in slender-stalked axillary racemes about twice as long as the leaves and with very small bracts; flower-stalks longer than the calyx, the latter (A, $\times 2\frac{1}{2}$) 4-lobed to the base, lobes ovate; corolla (B, $\times 2\frac{1}{2}$) dark sky-blue, 4-lobed; stamens 2, exserted, attached near the base of the corolla-tube; anthers ovoid; ovary 2-locular, with a slender style and capitate stigma; capsule (C, $\times 2$), rounded, shortly notched, glabrous, tipped by the persistent style; seeds (D, $\times 8$) rounded, straw-coloured, smooth (family *Scrophulariaceae*).

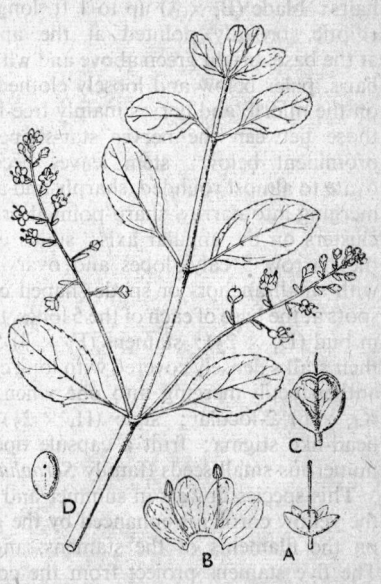

The dark sky-blue flowers expand in the sun to form a flat surface, from which the stigmas spread, the anthers being at a distance from the stigma when they open. In bad weather the flowers are half-closed, and automatic self-pollination takes place.

This species is like *Veronica scutellata* (see fig. 351), and is also spread across the northern hemisphere, but not in North America. It is also found in the same wet environment, but differs by the broader rounded leaves and by the racemes being in pairs at each node, i.e. one in the axil of each leaf. It flowers during the whole of the summer months.

BLACK MULLEIN, *Verbascum nigrum* L.

350. Black Mullein, *Verbascum nigrum* L. ($\times \frac{1}{2}$); biennial; stems simple or branched (see A), up to 3 or 4 ft. high; basal leaves on long stalks loosely clothed with branched (dendriform) hairs; blade (B, $\times \frac{1}{2}$) up to 1 ft. long and 6 in. broad, oblong-elliptic, broadly pointed at the apex, rounded-heart-shaped at the base, bright green above and with a few minute star-shaped hairs, paler below and loosely clothed with soft hairs, the hairs on the midrib and nerves mainly tree-like (dendriform) (C, $\times 2$), those between the nerves star-shaped (C, $\times 2$); nerves very prominent below; stem leaves becoming stalkless upwards, ovate to almost rounded, sharply and abruptly pointed, gradually merging into narrow sharp-pointed bracts; flowers numerous in clusters on the angular axis; stalks up to $\frac{1}{3}$ in. long, hairy like the narrow 5 calyx-lobes and ovary; corolla (E, $\times 0$) yellow with small anchor- or spade-shaped crimson or chestnut-brown spots at the base of each of the 5 lobes, these markedly overlapping in bud (D, $\times 2\frac{1}{2}$); stamens (F, $\times 3$) 5, alternate with the lobes, their stalks densely covered with long crimson gland-tipped hairs; anther-loculi merging into one when open, orange-red; ovary (G, $\times 6$) 2-locular; style (H, $\times 2\frac{1}{2}$) slender, with an orange head-like stigma; fruit a capsule opening by two valves, with numerous small seeds (family *Scrophulariaceae*).

This species flowers in summer and autumn and the colour of the yellow corolla is enhanced by the gland-tipped crimson hairs on the filaments of the stamens, and the orange-red anthers. The five stamens project from the corolla almost horizontally, and are only slightly bent upwards. The uppermost is short, and the lower 2 the longest. The style is a little shorter than the longer stamens, and is usually bent downwards, so that an insect alighting on the lowest corolla-lobe will generally touch the stigma first, bringing about cross-pollination.

G (A 180) 193

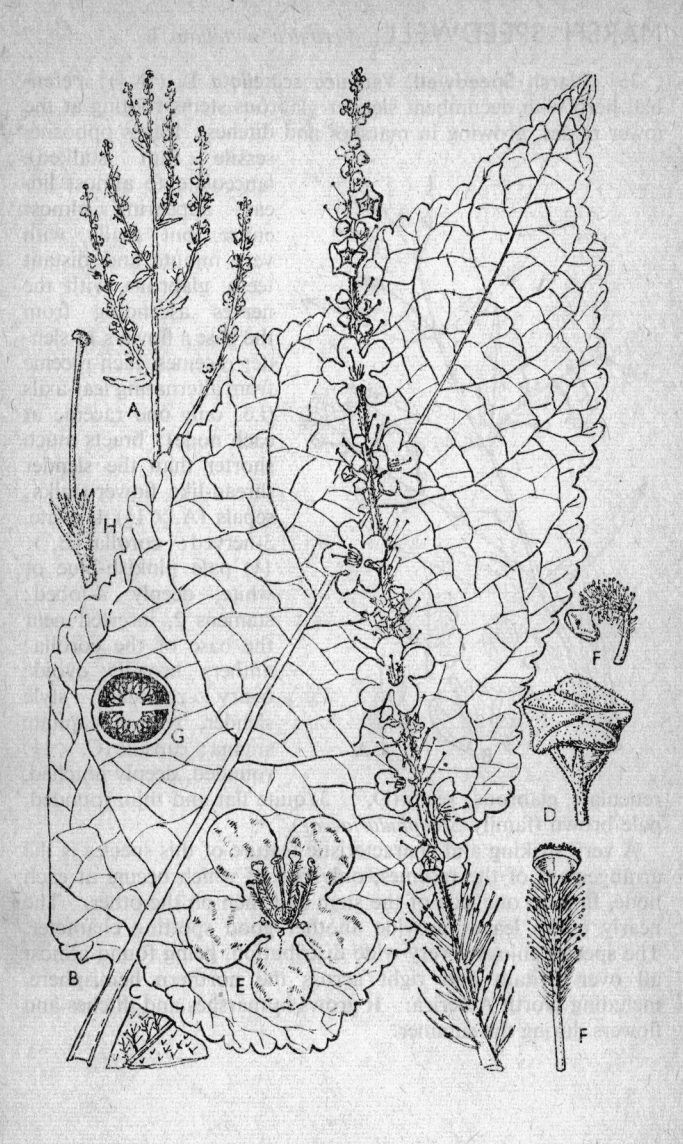

MARSH SPEEDWELL, *Veronica scutellata* L.

351. Marsh Speedwell, *Veronica scutellata* L. ($\times \frac{1}{3}$); perenbial herb with decumbent slender glabrous stems rooting at the lower nodes, growing in marshes and ditches; leaves opposite, sessile (not stalked), lanceolate to almost linear, appearing almost entire, but really with very minute and distant teeth, glabrous, with the nerves ascending from the base; flowers in slender racemes, each raceme from alternating leaf-axils (i.e., only one raceme at each node); bracts much shorter than the slender thread-like flower-stalks; sepals (A, $\times 1\frac{1}{2}$) 4, ovate, 3-nerved; corolla (B, $\times 1\frac{1}{2}$) pale pinkish-blue or white, deeply 4-lobed; stamens 2, inserted near the base of the corolla; anthers broadly ovoid; ovary rounded, style slender, with a capitate stigma; capsule (C, $\times 1\frac{1}{2}$) rounded, deeply notched, reticulate, glabrous; seeds (D, $\times 3$) quite flat and thin, rounded, pale brown (family *Scrophulariaceae*).

A very striking and characteristic feature of this species is the arrangement of the racemes, only one of which occurs at each node, first on one side of the stem and then on the other. The nearly entire leaves provide another good spotting character. The species enjoys a very wide distribution, being found almost all over Britain and right across the northern hemisphere, including North America. It grows in marshes and ditches and flowers during the summer.

COMMON SPEEDWELL, *Veronica officinalis* L.

352. Common Speedwell, *Veronica officinalis* L. ($\times \frac{1}{2}$); perennial herb usually much branched from the base and rooting at the lower nodes; stems thinly pubescent with rather long hairs all around; leaves (A, $\times 0$) opposite, very shortly stalked, ovate, wedge-shaped at the base, rounded or with a broad triangular top, very distinctly toothed (serrate), thinly hairy on both surfaces, with 3-4 pairs of lateral nerves; flowers (B, $\times 2$) in terminal stalked spike-like racemes (i.e., they are nearly sessile on the axis), the axis softly and rather densely pubescent; bracts about as long as the calyx, pubescent; sepals lanceolate, hairy; corolla pale blue, marked by darker veins, 4-lobed; stamens (C, $\times 4$) 2, inserted towards the base of the tube; anthers ovoid; ovary (D, $\times 4$) rounded, smooth, with a terminal rather long style, and seated on a nectariferous disk; capsule (E, $\times 2\frac{1}{2}$) rounded, notched, shortly pubescent; seeds (F, $\times 6$) yellow, flattened, smooth (family *Scrophulariaceae*).

Insects touch the stigma and anthers with various parts of their bodies, effecting either self- or cross-pollination. Failing these the filaments twist inwards and downwards as the corolla withers until the anthers touch the stigma.

A very widely distributed species on banks, heaths, and in dry pastures, flowering during the whole summer.

THYME-LEAVED SPEEDWELL, *Veronica serpyllifolia* L.

353. Thyme-Leaved Speedwell, *Veronica serpyllifolia* L. ($\times \frac{1}{2}$); perennial herb with tufted ascending stems up to about 9 in. high and minutely hairy all around; leaves opposite, shortly stalked, ovate to very broadly elliptic, more or less rounded at each end and obscurely crenate, 3-nerved at the base, and with only 1 or 2 pairs of additional lateral nerves, glabrous or very nearly so; flowers rather numerous in terminal leafy racemes, the leaves gradually decreased in size upwards and becoming alternate, the lower flowers already in fruit before the upper have done blooming; flower-stalks shortly pubescent; sepals (A, $\times 2$) oblong, slightly hairy; corolla (B, $\times 2$) whitish, marked by blue veins, 4-lobed to below the middle; stamens 2, inserted near the base of the corolla; anthers ovoid; ovary rounded, smooth, with a slender terminal style and capitate stigma; fruit (C, $\times 2$) a flat rounded notched capsule, slightly hairy, tipped by the slender persistent style; seeds (D, $\times 6$) pale straw-coloured, obovoid (family *Scrophulariaceae*).

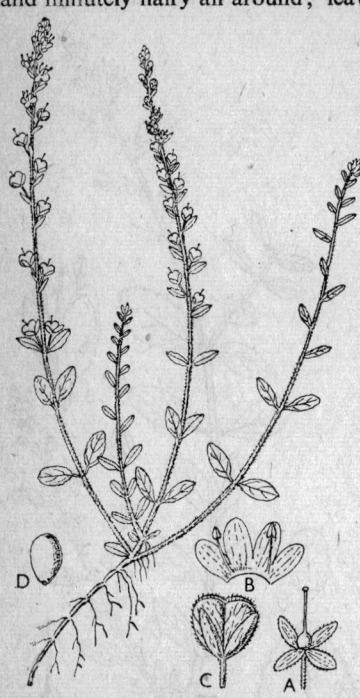

The anthers of this species lie close together on each side of the stigma, so that an insect visitor may effect self- or cross-pollination.

This is also a very widely spread species, found in fields and moist places, and flowering during spring and summer.

WALL SPEEDWELL, *Veronica arvensis* L.

354. Wall Speedwell, *Veronica arvensis* L. ($\times \frac{1}{2}$); a small very spreading thinly hairy annual, usually much branched from the base; leaves (A, $\times 0$) opposite, sessile (not stalked), ovate rounded at the base, with very few teeth, the upper bract-like ones becoming entire or nearly so, thinly hairy on both surfaces, but mainly on the nerves below; flowers (B, $\times 1\frac{1}{2}$) axillary and forming leafy racemes, though the flowers nearly sessile; sepals (C, $\times 1\frac{1}{2}$) linear-lanceolate, fringed with short hairs and glandular hairs; corolla (D, $\times 1\frac{1}{2}$) very much shorter than the sepals, dark sky-blue marked by darker streaks and with a whitish tube, 4-lobed; stamens 2, inserted towards the base of the tube; anthers ovoid; ovary rounded, with a very short style; fruit (E, $\times 2\frac{1}{2}$) rounded, notched, fringed with gland-tipped hairs; seeds (F, $\times 6$) ellipsoid, slightly compressed, straw-coloured (family *Scrophulariaceae*).

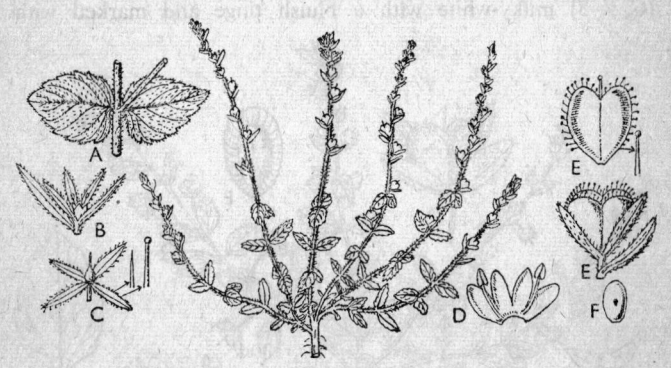

The anthers and stigma are at the same level, and so close together that self-pollination is easy, while insect visitors effect cross-pollination equally well.

Common in cultivated ground and waste places and on banks and old walls, where it flowers more or less during the whole of the year.

FIELD SPEEDWELL, *Veronica agrestis* L.

355. Field Speedwell, *Veronica agrestis* L. ($\times \frac{1}{2}$); a much-branched annual with procumbent or prostrate stems up to a foot or so long and slightly hairy all around; lower leaves (A, $\times$ 0) opposite, gradually becoming alternate upwards, ovate, abruptly narrowed into a broad short stalk, crenate-dentate, glabrous or very slightly hairy, with about 3 pairs of lateral nerves; flowers axillary sometimes only 1 to each pair of leaves (when opposite), the rather long stalk recurving in fruit; sepals (B, $\times$ 3) leafy, longer than the corolla, pubescent; corolla (C, $\times$ 3) milky-white with a bluish tinge and marked with convergent lines serving as nectar-guides; stamens 2, inserted near the base of the tube; anthers ovoid; ovary minutely hairy, with a slender style and capitate stigma; capsule (D, $\times$ 1$\frac{1}{2}$) compressed, deeply notched, thinly pubescent; seeds (E, $\times$ 5) grub-like, i.e. with wrinkled beady margins and scooped out in the middle (family *Scrophulariaceae*).

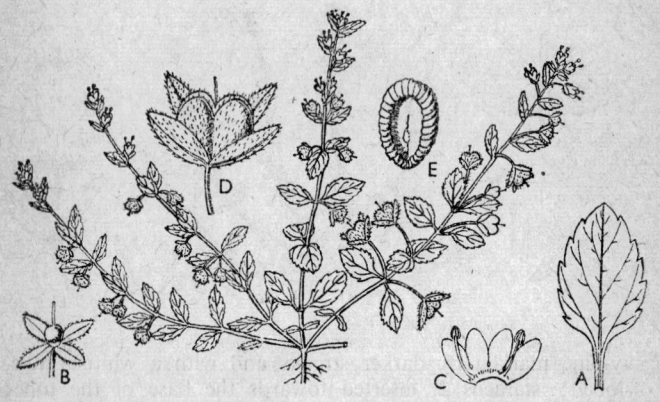

Nectar is secreted in a fleshy disk below the ovary and covered by hairs lining the tube of the corolla. During dull weather the flowers open less widely, so that the anthers and stigma lie in contact, automatic pollination being effective.

This is a common weed in waste and cultivated places, and it flowers during the whole season. The seeds are very remarkable, and are shown in fig. E.

IVY-LEAVED SPEEDWELL, *Veronica hederifolia* L.

356. Ivy-Leaved Speedwell, *Veronica hederifolia* L. ($\times \frac{1}{2}$); slender annual, often with long side-branches spreading from the base; stems green, thinly pubescent; seed-leaves opposite, persistent for some time, entire, yellowish-green, 1-nerved; stem-leaves alternate, broadly spade-shaped, coarsely 2-toothed or lobulate on each side with a broadly ovate end lobe, rounded or truncate at the base, 3-nerved, $\frac{1}{2}-\frac{3}{4}$ in. long and broad, bright green, minutely sponge-like below, loosely clothed on the upper surface with short stiff white hairs; stalk a little shorter than the blade; flowers (A, $\times$ 2) solitary, axillary, the stalks soon deflexed in fruit; sepals (B, C, $\times$ 2) 4, ovate-triangular, fringed with stiff white hairs; corolla (D, $\times$ 3) pale mauve-blue, shorter than the sepals, 4-lobed to the middle, lobes recurved; stamens 2; ovary 2-locular, with 2 ovules in each, sometimes only 1, 2, or 3 becoming seeds; style very short; fruit (E, $\times$ 3) slightly 2-lobed, enclosed by the persistent sepals; seeds (F, $\times$ 6) grub-like, i.e. ellipsoid and wavy, attached by a deep cavity to the central axis (family *Scrophulariaceae*).

A widely distributed weed of cultivation and in waste places, flowering most of the summer.

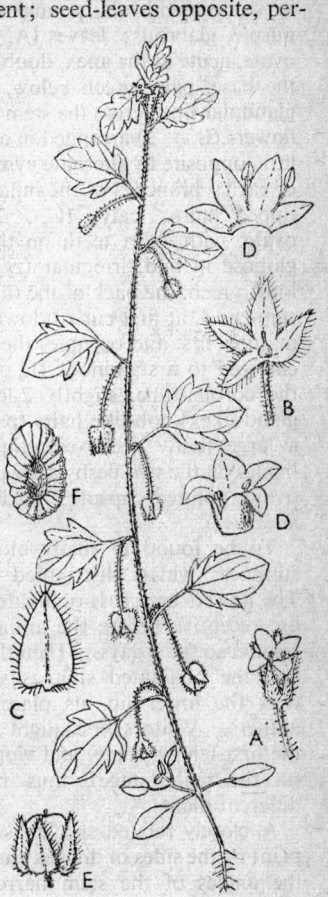

FIGWORT, *Scrophularia nodosa* L.

357. **Figwort, *Scrophularia nodosa* L.** ($\times \frac{1}{2}$); perennial with a tuberous root-stock; stems up to 3-4 ft. high erect, square in section with sharp angles, dull green finely speckled with purple, glabrous; leaves (A, $\times \frac{1}{2}$) opposite, stalked, triangular-ovate, acute at the apex, doubly dentate with larger teeth towards the base, paler green below, not hairy (glabrous); an oblique glandular line across the stem between the base of the leaf-stalks; flowers (B, $\times 2$) arranged in a loose terminal panicle made up of little opposite to alternate cymes, the oldest flowers in the middle of each; branches of the inflorescence covered with short gland-tipped hairs; calyx (C, $\times 2\frac{1}{2}$) saucer-shaped, 5-lobed, lobes ovate, with short teeth on the margin; corolla (D, $\times 2$) sub-globose in bud, irregular (zygomorphic), 2-lipped, nearly $\frac{1}{2}$ in. long, green, the back of the tube and two back lobes dull purple; stamens 4, at first curled downwards away from the style, which matures first and occupies the mouth of the corolla; 5th stamen changed to a staminode (E, $\times 6$) closely adnate to the back of the corolla-tube, slightly 2-lobed, on the inside covered with gland-like, knob-like hairs (papillae); ovary (F, $\times 5$) seated on a large fleshy nectar-secreting disk, 2-locular, with numerous ovules on the two fleshy axile placentas (G, $\times 5$); fruit a broadly ovoid pointed capsule; seeds rugose, brown (family *Scrophulariaceae*).

To be found in shady moist places, flowering most of the summer; widely distributed across the northern hemisphere. The flowers are cross-pollinated, mainly by wasps. The stigmas are receptive before the anthers open (protogynous), and they remain so for 2 days. Then the filaments of the stamens straighten, the pollinated stigmas wither and the style bends down over the lower lip, its place being taken by the discharging anthers. Visitors first alight on the upper younger flowers (in the first female stage) and work downwards to the older flowers (in the male stage), thus bringing about pollination from different plants.

A closely related species is *Scrophularia aquatica* L., a taller plant by the sides of ditches and streams and rather less branched, the angles of the stem narrowly winged, and the root-stock without tubers.

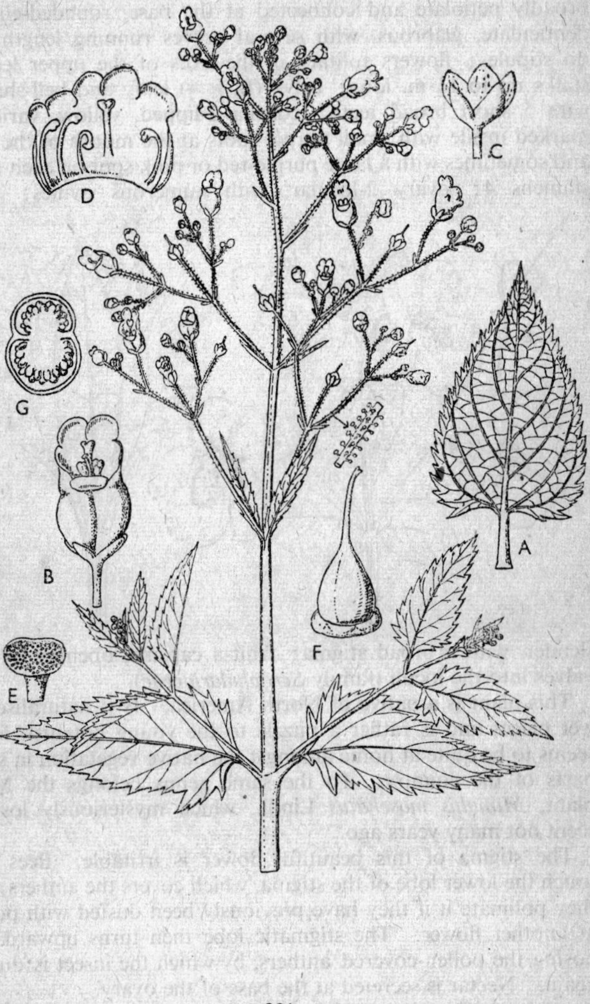
D
C
G
A
B
F
E

MONKEY FLOWER, *Mimulus guttatus* DC.

358. Monkey Flower, *Mimulus guttatus* DC. ($\times \frac{1}{2}$); herb up to about 1 ft. high, often found naturalised in or near brooks and by the sides of streams; leaves (A, $\times \frac{1}{2}$) opposite, lower broadly petiolate and connected at the base, rounded-elliptic, denticulate, glabrous, with several nerves running lengthwise; no stipules; flowers solitary in the axils of the upper leaves; stalks up to $1\frac{1}{2}$ in. long; calyx (B, $\times \frac{1}{2}$) leafy and bell-shaped, with 5 short broad teeth; corolla 2-lipped, yellow, variously marked inside with small purple spots at the mouth of the tube and sometimes with a large purple-red or pink spot on each lobe; stamens 4; ovary 2-locular, with numerous ovules; style slender, with a broad stigma; fruit a capsule, opening by two valves into the loculi (family *Scrophulariaceae*).

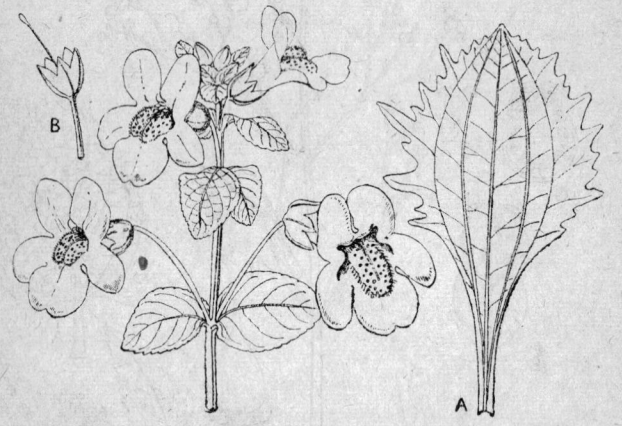

This plant is a native of North America. Is is naturalised in wet places and is rather a puzzle to the young botanist, for it seems to be quite at home amongst the native vegetation in some parts of the country. To the same genus belongs the Musk plant, *Mimulus moschatus* Lindl., which mysteriously lost its scent not many years ago.

The stigma of this beautiful flower is irritable. Bees first touch the lower lobe of the stigma, which covers the anthers, and they pollinate it if they have previously been dusted with pollen at another flower. The stigmatic lobe then turns upward, exposing the pollen-covered anthers, by which the insect is dusted again. Nectar is secreted at the base of the ovary.

MARSH LOUSEWORT, *Pedicularis palustris* L.

359. Marsh Lousewort, *Pedicularis palustris* L. ($\times \frac{1}{2}$); a much-branched annual up to $1\frac{1}{2}$ ft. high, leafy all over; stems slightly hairy below the nodes; leaves opposite or alternate, deeply pinnately divided into deeply cut or cristate segments, slightly hairy; flowers (A, $\times 1\frac{1}{2}$) nearly sessile in the axils of the upper leaves, but forming especially in fruit a dense spike; calyx large, with 2 broad irregularly toothed lobes thinly hairy outside; corolla deep purple-red, 2-lipped, upper lip hood-like and with 2 very small teeth on each side, lower lip with 2 large side lobes and a smaller middle lobe; stamens (B, $\times 1\frac{1}{2}$) 4, inserted near the base of the corolla-tube; anthers attached in the middle, glabrous; ovary (C, $\times 1\frac{1}{2}$) gradually narrowed into the very slender style with a club-like stigma; capsule (D, $\times 1\frac{1}{4}$) ovoid, with a hooked lateral tip, splitting obliquely at the top, longer than the calyx; seeds (E, $\times 3$) narrowly obovoid, brown, minutely and closely striate (family *Scrophulariaceae*).

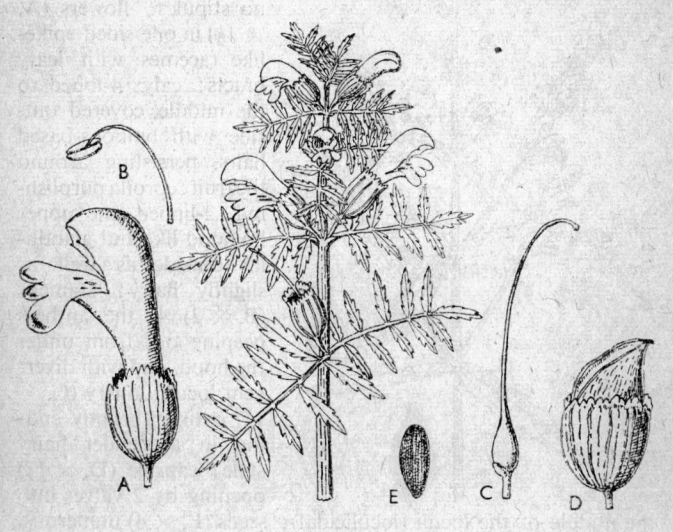

Nectar is secreted by the fleshy base of the ovary, and is collected in the bottom of the corolla-tube. The hooded upper lip of the corolla encloses the stamens, and the stigma protrudes obliquely downwards from between the anthers. Bees visiting a flower dust the stigma with pollen from one previously entered.

RED BARTSIA, *Bartsia odontites* Huds.

360. Red Bartsia, *Bartsia odontites* Huds. ($\times \frac{1}{2}$); semi-parasitical erect annual up to about 1 ft. high or more; stems bluntly 4-angled, hispid with short downwardly directed hairs; leaves opposite, sessile, lanceolate, rather remotely toothed, hispid on both surfaces with short bulbous-based hairs, 3-nerved from the base; no stipules; flowers (A, $\times 1\frac{1}{2}$) in one-sided spike-like racemes with leafy bracts; calyx 4-lobed to the middle, covered outside with bulbous-based hairs, persisting around the fruit; corolla purplish-red, 2-lipped, the upper lip hood-like and glandular outside as well as slightly hairy; stamens (B, $\times 2$) 4, the anthers peeping out from under the hood, and with divergent loculi; ovary (C, $\times 1\frac{1}{2}$) entire, abruptly ending in a slender hairy style; capsule (D, $\times 1\frac{1}{2}$) opening by 2 valves into the middle of the loculi (loculicidal); seeds (E, $\times 4$) numerous, brown, closely ribbed lengthwise (family *Scrophulariaceae*).

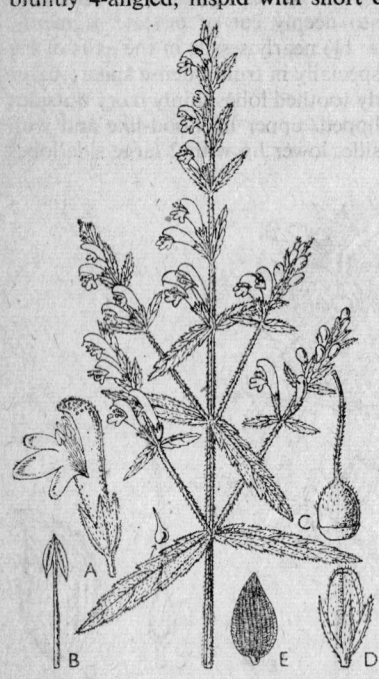

The beginner may mistake this plant for two other families than the one it belongs to; with its quadrangular stems, opposite leaves, and 2-lipped corolla it resembles *Labiatae*, whilst in its hairy covering of rough bulbous-based hairs it recalls some *Boraginaceae*. The entire ovary with a terminal style distinguishes it easily from both these families.

COMMON COW-WHEAT, *Melampyrum pratense* L.

361. Common Cow-Wheat, *Melampyrum pratense* L. ($\times \frac{1}{2}$); annual herb chiefly in woods and parasitic on roots; stems branched from well above the base, glabrous or minutely hairy; leaves opposite, sessile or nearly so, linear-lanceolate to lanceolate, narrowed to the base, tapered to the apex, but rather blunt, most of them entire, but the uppermost among the flowers often pinnately lobulate or toothed towards the base; no stipules; flowers (A, $\times$ 2) mostly all turned one way, axillary, solitary, shortly stalked; calyx (B, $\times 1\frac{1}{2}$) deeply 4-lobed, lobes linear, longer than the tube; corolla pale pure yellow, about twice as long as the calyx, 2-lipped, the upper lip hood-like, the lower flat with 3 short lobes, the mouth of the tube nearly closed; stamens (C, $\times$ 5) 4, hidden in the corolla; ovary (D, $\times$ 5) not lobed, with 2 loculi and 2 ovules in each attached near the base; capsule (E, $\times 1\frac{1}{2}$) obliquely ovate, compressed, splitting on one side; seeds (F, $\times$ 2) 4, oblong-obovoid, contracted at the base, blackish and smooth (family *Scrophulariaceae*).

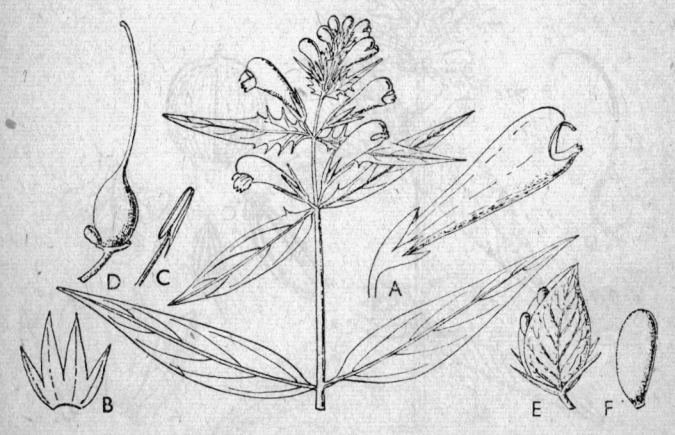

The upper lip of the corolla acts as a hood and protects the anthers from rain. Nectar is secreted by a lobe projecting downwards from the base of the ovary, and is stored at the base of the corolla. It is protected from rain by a circle of converging hairs. In addition to the floral nectary the bracts are provided with nectar-secreting hairs (extra floral nectaries).

COMMON CORN RATTLE, *Rhinanthus minor* L.

362. Common Corn Rattle, *Rhinanthus minor* L. ($\times \frac{1}{2}$); an annual with simple or branched stems up to about 1 ft. high, slightly hairy on the flattened part below the nodes; roots semi-parasitic on those of grasses and other herbs; leaves opposite, sessile, narrowly lanceolate, very coarsely toothed (serrate), clothed with very short stiff hairs like some of the Borage family; flowers in a rather dense spike-like raceme, with spreading leafy bracts; calyx (A, $\times 2$) inflated and nearly orbicular, contracted into 4 small short teeth and covered with a close network of veins; corolla 2-lipped, yellow, sometimes with a purple spot on the upper or both lips, upper lip hooded, hiding the stamens and style, lower lip (B, $\times 1\frac{1}{2}$) 3-lobed; stamens (C, $\times 2$) 4, in pairs; anthers held together by woolly hairs; ovary ellipsoid (D, $\times 1\frac{1}{2}$); style arched inside the hood, slightly hairy, stigma capitate; capsule (E, $\times 1\frac{1}{4}$) enclosed in the persistent inflated membranous calyx, compressed, splitting into 2 halves; seeds (F, $\times 2$) compressed, kidney-shaped, broadly winged (family *Scrophulariaceae*).

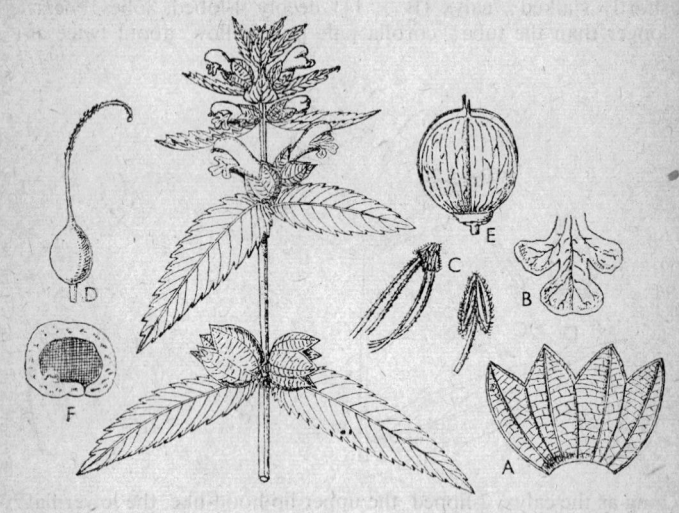

In pastures, and widely distributed in the northern hemisphere.

TOOTHWORT, *Lathraea squamaria* L.

363. Toothwort, *Lathraea squamaria* L. ($\times \frac{1}{3}$); perennial growing on roots chiefly of hazel and poplar; stems thick and fleshy, creamy-white or purplish, becoming black when dry, glabrous or thinly pubescent; root-stock densely covered with broad overlapping cream-coloured scales; buds rounded, densely scaly; flowers in a dense bracteate raceme; bracts oblong-ovate; flower-stalks stout, shorter than the bracts; calyx (A, $\times$ 0) cream-pink, 4-lobed, the tube furnished with a few long several-celled gland-tipped hairs (B, $\times$ 4); corolla (C, $\times$ 0) pink in bud, turning dark brown with age, irregularly lobed and 2-lipped; stamens (D, $\times$ 2) 4, inserted on the corolla; anthers at first connivent, hairy; ovary (E, $\times$ 3) ovoid, 1-locular, with 2 placentas nearly meeting in the middle and bearing numerous ovules (F, $\times$ 5); style with a large shortly 2-lobed hairy pale green stigma; capsule 2-valved, many-seeded (family *Orobanchaceae*).

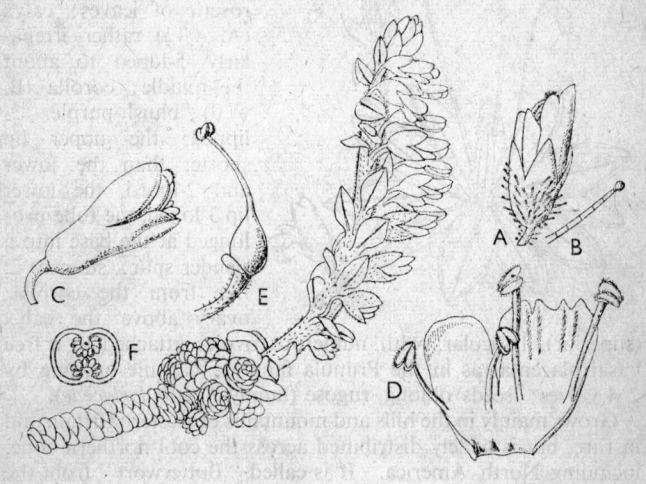

This plant flowers in early spring, before the leaves of the trees on the roots of which it grows are produced; it is widely distributed to North and Western Asia, and south to the Himalayas. Nectar is produced on the lower side of the ovary and secreted by a gland resembling a flattened bag. The flowers are at first insect-pollinated, and later tend towards wind pollination.

COMMON BUTTERWORT, *Pinguicula vulgaris* L.

364. Common Butterwort, *Pinguicula vulgaris* L. ($\times \frac{2}{5}$); a herb growing in mountain bogs or on wet rocks; leaves forming a rosette, spreading, ovate to oblong and narrowed to the base, rather fleshy and covered with small crystalline points and clammy to the touch, margins entire; flowers 3 or 4 to each plant, on stalks up to about 6 in. long from the rosette of leaves; calyx (A, $\times 1\frac{1}{2}$) rather irregularly 5-lobed to about the middle; corolla (B, $\times 0$) bluish-purple, 2-lipped, the upper lip shorter than the lower and 2-lobed, the lower lip 3-lobed, the tube prolonged at the base into a slender spur; stamens 2, free from the corolla; ovary above the calyx (superior), 1-locular, with numerous ovules attached to a free basal placenta (as in the Primula family); capsule opening by 2–4 valves; seeds oblong, rugose (family *Lentibulariaceae*).

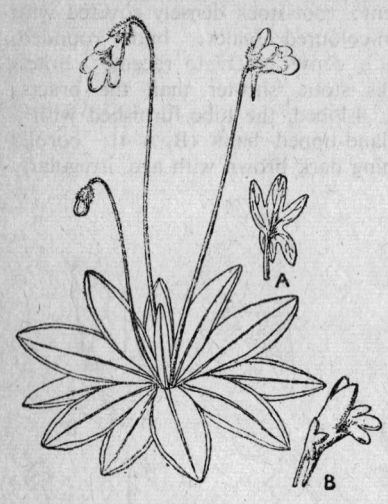

Grows mainly in the hills and mountains of western Britain and in Eire, but is widely distributed across the cool northern zone, including North America. It is called "Butterwort" from the greasy feel of the leaves, as if melted butter had been poured on them.

The downwardly curved spur of the corolla secretes and conceals nectar in its basal part, and the lower lip acts as a platform for insect visitors, mainly bees. These touch the stigma first, and dust it with pollen from a flower previously visited. On probing further into the corolla, the bee's head and back are dusted with fresh pollen, which is carried to another flower.

BLOODY CRANE'S BILL, *Geranium sanguineum* L.

365. Bloody Crane's Bill, *Geranium sanguineum* L. (×⅔); perennial with a blunt root-stock; stems covered at the base by overlapping scales, 1–2 ft. long, very slender, but thickened at the nodes, and with slender hairs spreading at right angles; leaves opposite, shortly stalked, each stalk with a pair of brown oblong stipules (A, × 2) at the base, which soon shrivel up; leaf-blade rounded in outline, deeply divided into 5 main parts, the lower divisions usually with 2 lanceolate lobes, the other 3 rather deeply 3-lobed, thinly clothed above with short bristle-like hairs, paler below and with a few hairs on the nerves; flowers axillary, in the alternate axils of the leaves, the end one flowering last; stalk with a pair of stipule-like bracts above the middle and fringed with hairs; sepals (B, × 2) 5, elliptic, green and 3-nerved with pale thinner margins and ending in a long narrow point; petals (D, × 2) 5, crimson or pink with 5 deeper crimson nerves, fringed with long soft hairs at the base; stamens (E, × 3) 10, their stalks close together; anthers attached in the middle, deep violet; nectaries 5, green, fleshy; ovary (F, × 2) 5-lobed, each lobe narrowed into a long reddish style; fruit (G, × ⅘) dividing from the base into 5 parts which curl upwards and disperse the seeds (C, flower, petals removed) (family *Geraniaceae*).

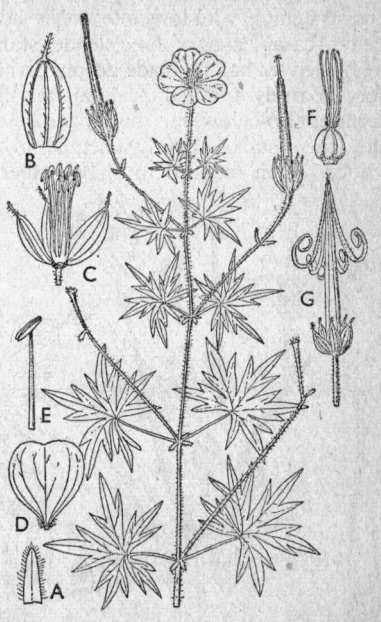

Grows in shady places on rocky cliffs and is partial to limestone; generally distributed, and in the greater part of Europe as far as the Caucasus; a decumbent variety (var. *lancastriense* Mill.), more hairy and sometimes with white or pale pink flowers, is found on an island near the Lancashire coast.

PENCILLED GERANIUM, *Geranium versicolor* L.

366. Pencilled Geranium, *Geranium versicolor* L. ($\times \frac{1}{2}$); perennial with ascending root-stock, the latter densely clothed with the persistent sheathing bases of former leaves; stems weak and straggling, with long internodes, laxly clothed with long weak hairs; basal leaves on long slender stalks, these also clothed with weak slender hairs; blade deeply divided into 5 lobes, the lobes very coarsely toothed or lobulate, thinly hairy on the upper surface, also below, but mainly on the nerves; stem-leaves opposite, their stalks slightly unequal in length in each pair, the 5 lobes often reduced to 3, but otherwise similar to the basal leaves; stipules paired at the base of each stalk, about $\frac{1}{2}$ in. long, long-pointed from a narrowly lanceolate base, fringed with slender hairs on the margin; flowers few, and only 1 or 2 out at a time, shortly stalked; sepals (B, $\times$ 0) 5, lanceolate, about $\frac{1}{2}$ in. long, with long slender tips, slightly hairy on the 3 nerves and margin; petals (A, $\times$ 0) 5, spreading from the broadly clawed base, prominently nerved, rather deeply 2-lobed; stamens (B, $\times$ 0) 10, the filaments united around the ovary; ovary (C, $\times$ $2\frac{1}{2}$) 5-locular, the 5 styles united in a column with 5 free stigmas; disk of 5 separate fleshy nectaries; fruit (D, $\times$ $\frac{3}{4}$) of 5 dehiscent 1-seeded carpels united together in a column, but separating elastically from the top; seeds (E, $\times$ 2) ellipsoid, dark brown (synonym *Geranium striatum* L.) (family *Geraniaceae*).

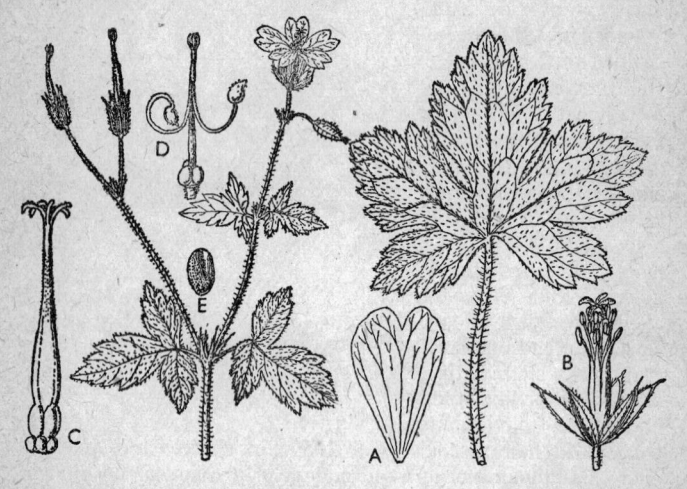

MEADOW GERANIUM, *Geranium pratense* L.

367. Meadow Geranium, *Geranium pratense* L. ($\times \frac{1}{2}$); perennial; basal leaves on long stalks, orbicular, deeply 5–9 lobed, the lobes deeply lobulate and coarsely toothed, strongly nerved below and hairy on the nerves, thinly downy above; leaf-stalks with very short downwardly directed hairs; stem-leaves opposite, shortly stalked to nearly sessile, with a pair of interpetiolar stipules to each; stipules narrowly triangular, 1-nerved, fringed with hairs; upper part of stem and flower-stalks covered with spreading gland-tipped hairs; flowers large, mostly in pairs on long peduncles; bracts crimson; buds (A, $\times 1\frac{1}{2}$) closely ribbed, covered with glandular hairs; sepals 5, beaked, 5-nerved, glandular-hairy; petals (C, $\times 2$) hairy on the margin near the base, deep violet-blue, with crimson nerves, nearly 1 in. long and broad; stamens (D, $\times 2\frac{1}{2}$) 10; anthers pale purple; carpels 5, united, the styles united in a column, hairy, with 5 recurved softly hairy stigmas; ovule solitary in each loculus; fruit (E, $\times 1\frac{1}{2}$) splitting into 5 carpels with long beaks, which open and release the seed (B, flower with petals removed, $\times 1\frac{1}{2}$) (family *Geraniaceae*).

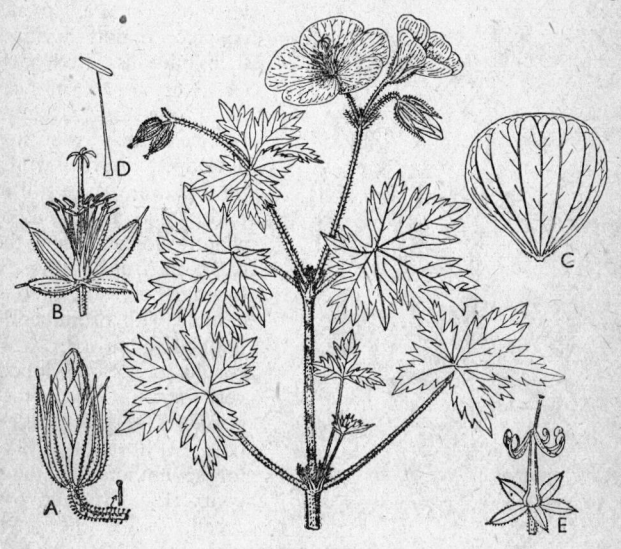

FIELD MYOSOTIS, *Myosotis arvensis* (L.) Hill

368. **Field Myosotis,** *Myosotis arvensis* (L.) Hill (× ⅔); annual or biennial, mostly more or less branched from the base, occasionally very much branched; stems up to about 1 ft. high, clothed with rather long weak hairs, with a few scattered leaves; basal leaves spathulate-obovate, narrowed into a short stalk, stem-leaves spathulate-oblanceolate, sessile, covered on both surfaces with bulbous-based hairs (A, × 6); flowers in scorpioid one-sided (secund) racemes, the lowermost developed into fruit whilst the uppermost are still in bud; stalks as long as or slightly longer than the calyx in fruit; calyx 5-lobed to below the middle, clothed with prominently hooked hairs (B, × 5); corolla (C, × 6) 5-lobed, very small, pale blue; stamens (D, × 8) 5, alternate with the corolla-lobes; anthers apiculate; ovary (E, × 6) deeply 4-lobed, with the style between the lobes (gynobasic); nutlets (F, × 5) obovoid, nearly jet black, shining (family *Boraginaceae*).

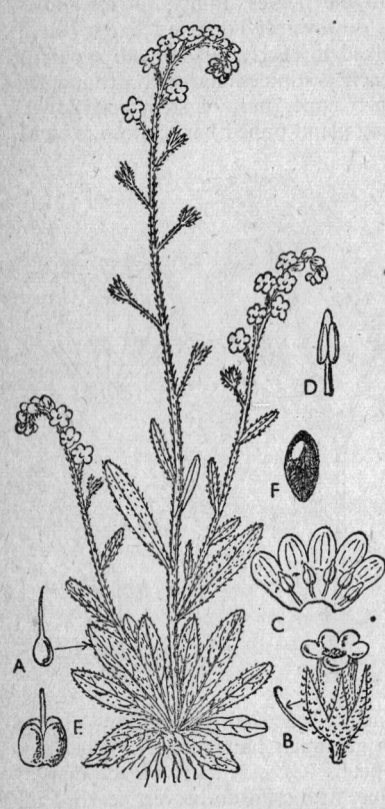

Hairs with a much swollen base (bulbous based hairs) are very characteristic of most of the Borage family. Another and more constant character is the ovary, which is vertically divided into 4 nearly separate lobes, with the single style inserted in the middle between them. A good spotting feature for *M. arvensis* is the nature of the hairs on the calyx, which are hooked at the top (see fig. B).

CREEPING FORGET-ME-NOT, *Myosotis repens* (Don) Reichb.

369. Creeping Forget-Me-Not, *Myosotis repens* (Don) Reichb. ($\times \frac{1}{2}$); perennial herb with slightly creeping root-stock; stems more or less decumbent and then ascending, hairy, sometimes almost villous with spreading hairs; leaves (A, $\times \frac{1}{2}$) sessile, narrowly oblong-oblanceolate, rounded at the apex, up to 3 in. long and $\frac{3}{4}$ in. broad, the very few lateral nerves forming a continuous line well within the margin, hairy, with bulbous based hairs (B, $\times 2$); flowers (D, $\times 1\frac{1}{2}$) in a loose 1-sided raceme, the lower flowers often forming fruits whilst the upper are still in bud; stalks becoming more or less deflexed and about $\frac{1}{2}$ in. long in fruit; calyx (C, $\times 2$) 5-lobed to below the middle, the hairs on it very short and adpressed; corolla (E, $\times 2\frac{1}{2}$) bright blue with a yellow " eye ", 5-lobed; stamens (F, $\times 5$) 5, alternate with the lobes and hidden in the tube of the corolla; ovary (G, $\times 6$) seated on a fleshy nectariferous disk, deeply 4-lobed, with the style between the lobes; nutlet (H, $\times 5$) black and shining (family *Boraginaceae*).

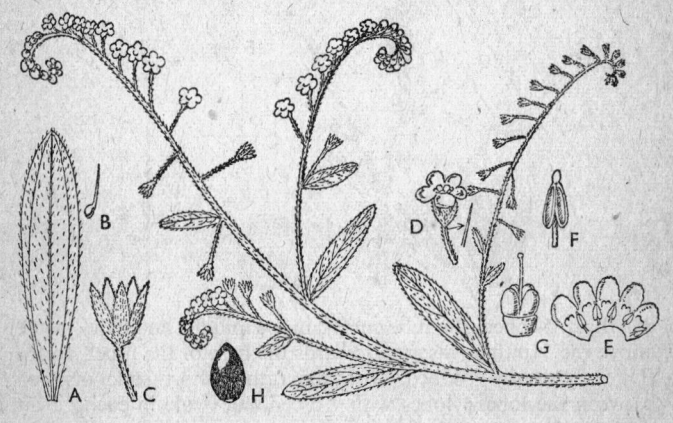

Myosotis repens is mentioned in *Common Wild Flowers* in the notes on the Water Forget-Me-Not, *Myosotis palustris*. The drawings of the calyx should be compared, when it will be seen that in *M. repens* it is much more deeply divided than in *M. palustris*.

BUGLOSS, *Lycopsis arvensis* L.

370. Bugloss, *Lycopsis arvensis* L. ($\times \frac{1}{2}$); a rough, spreading annual up to about 2 ft. high, covered all over with bristly bulbous-based hairs; leaves alternate, sessile, oblong-lanceolate or oblanceolate, with wavy margins and rather obscure lateral nerves, bristly on both surfaces and margins with longer and shorter bulbous-based hairs; flowers (A, $\times 1\frac{1}{2}$) in simple or branched bracteate clusters which lengthen and become one-sided in fruit; calyx (C, $\times 1\frac{1}{2}$) 5-lobed to the base, lobes linear-lanceolate, nearly as long as the corolla, very bristly; corolla (B, $\times 4$) pale-blue, 5-lobed, the tube curved in the middle, and hairy inside above the 5 anthers inserted towards the base of the tube; ovary (D, $\times 3$) deeply 4-lobed, with the rather short style inserted between the lobes; lobes with 1 ascending ovule in each; fruit (E, F, $\times 2$) composed of 4 separate ovoid densely warted nutlets (family *Boraginaceae*).

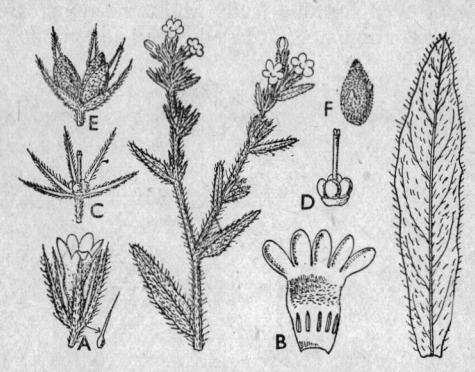

Nectar is secreted by the base of the 4-lobed ovary and stored in the lower part of the corolla-tube. The corolla-tube is bent in the middle. Should insect visitors not effect cross-pollination, automatic self-pollination is brought about by the dropping off of the corolla, in the process of which the anthers, to which some pollen still clings, are drawn over the stigma.

CORN GROMWELL, *Lithospermum arvense* L.

371. Corn Gromwell, *Lithospermum arvense* L. ($\times \frac{2}{3}$); a strong-growing annual becoming hard and almost woody at the base, up to 1½ ft. high, rough and hoary all over with rather short bulbous-based hairs (A, $\times 1$); stems slightly angular; leaves lanceolate to almost linear, entire and without visible side-nerves, hairy on both surfaces; flowers small, in leafy terminal cymes which elongate in fruit and become zig-zag; stalks very short; calyx 5-lobed nearly to the base, lobes linear, nearly as long as the corolla; corolla (B, $\times 2$) white, 5-lobed, without scales in the throat, hairy half-way down inside the tube; stamens 5, inserted below the middle of the tube; ovary (C, $\times 3$) on a fleshy disk, deeply 4-lobed, with the style inserted between the lobes (gynobasic); style about half as long as the tube; fruit (D, $\times 2$) composed of 4 separate closely warted nuts (E, $\times 4$) (family *Boraginaceae*).

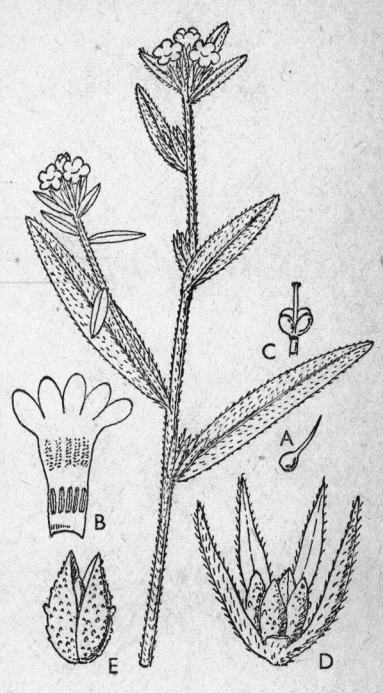

To be found mostly in cornfields and waste places, flowering during spring and summer.

The hairs above the anthers prevent rain from entering the corolla-tube. The anthers open before the corolla opens, but insect visitors are few. As the entrance to the nectar, which is secreted by the ovary and stored in the base of the corolla-tube, is completely closed, an insect-visitor brings fresh pollen, and may effect cross-pollination. Eventually the anthers discharge such a quantity of pollen that the stigma becomes covered with it and self-pollination is effected.

HOUND'S TONGUE, *Cynoglossum officinale* L.

372. Hound's Tongue, *Cynoglossum officinale* L. ($\times \frac{1}{3}$); biennial; stems simple or branched, up to 2 ft. high, thick and fleshy, pale green, with brownish-green ribs, softly but thinly villous; leaves spirally arranged, sessile, linear-lanceolate, gradually subacute, bright green above, paler below, covered with short soft hairs; flowers in nodding scorpioid cymes in the axils of most of the leaves; stalks pubescent; sepals 5, free, ovate-elliptic, densely pubescent; corolla (B, $\times 1\frac{1}{4}$) dull purplish-red, 5-lobed, nearly closed at the mouth by 5 humps, each opposite a lobe; anthers 5, alternate with the lobes; ovary (A, $\times 0$) deeply divided into 4 lobes, with a stiff awl-shaped style between them; fruit (C, $\times 0$) of 4 separate depressed nutlets covered with short hooked prickles (family *Boraginaceae*).

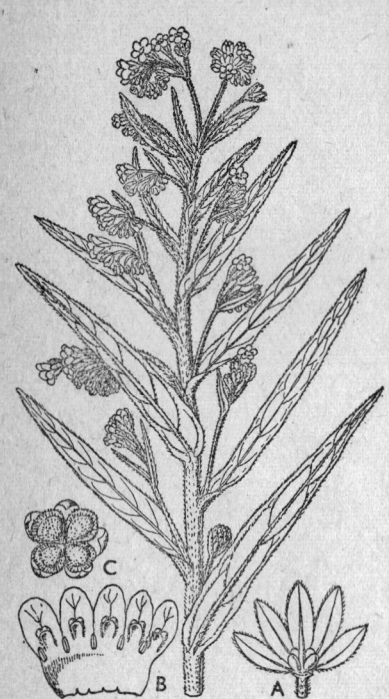

When bruised, the plant, and especially the flowers, have a disagreeable mouse-like smell; it grows on roadsides and waste places and on maritime chalky downs, flowering from early summer. In former times, among its many supposed virtues, it was recommended, curiously enough, for stuttering, and was also considered to be antiscorbutic.

Nectar is secreted by the fleshy receptacle below the ovary and concealed in the base of the corolla-tube. The 5 darker-coloured pocket-shaped hollow scales at the entrance to the corolla-tube serve as nectar-guides and their velvety covering of hairs as nectar-covers. The stigma of the short style is receptive at the same time as the anthers release their pollen, and self-pollination takes place if no insect has visited the flower.

GIPSYWORT, *Lycopus europaeus* L.

373. Gipsywort, *Lycopus europaeus* L. ($\times \frac{1}{2}$); a tall perennial with the habit of mint; root-stock creeping; stems up to 3 ft. high, erect, very slightly hairy; leaves nearly sessile, opposite, all coarsely toothed or lobulate, the lower pinnately divided near the base almost to the midrib (A, $\times \frac{1}{2}$), glandular-pitted on the lower surface, otherwise nearly glabrous; lateral nerves several, prominent below, ending in the teeth; flowers (B, $\times 2\frac{1}{2}$) bisexual or female, numerous, sessile, in dense axillary clusters; calyx (C, $\times 2$) 5-lobed, lobes narrowly triangular, with rigid very sharp points; corolla (D, $\times 2\frac{1}{2}$) bluish-white, dotted with purple, scarcely longer than the calyx-lobes, nearly equally 4-lobed and almost quite regular (actinomorphic), the inner surface of the tube covered with vertical hairs protecting the nectar from rain; stamens 2, shortly exserted from the corolla; anthers (E, $\times 7$) with 2 divergent loculi; vestiges of two stamens between the others; ovary (F, $\times 2\frac{1}{2}$) of 4 very blunt lobes; style inserted between the lobes of the ovary (gynobasic), 2-lobed; nutlets (G, $\times 2\frac{1}{2}$) truncate with thickened margins (family *Labiatae*).

The flowers may be bisexual or female, the latter generally being smaller. Nectar-guides in the form of red spots on the lower lip are provided, the nectar being secreted by the large fleshy base of the ovary. This is accessible to very short-tongued insects, as the corolla-tube is short and wide.

MARJORAM, *Origanum vulgare* L.

374. Marjoram, *Origanum vulgare* L. ($\times \frac{1}{2}$); strongly aromatic herbaceous perennial with creeping root-stock and annual stems up to 2 ft. high, these softly hairy and more or less crimson; leaves opposite, ovate, rounded to shortly wedge-shaped at the base, not pointed at the apex, slightly dentate, thinly hairy on both surfaces, markedly punctate-glandular especially below (A, $\times$ 0); stalks nearly quarter as long as the blade, bristly hairy; no stipules; very short leafy branchlets in the lower leaf-axils; flowers (B, $\times 2\frac{1}{2}$) in terminal clusters, these forming a leafy panicle; bracts ovate, longer than the calyx and often tinged with crimson or purple; calyx (C, $\times 1\frac{1}{2}$) very small, equally 5-toothed, shortly hairy; corolla dull-purple, twice as long as the calyx, nearly equally 4-lobed, the upper lobe sub-erect, slightly hairy outside; stamens (D, $\times 2\frac{1}{2}$) 4, two longer, all well exserted from the corolla; anther-loculi 2, separate; ovary (E, $\times 2\frac{1}{2}$) on a large fleshy disk, deeply 4-lobed, with the bifid style inserted between the lobes; nutlets smooth (family *Labiatae*).

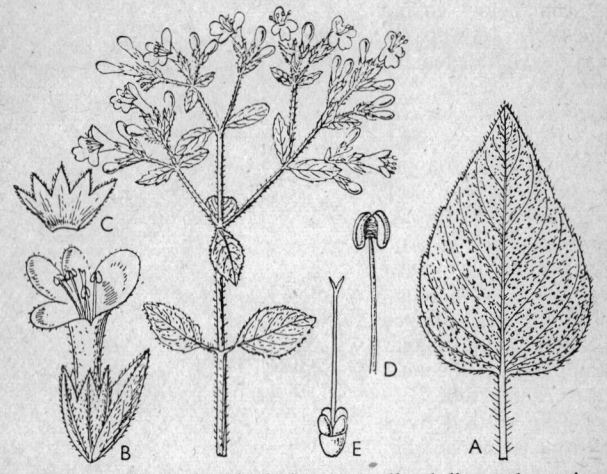

The flowers are either bisexual or female, the former being larger. They are crowded into dense clusters, and they are much visited by insects. Stamens and style project from the corolla, but self-pollination is prevented by the anthers opening before the stigmas are receptive. The bodies of insects are dusted with pollen, thus effecting cross-pollination.

WILD BASIL, *Clinopodium vulgare* L.

375. Wild Basil, *Clinopodium vulgare* L. (× ⅓); perennial with annual stems up to 2 ft. high and a slender creeping rootstock; stems square in cross-section, densely covered with soft reflexed or spreading hairs; leaves opposite, shortly stalked, ovate to triangular-ovate, obtuse at the apex, rounded at the base, obscurely toothed, loosely covered on both surfaces with soft spreading hairs; flowers in axillary shortly stalked clusters, each short flower-stalk with a pair of very narrow (subulate) hairy bracts at the base (A, ×2); calyx tubular, with 5 very narrow hairy subequal lobes and about 15 ribs, these clothed with gland-tipped hairs; corolla (B, × 1½) purple-red, nearly twice as long as the calyx, unequally 4-lobed; stamens 4, exserted; ovary (C, × 2) deeply 4-lobed, on a fleshy disk, with the style between the lobes; nutlets (D, × 4) very small and smooth (family *Labiatae*).

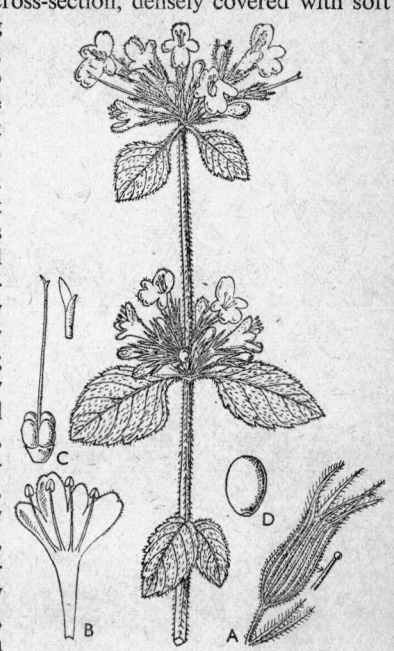

This is a bee or humble-bee flower with abundant nectar secreted by the base of the ovary and stored in the base of the corolla-tube even to a height of 3 millimetres. There are 2 kinds of flowers, bisexual and female, sometimes on the same plant (described as *gynomonoecious*!) or on different plants (*gynodioecious*!).*

* In the first volume (*Common Wild Flowers*) as few botanical terms as possible were used in the descriptions. However, one correspondent complained in an amusing letter (see p. 265) that his enthusiasm for the study of the book had been completely shattered by the few which were introduced and which he could not find in the dictionaries in his local library.

SKULL CAP, *Scutellaria galericulata* L.

376. Skull Cap, *Scutellaria galericulata* L. (× ⅖); perennial with creeping root-stock, flowering from July to September; stems usually about 9 in. to 1 ft. high, erect, square in section, the edges covered with minute downwardly directed hairs (H, × 2); leaves opposite, very shortly stalked, lanceolate, heart-shaped (cordate) at the base, 1–1½ in. long, rather wrinkled (bullate), crenate, very minutely hairy on the margin and nerves below; a distinct ridge between the leaf-stalks; flowers (A, × 2) borne towards one side of the stem, solitary, axillary, only a few out at one time, stalks with 2 very narrow bracteoles near the base, shorter than the tubular slightly 2-lipped calyx, the latter with a large leafy outgrowth on the back (B, × 3); corolla mauve-blue, ½ in. long, covered with soft white hairs, 2-lipped, the upper lip concealing the stamens, the lower forming a platform and beautifully mottled with deep-blue spots (C, corolla opened out, × 2); stamens (D, × 3) 4, the longer 2 with only 1 perfect anther-lobe (loculus), the shorter 2 with 2 perfect lobes, lobes hairy; ovary of 4 rounded separate lobes (E, × 2½), supported on a fleshy disk; style slender; nutlets granular, enclosed in the calyx (family *Labiatae*).

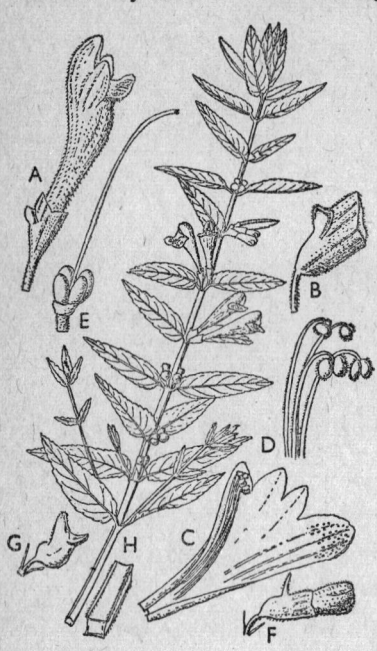

In the bud stage the flowers recall an old and very short blunderbuss or highwayman's pistol, the process on the top of the calyx representing the hammer (F, × 2). In the fruiting stage the calyx assumes the shape of an ugly duckling (G, × 1½).

A familiar water-side plant, generally distributed in England and Wales; locally common in Scotland and rather local in Eire. It also grows in shady places in damp woods and in bogs and marshes.

BLACK HOREHOUND, *Ballota nigra* L.

377. Black Horehound, *Ballota nigra* L. ($\times \frac{1}{2}$); a strong-growing rather densely leafy and hairy perennial; stems square in section, purplish, clothed with short white reflexed hairs; leaves (A, $\times$ 0) opposite, petiolate, ovate, coarsely toothed, the teeth with little blunt tips, undulate (bullate), shortly hairy mainly on the nerves below; flowers (B, $\times$ 2) in axillary clusters, the clusters very shortly stalked, each flower with 2 or 3 long sharp very narrow bracts (C, $\times$ 2) at the base; calyx (C, $\times$ 2) green-crimson, funnel-shaped, 5-toothed, 10-ribbed, the teeth ovate, with sharp tips; corolla mauve-purple, 2-lipped, the upper lip at length recurved and villous, the lower 3-lobed, the lateral lobes small and bifid; stamens (D, $\times$ 4) 4, a little shorter than the back lip; anther-loculi divergent (D, $\times$ 4); ovary (E, $\times$ 2) deeply 4-lobed with the long slender style between the lobes; nutlets obtusely 3-angled, smooth (family *Labiatae*).

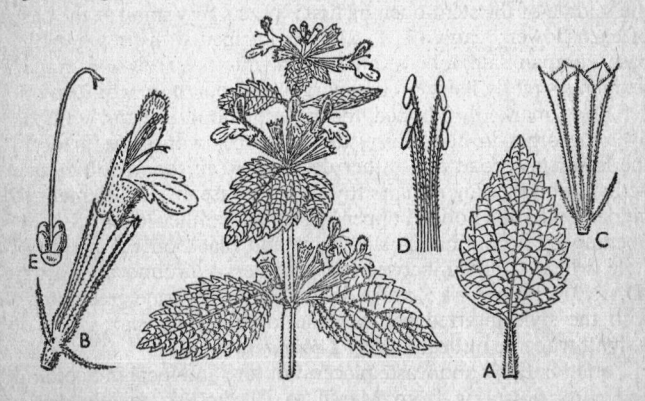

The corolla has a nectar-guide on the lower lip in the form of white lines pointing towards the corolla-tube, and a longitudinal furrow on the lip serves as a guide for the proboscis. The nectar is secreted by the base of the ovary and stored at the bottom of the corolla-tube. A nectar-cover is provided by stiff hairs as a protection, not from rain, as the flower is horizontal, but from nectar-seeking flies, preventing their broad proboscides from entering. After the anthers have shed their pollen the style bends downwards away from them.

DEAD NETTLE, *Lamium album* L.

378. Dead Nettle, *Lamium album* L. ($\times \frac{1}{2}$); perennial with a creeping rhizome and giving off stolons; stem up to about $1\frac{1}{2}$ ft. high, bearing whorls of flowers at each node almost to the base, square in section, pale green, slightly pubescent, especially in the upper part, hairs spreading; leaves opposite, in 2 ranks (decussate), stalked, broadly ovate, rounded to slightly cordate at the base, acutely acuminate, up to about 2 in. long and $1\frac{1}{2}$ in. broad, coarsely crenate-serrate, pale green, bullate-reticulate, very slightly hairy on both surfaces; leaf-stalks connected across the stem by a narrow ridge; flowers (B, $\times 1\frac{1}{2}$) axillary (pseudo-verticillate), about 7–8 in each leaf-axil, sessile, those towards the middle of the stem-opening first; bracts very small at the base of each flower; calyx (A, $\times 2$) green, striped with brown at the base, campanulate, lobed to the middle into 5 narrow awl-shaped segments slightly hairy on the margin; corolla pure white, about 1 in. long, markedly 2-lipped, the upper lip hood-like and wrapped over the other in bud, hairy, the side lobes with a small tooth, the lower lip broad and rather deeply split in the middle; tube with an oblique ring of hairs towards the base inside; stamens 4, hidden under the hooded upper lip, the two anther-lobes (C, $\times 4$) opening by a continuous slit, hairy and black on the margins; style white, 2-lobed between the anthers; around the ovary (D, $\times 3$) a fleshy disk; ovary divided into 4 separate green lobes, with the style inserted between the lobes (gynobasic); fruit of 4 small truncate nutlets (family *Labiatae*).

Found in fields and waste places, but rare and local in Scotland and Eire, flowering from March to December; widely distributed eastward to North Asia and in North Africa; introduced in North America.

Nectar is secreted by the base of the ovary and stored at the bottom of the corolla-tube. The oblique ring of hairs described above acts as a nectar cover. The upper lip shelters the anthers and stigma, and the lower lip forms a convenient alighting platform for insect-visitors. On account of the length of the corolla-tube the nectar is only accessible to long-tongued humble-bees and bees.

223

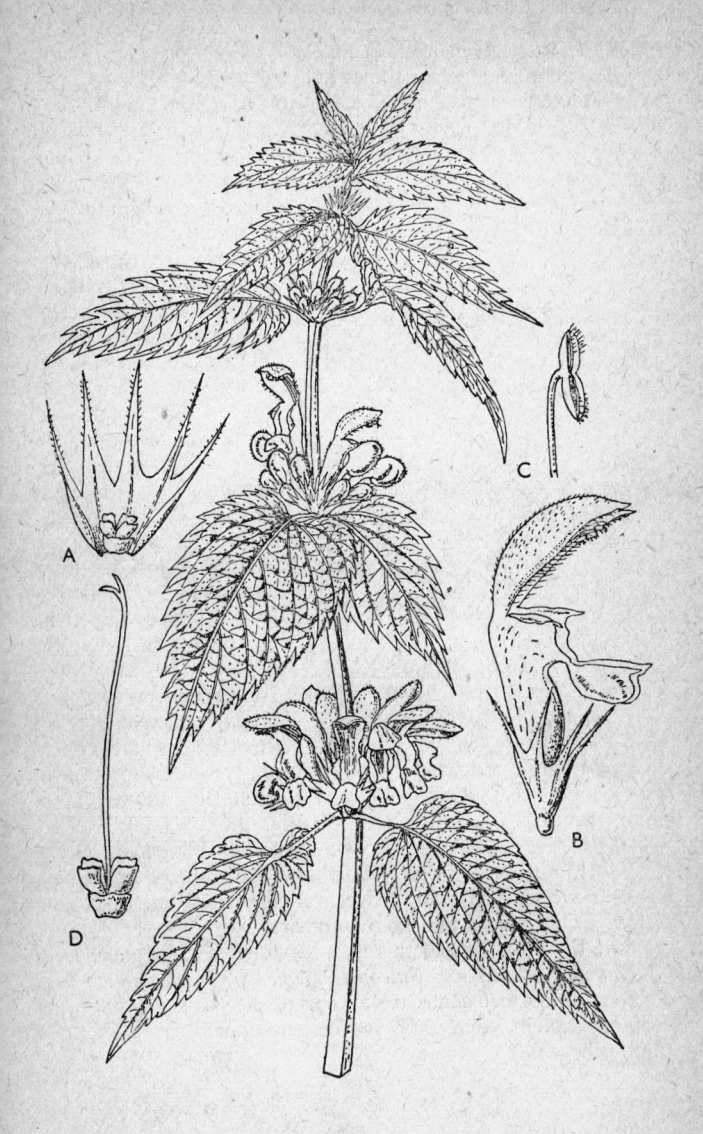

YELLOW ARCHANGEL, *Lamium galeobdolon* (L.) Crantz

379. Yellow Archangel, *Lamium galeobdolon* (L.) Crantz (× ½); perennial with somewhat tuberous root-stock and long stolons; stem simple, leafy, up to about 1½ ft. high, square in section, covered with short deflexed hairs (A, × 2); leaves opposite, connected at the base by a narrow rim, shortly stalked, the lowermost ovate and slightly heart-shaped (cordate) at the base, gradually narrowing upwards, coarsely toothed, bullate, thinly hairy above and mainly on the nerves below; stalks clothed with slender hairs; flowers (C, × 2) in dense axillary whorls, sessile; calyx tubular, almost equally 5-lobed, lobes very acute; corolla yellow, 2-lipped, upper lip hood-like and hiding the stamens and style, lower 3-lobed and mottled with brown; stamens 4; anthers (D, × 5) with 2 divergent loculi, not hairy; style crimson, arising from between the 4 lobes of the ovary (E, × 2); fruit of 4 nutlets, very blunt (truncate) (B, flower bud, × 3) (family *Labiatae*).

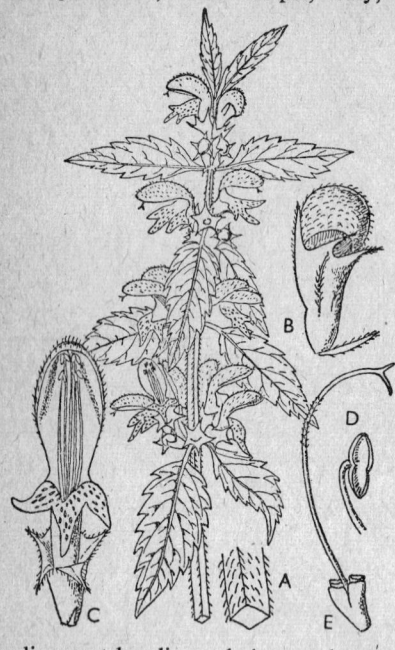

A distinctive species, and very similar to the White Dead Nettle (fig. 378), but the corolla yellow and the anthers not hairy; grows in woods and shady places, ranging to western Asia, and flowers in late spring and early summer.

Some botanists regard this as a separate genus, *Galeobdolon* (*G. luteum* Huds.) or *Galeopsis* (*Galeopsis Galeobdolon* L.). There is no correct genus name, because it is just a matter of opinion, though young and inexperienced botanists sometimes think otherwise!

CLARY, *Salvia verbenaca* L.

380. **Clary**, *Salvia verbenaca* L. (× ⅓); perennial, with a woody root-stock; stem up to about 2 ft., erect and rigid, square, softly pubescent; lower leaves long-stalked, oblong or elliptic, irregularly serrate or sometimes coarsely pinnately lobed; stalks tinged with crimson; stem-leaves opposite, sessile, ovate, rounded or slightly cordate at the base, triangular or ovately pointed, coarsely dentate with ovate teeth, bullate-reticulate above, very veiny beneath and paler, glabrous or nearly so; upper leaves reduced, acuminate, each with 3 flowers in its axil, forming a whorl of 6 flowers at each node; calyx (A, × 2½) 2-lipped, the upper lip of 3 united sepals, the lower of 2 united sepals, but split to the middle (B, × 1½), strongly ribbed, gland-dotted between the ribs; corolla (C, × 2½) bright blue, 2-lipped, upper lip hood-like, lower scoop-shaped, side-lobes ovate; stamens (D, × 3) 2, hidden under the hood; anthers 1-locular; style with 2 blue exserted branches; ovary (E, × 4) deeply 4-lobed, sometimes 2 of the lobes not bearing seeds, lobes inserted in a large fleshy disk (family *Labiatae*).

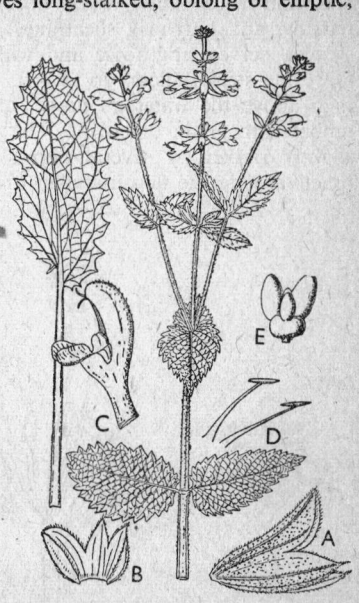

Clary grows in dry fields, by the roadsides and in waste places; fairly common in England, but rare in Scotland, and in Eire is confined to the south; it flowers from late spring until autumn. It is widely distributed into North Africa and western Asia. The seeds when soaked in water form a thick mucilage, which was formerly used as an eye-wash.

FLOWERING RUSH, *Butomus umbellatus* L.

381. Flowering Rush, *Butomus umbellatus* L. ($\times \frac{1}{2}$); an aquatic perennial with a thick horizontally creeping root-stock and numerous rather thick fibrous roots; leaves long and narrow, and narrowly sheathing at the base, closely lined by slender nerves lengthwise and with a distinct thicker midrib; flowering stem leafless, up to 4 ft. high, bearing at the top and high above the water an umbel of 20–30 pretty pink flowers; umbel with an involucre of 3 large triangular pointed bracts, slightly ribbed by several nerves lengthwise; a few smaller bracts among the flower-stalks; flower-stalks (pedicels) 3–4 in. long; perianth of 6 parts in 2 whorls, all petal-like, overlapping in bud; stamens (A, $\times$ 2) 9, with long anthers in bud becoming rounded after opening (B, $\times$ 2); carpels (C, $\times$ 2) 6, free, narrowed into a short style, each with numerous ovules spread over the inside of the carpellary wall (D, $\times$ 4); seeds numerous and very small (family *Butomaceae*).

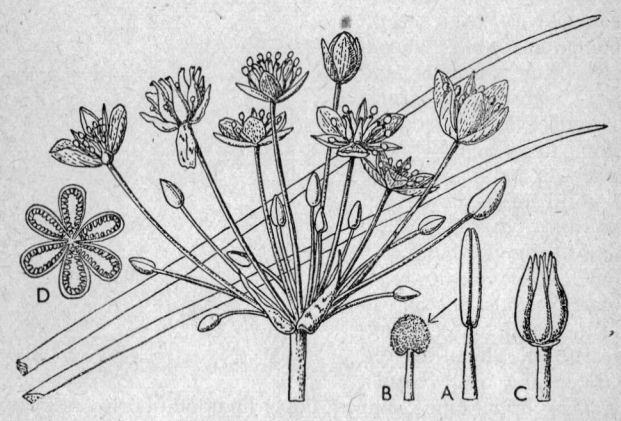

The stamens as well as the carpels are red and help to make the flower conspicuous. Of the 9 stamens, 6 not superposed on the petals open first, and their filaments at the same time bend backwards and outwards. When the 6 have withered, the anthers of the other 3 open, and their filaments remain nearly erect. The carpels now mature and become dark red, the stigmas appearing in the form of slits, which expand gradually below the pollen-covered anthers of the 3 stamens. Thus cross- or self-pollination may take place.

ARROWHEAD, *Sagittaria sagittifolia* L.

382. Arrowhead, *Sagittaria sagittifolia* L. ($\times \frac{1}{2}$); aquatic perennial with milky juice and with creeping root-stock, with bulb-like tubers; leaves rising above the water on long 3-sided stalks, arrow-shaped (sagittate), the 2 "barbs" almost as long as the end lobe, the latter with 3 main parallel nerves; flowers arranged in distant whorls of 3, each pedicel with a thin triangular bract at the base, upper flowers usually male, lower female on shorter stalks; sepals 3, ovate, deeply saccate, rather crimson and lined with closely parallel nerves; petals 3, broad and rounded, white, crimson at the base; stamens (A, $\times 4$) about 25; anthers dark brown, sagittate; carpels (B, $\times 7$) few in the male flowers, very numerous in the females, free from one another (apocarpous), arranged on a large fleshy axis (C, $\times 0$), each with a single erect ovule (family *Alismataceae*).

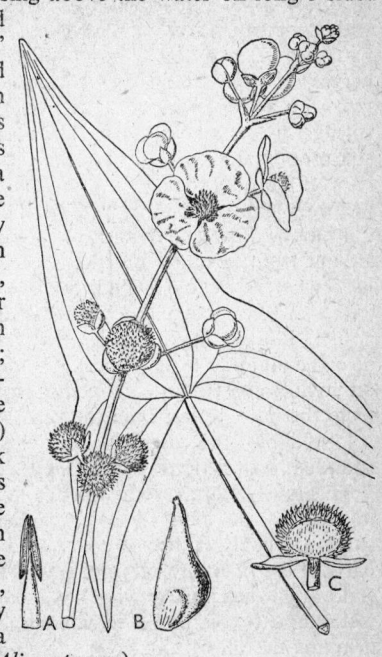

This water-plant is easily recognised by its handsome white flowers over an inch in diameter, the upper ones being male, with numerous stamens and few abortive carpels; the females have much shorter stalks and very numerous carpels. When the individual flower-stalks are cut, a white juice exudes from parts of the section.

The flowers are unisexual, but both sexes are found on the same plant. The females are smaller than the male, and the white petals have a red nectar-guide at their base. The females are mature before the males. The anthers of the latter are of a beautiful dark-brown colour and open at the side.

AUTUMN CROCUS, MEADOW SAFFRON,
Colchicum autumnale L.

383. Autumn Crocus, Meadow Saffron, *Colchicum autumnale* L. ($\times \frac{1}{2}$); perennial with a preference for limestone soil, with a deeply placed narrowly ovoid acuminate corm covered with a thin shining, chestnut-brown coat lined with parallel nerves; flowers and leaves produced at different times of the year, the flowers in early September, the leaves and fruits in late spring; leaves several, linear-lanceolate, up to about 9 in. long, sharp-pointed, green; in the middle of the leaves 1 or 2 fruits (F, $\times$ 0) produced in May or June and soon ripening; these narrowly ellipsoid and tipped by the bases of the styles, about 2 in. long; flower long and tubular, pale purple or deep mauve, arising from near the base of the corm; perianth-segments 6, in 2 whorls, the outer slightly wider than the inner; stamens (A, $\times$ 2) 6, opposite the segments and inserted in the throat; anthers long, facing outwards, arrow-shaped at the base, attached near the middle; ovary superior, 3-locular (B, $\times$ 2), with numerous ovules inserted on the central axis; styles (C, $\times$ 0) 3, free from the base, longer than the tube, the exserted parts (D, $\times$ 2) coloured like the filaments of the stamens; seeds (G, $\times$ 1$\frac{1}{2}$) rounded, brown (family *Liliaceae*).

This lovely plant is sometimes called Naked Ladies, and occurs in meadows in many districts of England and Wales. Where stock are likely to browse, it should be rooted out because all parts of the plant are very poisonous both in the green and dried state and when mixed with hay. Domestic animals have been lost after eating it, and even calves and infants have died through drinking the milk from cows which had eaten the plant a short time previously. A case is recorded of the death of a woman at Covent Garden who ate the corms in mistake for onions.

From a biological point of view the Autumn Crocus is one of our most interesting native species. Unlike most bulbous or cormous plants, it flowers in the autumn. The styles are very long and free from one another, and the pollen tubes do not reach the ovules until the beginning of November. But the ovary remains dormant, and the embryo is not formed until the next May, when the fruits are developed, being then carried above the surface in the middle of a bunch of green leaves. In the wild state, like many ground orchids, the position in the soil of the corms may indicate how deeply in a given neighbourhood the ground is usually frozen, for they are imbedded just far enough to avoid injury.

229

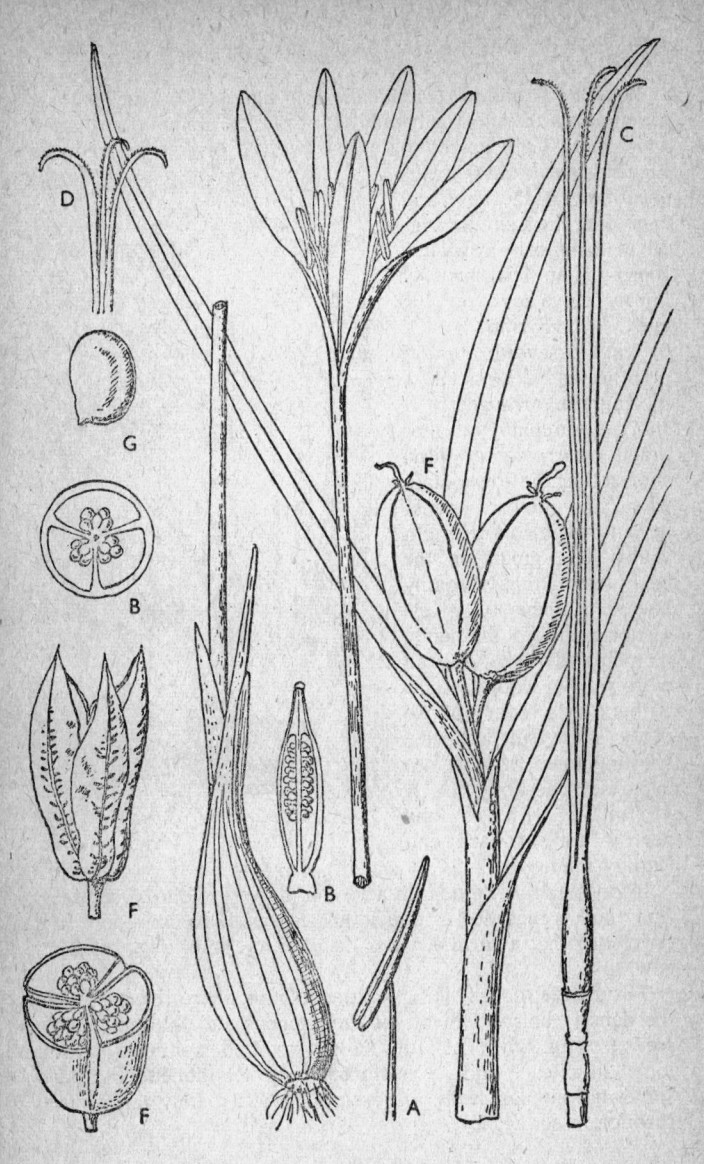

BOG ASPHODEL, *Narthecium ossifragum* (L.) Huds.

384. Bog Asphodel, *Narthecium ossifragum* (L.) Huds. ($\times \frac{1}{2}$); perennial with short creeping root-stock; stem up to about 1 ft. high, leafy at the base and with 2 or 3 much-reduced higher leaves; basal leaves sheathing at the base and encircling the stem, arranged in 2 opposite rows like those of an Iris, broadly linear, very acute at the apex, strongly ribbed (A, $\times$ 0) lengthwise with about 5 or 6 nerves; flowers (B, $\times$ 0) fragrant, arranged in a short terminal raceme; bracts narrow, a little shorter than the flower-stalk when the flower opens; perianth-segments 6, bright yellow but green on the back, spreading, broadly linear; stamens (C, $\times 2\frac{1}{2}$) 6, shorter than the segments; filaments densely covered with yellow woolly hairs; anthers red; ovary above the perianth, fruit, a capsule splitting from the top into 3 parts; seed-body (D, $\times$ 4) small, with a long narrow tail at each end (family *Liliaceae*).

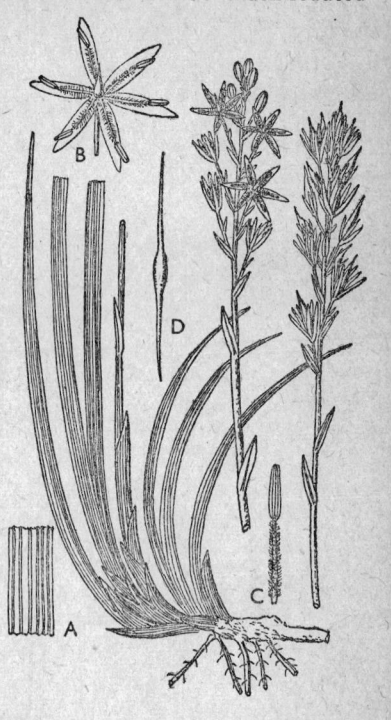

In bogs and wet moors in acid soil, flowering during summer. The plant is regarded as poisonous, especially to cows, and it is on record that a cat died after drinking the milk of an affected cow.

Two of the most striking features of this interesting plant are the densely hairy filaments of the stamens and the remarkable seeds (see fig. D). The latter have a small ellipsoid body with a long tail at each end. Certain epiphytic Rhododendrons have somewhat similar seeds. Cross-pollination mainly takes place through insect agency.

SIMPLE BUR-REED, *Sparganium simplex* Huds.

385. Simple Bur-Reed, *Sparganium simplex* Huds. ($\times \frac{1}{3}$); perennial aquatic herb with erect stems; leaves erect and partly out of the water, completely encircling the stem at the base and with membranous margins in the lower part, flattened upwards but keeled below, narrowly linear, bright green and with about 3 longitudinal nerves on each side of the midrib; flowers unisexual, crowded into globose heads on a simple main axis, the upper male (A, $\times 0$) and sessile, the lower female (C, $\times 2$) and pedunculate, or sometimes the peduncle adnate to the axis (extra-axillary); male flowers consisting of slender stamens surrounded by free yellowish-green perianth-segments; anthers (B, $\times 2$) linear-oblong, opening at the side; female flowers of a single long-beaked carpel surrounded by jagged scales, with 1 pendulous ovule (D, $\times 2$) (family *Sparganiaceae*).

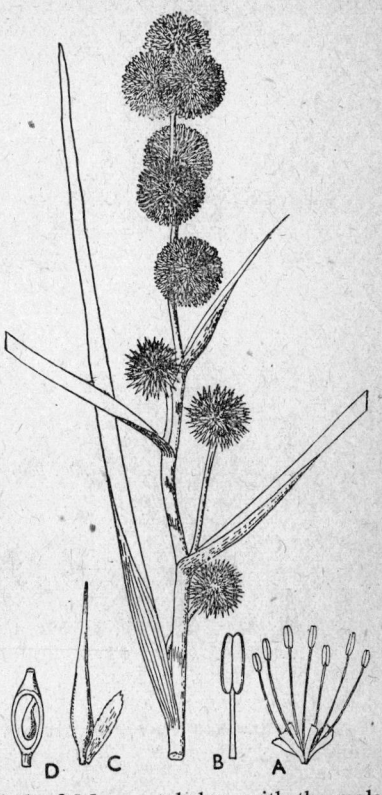

This is a very advanced (highly evolved) kind of Monocotyledon, with the male and female flowers in separate heads, and a single pendulous ovule in the solitary carpel of the female flower.

TOAD RUSH, *Juncus bufonius* L.

386. Toad Rush, *Juncus bufonius* L. ($\times \frac{1}{3}$); a small annual plant often growing in dense tufts like a perennial, with numerous stems up to nearly 1 ft. high; leaves very few, mostly from the base, much shorter than the flowering stems, very narrow; flowers (A, $\times$ 0) solitary or rarely 2–3 together at the main forks of the branches, sessile or nearly so, each subtended by 2 small ovate very thin bracts; perianth (B, $\times$ 0) of 6 unequal segments, the outer 3 longer and very sharply pointed, the inner 3 shorter and wider, and more membranous, but all longer than the capsule; stamens 6, opposite to the segments; ovary with 3 parietal placentas nearly meeting in the middle; capsule (C, $\times$ 2) splitting into 3 boat-shaped parts, each part (D, $\times$ 2) with a wide parietal placenta down the middle; seeds (E, $\times$ 6) very minute and numerous, pale brown, faintly lined (family *Juncaceae*).

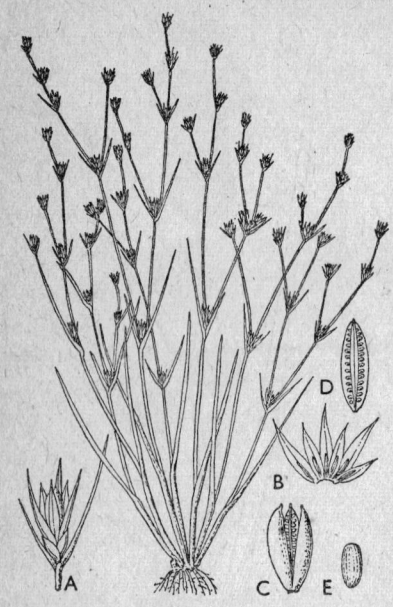

This species is very abundant in Britain, and is widely spread over many parts of the world. It flowers during the whole of the summer.

COMMON RUSH, *Juncus effusus* L.

387. **Common Rush,** *Juncus effusus* L. ($\times \frac{1}{3}$); perennial with closely matted root-stocks bearing dense tufts of rounded leafless stems 2–3 ft. high, clothed at the base with rather long brown sheaths and full of soft pith; only some of the stems bear a bunch of flowers about 6–8 in. below the tip; flowers (A, $\times$ 0) in much-branched loose cymes varying greatly in number, sometimes quite few; each flower (B, $\times 2\frac{1}{2}$) with a pair of thin lanceolate bracts at the base; perianth-segments (C, $\times 2\frac{1}{2}$) subequal, very sharply pointed, about as long as the fruits (E, $\times 1\frac{1}{2}$); stamens 3, opposite the outer segments; ovary (D, $\times$ 4) ovoid; styles 3; capsule rounded at the top, with numerous very small yellowish seeds (F, $\times$ 5) (family *Juncaceae*).

This is very common in Britain, and grows in moist places in woods and on heaths. It is widely distributed in Asia and in both North and South America.

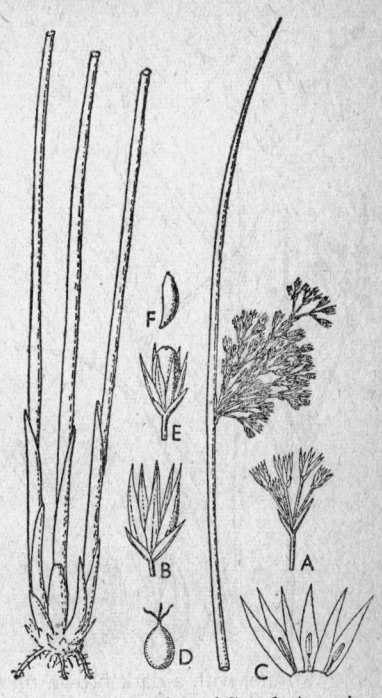

JOINTED RUSH, *Juncus articulatus* L.

388. Jointed Rush, *Juncus articulatus* L. ($\times \frac{1}{3}$); perennial with short knotted root-stock; stems slender, crowded in tufts; leaves with long open sheathing bases and ligule-like at the top of the sheath, the blade cylindrical upwards and hollow, but divided inside by cross partitions of pith giving a knotted or jointed appearance; flowers (A, $\times 2$) in small dense "prickly" clusters arranged in panicles; lowermost bract of each cluster sheath-like and shortly pointed; smaller bracts lanceolate, acute; perianth (B, $\times 3$) of 6 free segments, these lanceolate, acute, keeled; stamens 6, opposite the segments and about half as long; ovary (C, $\times 3$) ellipsoid, with 3 short styles; capsule (D, $\times 2$) 3-angled, splitting into 3 valves (E, $\times 2$), each with seeds arranged down the middle; seed (F, $\times 6$) faintly striate, with a dark brown tip (family *Juncaceae*).

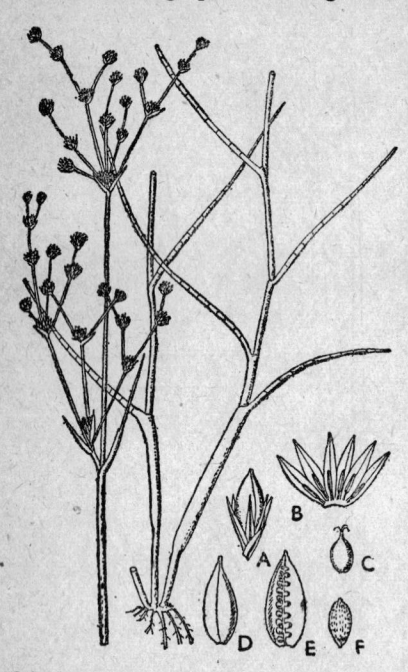

This species is very easily recognised by its distinctive leaves, which are described above. It is very widely distributed in various parts of the world, and is sometimes split up under several names.

LESSER-JOINTED RUSH, *Juncus bulbosus* L.

389. **Lesser-Jointed Rush,** *Juncus bulbosus* L. ($\times \frac{1}{2}$); perennial herb with tufted stems about 6 in. high and the root-stock sometimes tuberous; leaves shorter than the flowering stems, needle-like, sheathing at the base and with a large membranous ligule-like appendage at the top of the sheath; flowers (B, $\times$ 3) in a few small sessile or shortly stalked clusters (A, $\times$ 0) the

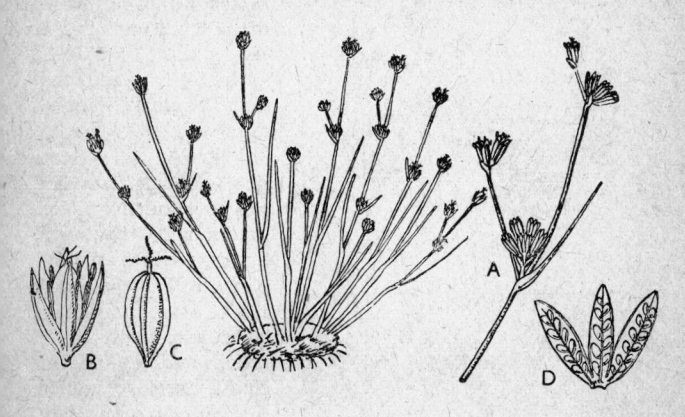

lowermost with a leaf-like bract at the base, the others with much smaller membranous bracts about half the length of the perianth; perianth of 6 free lanceolate segments tinged with brown or reddish; stamens 6, opposite the segments; ovary (C, $\times$ 3) 3-sided, winged; capsule (D, $\times$ 2$\frac{1}{2}$) as long as the perianth, opening into 3 valves, each with 2 rows of seeds up the middle (family *Juncaceae*).

A common dwarf species in bogs, and especially in acid soils.

HEATH RUSH, *Juncus squarrosus* L.

390. Heath Rush, *Juncus squarrosus* L. ($\times \frac{1}{3}$); a perennial with a bunch of numerous leaves from the base, and these broadly sheathing in the lower part; leaf-blades stiff and spreading, very narrow, rounded below and grooved above, usually about as long as the flowering stems; the latter usually 2-3 to each plant, 9 in. to 15 in. high, very rigid, ending in a shortly branched cyme-like panicle; flowers (A, $\times 1\frac{1}{2}$) separate, though crowded, sessile or shortly stalked; bracts paired below the flower, ovate, short; perianth-segments (B, $\times 1\frac{1}{2}$) 6, equal in length, lanceolate, glossy, with a broad middle and thin chaffy margins; stamens 6, opposite the segments; ovary (C, $\times 3$) with a short style and 3 stigmas; capsule (D, $\times 2\frac{1}{2}$) about as long as the segments, obovoid, shining, splitting into 3 parts, each part (E, $\times 2$) boat-shaped, with a placenta in the middle and numerous, brown, closely pitted seeds (F, $\times 10$) (family *Juncaceae*).

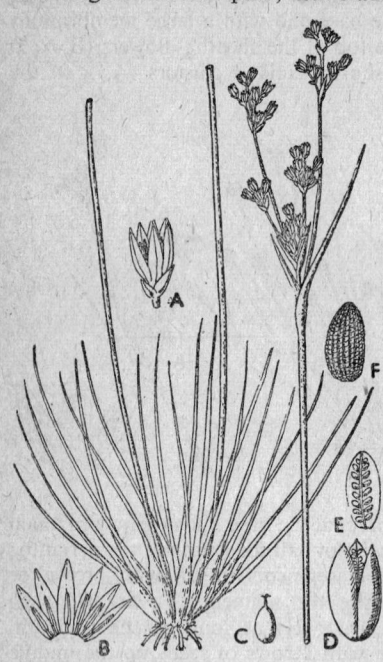

This species grows on moors and heaths, and is found in drier places than most other rushes. The seeds (fig. F) are very distinctive. It flowers in summer, and is widely distributed in Europe and Asia.

BULRUSH, *Scirpus lacustris* L.

391. Bulrush, *Scirpus lacustris* L. ($\times \frac{2}{3}$); perennial with creeping root-stock covered with brown closely ribbed scales; stems erect, even up to 8 ft. high, cylindrical at the base and embraced with a few overlapping narrow pointed leaf-sheaths, the latter thin and closely marked with numerous parallel nerves; the stem towards the top becoming obtusely triangular; flower-spikes (A, $\times$ 3) 3 or more together in sessile and stalked clusters, ovoid, $\frac{1}{2}-\frac{3}{4}$ in. long; outer bract stiff and continuing the stem and 1–2 in. long; flowers (B, $\times$ 4) bisexual; floral bracts (glumes) numerous, overlapping all around the axis, ovate, acute, jagged at the margins; hypogynous bristles (C, $\times$ 10) 5–6, shorter than the bracts, with numerous reflexed barbs; stamens (D, $\times$ 8) 3; anthers apiculate, attached at the base; ovary (E, $\times$ 4) obovoid; style divided into 2 arms; nut obovoid, smooth (family *Cyperaceae*).

The Bulrush is very widely distributed, and is typical of the vegetation in almost every piece of water landscape, particularly in the Fen districts of East Anglia, reaching in some places up to 8 ft. high. It flowers in July and August. The leaves have been much used for matting, chair seats ("rush-bottomed chairs"), mats and hassocks, and thatching. At one time pack-saddles were stuffed with bulrushes.

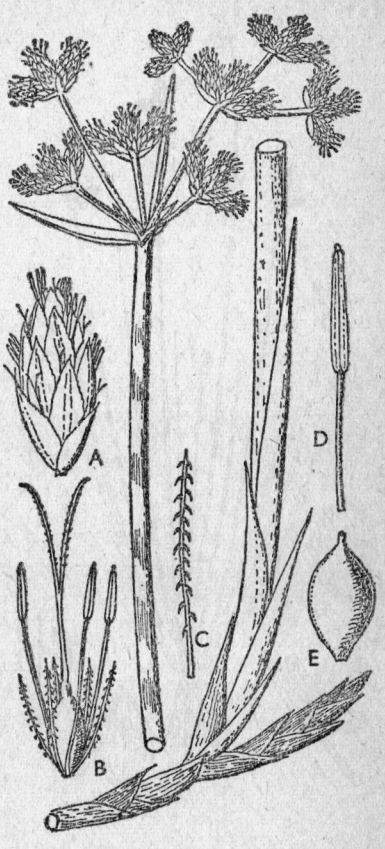

BRISTLY SCIRPUS, *Scirpus setaceus* L.

392. Bristly Scirpus, *Scirpus setaceus* L. ($\times \frac{2}{3}$); one of the very smallest sedges growing in sandy or gravelly soil on the margins of ponds; plants forming dense tufts with matted roots; leaves very short and subulate, purplish at the base; flowering stems up to about 6 in. high, like fine wire, closely ribbed, smooth, bearing at the top 1–3 sessile spikelets (A, $\times$ 4), subtended by the shortly produced subulate bract-leaf; spikelets ovoid, about $\frac{1}{4}$ in. long; bracts (B, $\times$ 6) ovate, streaked with brown and with a green midrib; flowers (C, $\times$ 8) bisexual; no hypogynous bristles; stamens 3, anthers comparatively short; ovary smooth, with a slender 3-armed style; nut (D, $\times$ 12) very small, broadly obovoid, marked with several longitudinal brown ribs (family *Cyperaceae*).

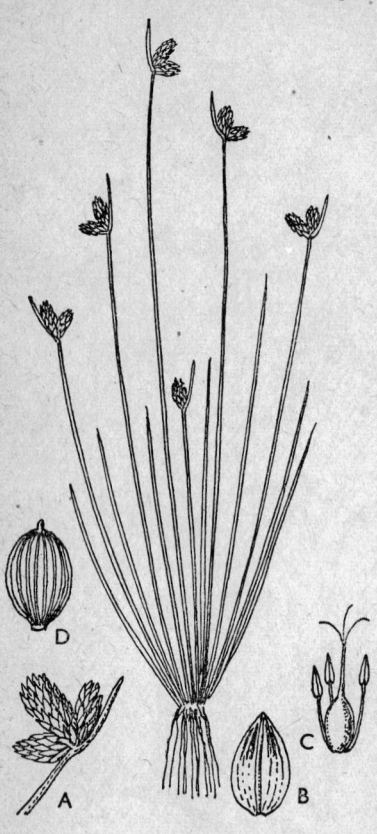

Easily distinguished by its diminutive size, and differing from the rather similar *S. riparius* by the nut marked with longitudinal ribs, a feature only observable through a fairly strong lens.

DEER'S GRASS or DEER'S HAIR, *Scirpus caespitosus* L.

393. Deer's Grass or Deer's Hair, *Scirpus caespitosus* L. ($\times \frac{1}{2}$); a very densely tufted perennial with numerous fairly thick roots; flowering stems up to 1 ft. high, covered with closely overlapping shining sheaths in the lower part, the lower brown, the upper green and with very short narrow leafy tips; spikelet (A, $\times$ 2) solitary at the apex of each stiff wiry peduncle, about $\frac{1}{4}$ in. long, ovoid, brown, the outermost bract the largest, but not exceeding the length of the spikelet, with a short leafy top (B, $\times$ 3); flowers (C, $\times$ 5) bisexual, about 6–8 to each spikelet; stamens 3; anthers (D, $\times$ 4) with a barren tip; hypogynous bristles about 6, very fine and hair-like and smooth; style with 3 branches; nut obovoid, 3-sided, pointed (family *Cyperaceae*).

Locally abundant in moorland and heath districts, but not found in cultivated land and areas with chalky soil. It is very widely distributed in the northern hemisphere.

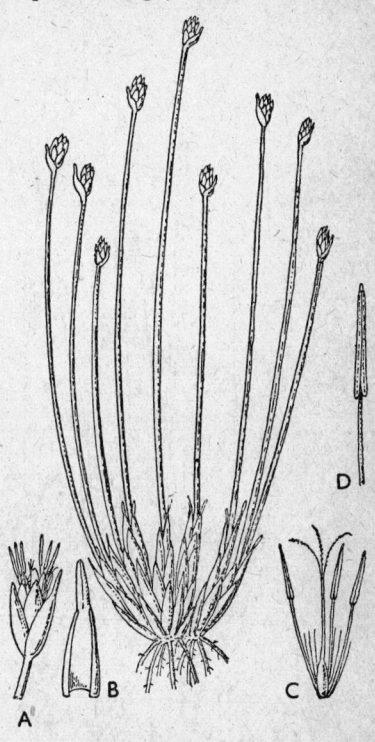

MARSH CLUB RUSH, *Eleocharis palustris* (L.) R.Br.

394. Marsh Club Rush, *Eleocharis palustris* (L.) R.Br. (× ⅔); perennial with creeping blackish root-stock, on the edges of ponds, pools and wet ditches; roots slender and fibrous; tufts of leaves and flowering stems numerous, often about 9 in. to 1 ft., but occasionally up to 2½ ft. high; peduncles with a tubular sheath about 1–2 in. long at the base, the sheath truncate at the top, tinged with reddish-crimson; spikelets (A, × 3) solitary at the top of the peduncle, lanceolate in outline, composed of several spirally arranged imbricate reddish-brown bracts (glumes); lowermost bract (B, × 4) ovate, shorter and broader than the others and without a flower inside; other bracts all with a flower in their axils, broadly lanceolate, with green middle part, brown or reddish towards the membranous margin; stamens (D, × 10) 3; anthers basifixed, apiculate; hypogynous bristles 4, with reflexed barbs (C, × 6); ovary (E, × 6) obovoid, smooth, the base of the style much swollen into a thick cone-like paler body; style 2-lobed; nut obovoid, rather compressed, tipped by the swollen persistent base of the style (family *Cyperaceae*).

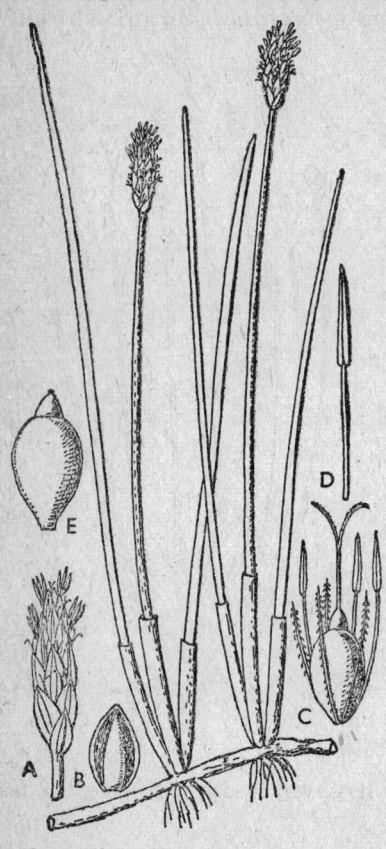

Like many other aquatic or semi-aquatic plants, this has a wide range of distribution, south to northern Africa, and in North America; it is common and widely distributed throughout Britain.

BLACK BOG-RUSH, *Schoenus nigricans* L.

395. Black Bog-Rush, *Schoenus nigricans* L. ($\times \frac{1}{2}$); a densely tufted perennial with very numerous thick roots, up to $1\frac{1}{2}$ ft. high, but usually 9 in. to 1 ft.; leaves very narrow and rigid, their sheaths dark brown or reddish and shining, ribbed; flowers crowded in terminal heads subtended by a pair of opposite bracts (B, $\times$ 0), 1 or both with a leaf-like upper portion; spikelets (A, $\times$ 2) crowded together into a head, each spikelet shortly stalked and consisting of a few bracts (glumes) arranged in opposite rows, only the upper bracts containing bisexual flowers (C, $\times$ 4), the lower ones empty; bracts dark brown or nearly black, lanceolate, keeled, the keel slightly rough; stamens (D, $\times$ 8) 3; anthers with rather long barren tips; ovary ellipsoid, with a slender style and 3 slender style-arms; nut (E, $\times$ 5) triangular, pale-grey and smooth (family *Cyperaceae*).

This is locally common and more frequent in northern Britain. It is a very widely distributed species in the northern hemisphere.

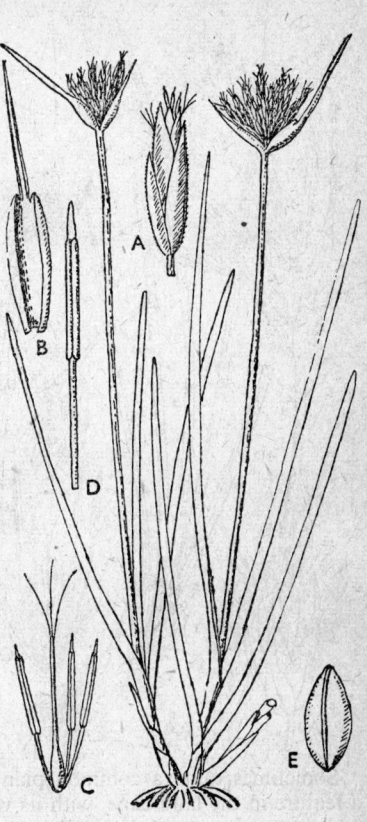

COTTON GRASS, *Eriophorum angustifolium* Roth.

396. Cotton Grass, *Eriophorum angustifolium* Roth. ($\times \frac{2}{3}$); perennial with creeping root-stock covered with strongly nerved sheaths; leaves few from the base of the stem, very narrow and tough, closely ribbed when dry, glabrous; flowering stem about 1–1½ ft. high, bearing at the top usually more than 1 spike of flowers arranged in an irregular umbel, some with longer stalks than others: spike (in flower) (A, $\times 1\frac{1}{3}$) ¾–1 in. long, narrowly ellipsoid, with conspicuous long anthers projecting beyond the bracts (glumes); all the bracts (B, $\times 2$) except the lowermost with a flower (C, $\times 2$) in their axil, thin and membranous, with a very narrow midrib; stamens (D, $\times 3$) 3; anthers very long, basifixed; hypogynous bristles numerous, very fine and hair-like, growing out in fruit and resembling cotton, hence the common name; ovary ellipsoid, with a slender 3-branched style; nut very small (family *Cyperaceae*).

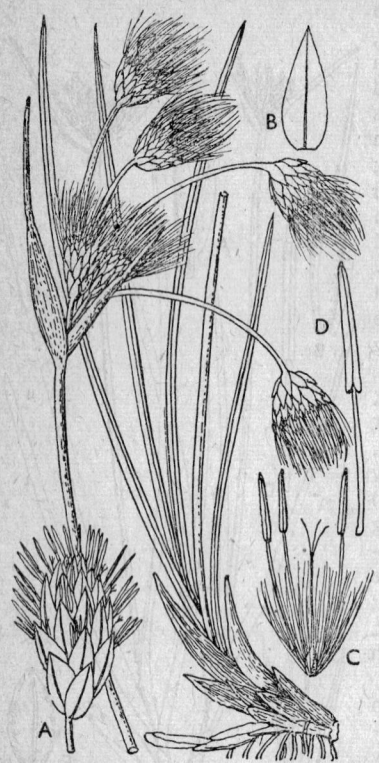

Sometimes quite a common plant in marshes and bogs and a feature in the landscape, with its white cotton-like balls; it is widely spread around the north temperate zone.

BLACK SEDGE, *Carex nigra* (L.) Reichard

397. Black Sedge, *Carex nigra* (L.) Reichard ($\times \frac{2}{5}$); a perennial with long stoloniferous shoots, these clothed with fibrous leaf-sheaths; leaves few in the lower part of the stem, some as long as the flowering-stem, narrow, closely nerved, tapered to a fine point, the basal sheath with wide membranous margins; spikelets containing flowers of 1 sex only (unisexual) the terminal male (A), the others female (B, $\times$ 0); male spikelet narrow and slender, about $\frac{3}{4}$–1 in. long; bracts (glumes) (C, $\times$ 2) oblong-elliptic, rounded at the top; stamens (D, $\times$ 2) 3; female spikelets axillary, nearly sessile, about $\frac{3}{4}$ in. long in flower, or 1 in. in fruit; bracts (glumes) narrowly ovate, shorter than the utricle in fruit (E, $\times$ 2); utricle (F, $\times$ 2$\frac{1}{2}$) broadly bottle-shaped, shortly beaked, ribbed lengthwise; style-arms 2 or occasionally 3; nut (G, $\times$ 2) somewhat flattened, beaked; bracts in fruit black or nearly so (family (*Cyperaceae*). Male spikelets marked ♂, female ♀.

This species is usually called *C. goodenowi* Gay or *C. vulgaris* Fries in British Floras, but *C. nigra* is the name to be used according to the most recent research into the nomenclature. It is widely distributed in Europe, northern Asia, and in north-eastern America.

BEAKED CAREX, *Carex rostrata* Stokes

398. Beaked Carex, *Carex rostrata* Stokes (× ⅖); tufted perennial up to 3 ft. high; leaves longer than the flowering stem, ½ in. broad, tapered to a fine point, margins finely toothed, the lower reduced to sheaths; spikelets with flowers of 1 sex only (unisexual), 2–4 of the upper entirely male and sessile (A), the remainder (D) female and more or less shortly stalked, the stalks much elongating in fruit; terminal male spikelets (A) the longest, about 2 in. long; bracts (B, × 2) narrow; stamens (C, × 2) 3; female bracts also narrow (E, × 3), with a broad pale middle and brownish margins; utricle (F, × 2½) longer than the bract in fruit and beaked; style-arms 2; nut ellipsoid, smooth (family *Cyperaceae*).—Male spikelets marked ♂, female marked ♀.

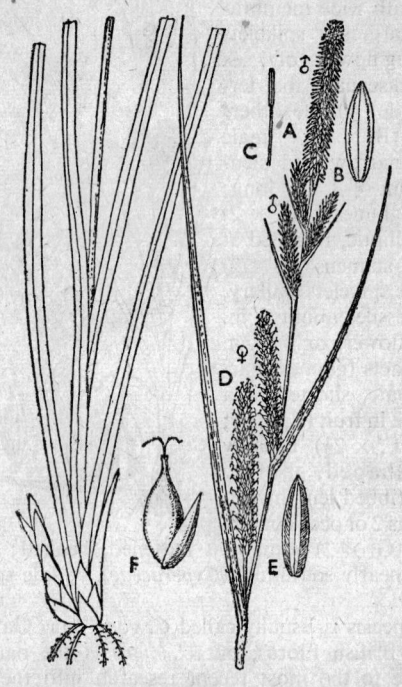

In British Floras and lists this species is usually called *C. ampullacea* Gooden. It is widely distributed from Europe to Asia Minor and as far east as Siberia.

FLEA SEDGE, *Carex pulicaris* L.

399. Flea Sedge, *Carex pulicaris* L. ($\times \frac{2}{3}$); a densely tufted perennial up to 9 in. high; roots very fine and fibrous; leaves very slender and wiry, some as long as the flowering stems; sheaths at the base narrow and strongly ribbed; spikelets (A, $\times 1$) solitary at the top of each stem, $\frac{1}{2}-\frac{3}{4}$ in. long, bisexual, i.e. the upper slender portion with male flowers, the lower thicker half with female flowers: bracts ovate-lanceolate, with a green mibrib and brown towards the thin margins, the lowermost bract like the others; each female flower (B, $\times 3$) with a membranous brown bract; utricle (C, $\times 4$) rather narrow and pointed; style with 2 branches; nut (D, $\times 4$) oblong-ellipsoid, partly compressed, pale brown; fruiting spike (E, $\times 2$) very loose, with the fruits spreading or drooping (family *Cyperaceae*).—Male part of spikelet marked ♂, female marked ♀.

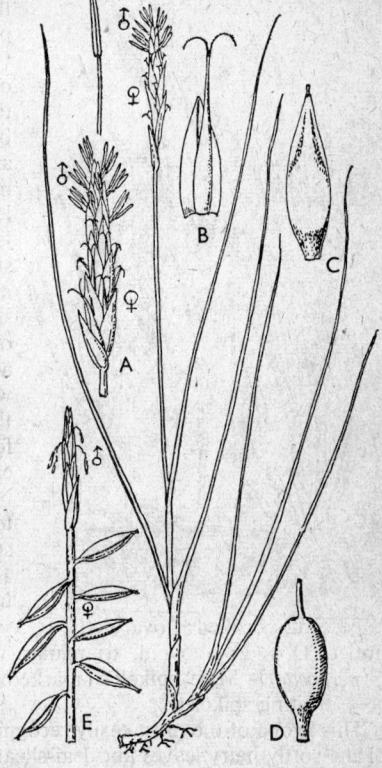

Widely spread in north and central Europe, like most other species growing in wet fields and bogs or in moist mountain pastures.

HAIRY SEDGE, *Carex hirta* L.

400. Hairy Sedge, *Carex hirta* L. ($\times \frac{2}{5}$); perennial herb with long creeping root-stock covered with closely ribbed old leaf-sheaths and with very fine fibrous roots; stem slender, leafy throughout, rather sharply three-sided; leaves thinly pilose on both surfaces and very densely woolly-hairy on the margins towards the top of the sheath, the blade about $\frac{1}{4}$ in. broad and closely ribbed with nerves lengthwise; spikelets unisexual; male spikelets 1–3 at the top of the stem, the terminal about 1 in long, the lower males shorter; glumes (A, $\times$ 3) oblong-obovate, shortly acuminate, pubescent towards the top; stamens 3, the anthers exserted; female spikelets 2–3, 1 in each axil of the leaves below the males, elongating to 2 in. long in fruit and stalked; glumes (B, F, $\times$ 1½) very long-pointed; utricle exceptional in being pubescent, beaked; ovary (C, $\times$ 3) narrow; style 3-lobed; nutlet (D, $\times$ 2) obovoid, triangular, pale and smooth (family *Cyperaceae*).—Male spikelets marked ♂, female marked ♀ (E. $\times \frac{4}{5}$, fruiting spikelet).

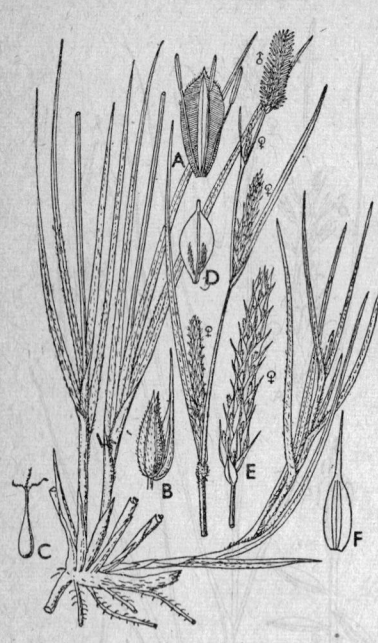

This is one of the most easily recognised of the sedges because of the softly hairy leaves and leaf-sheaths and hairy utricles. It is very common in Europe, Asia Minor, and is also found in northern Africa.

MARSH SEDGE, *Carex acutiformis* Ehrh.

401. Marsh Sedge, *Carex acutiformis* Ehrh. ($\times \frac{2}{5}$); perennial with creeping root-stock; stems triangular, 2–3 ft. high; leaves very long and erect, densely overlapping at the base, and with thread-like margins, about ½ in. broad, with sharply serrulate margins, and with nearly 20 close parallel nerves on each side of the midrib; leaf below the lowest female spikelet overtopping the terminal males; male spikelets usually 2 or 3 together at the top and nearly sessile, the end one the longest and about 1½ in. long, covered with densely crowded exserted anthers; glumes (A, $\times 4$) oblong, not pointed; stamens (B, $\times 2$) 3; female spikelets (H, $\times 1\frac{1}{2}$) nearly sessile, lengthening to 3 in. in fruit; glumes (C, $\times 4$) elliptic, with an acuminate slightly hairy tip; utricle (D, F, $\times 2$) ellipsoid, shortly beaked, distinctly ribbed lengthwise; ovary (E, $\times 2\frac{1}{2}$) ellipsoid, with a long 3-lobed style; nut (G, $\times 2\frac{1}{4}$) longer than the perianth, 3-angled beaked by the persistent style (family *Cyperaceae*).—Male spikelets marked ♂, female marked ♀.

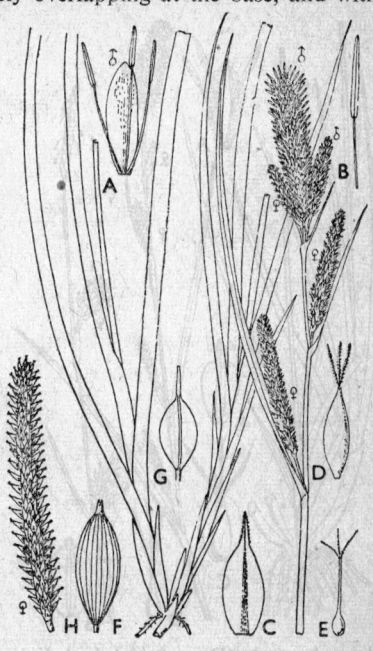

This species flowers in May and fruits in June, and grows in wet meadows and marshes. It is widely distributed in Europe and central Asia to Siberia, and in North Africa. Another name for the plant is *C. paludosa* Gooden.

DISTANT SEDGE, *Carex distans* L.

402. Distant Sedge, *Carex distans* L. ($\times \frac{2}{5}$); a slender perennial herb up to about 15 in. high; stems tufted from a creeping root-stock, leafy below the middle, the longest leaves up to about half as long as the flowering stems; lower leaves recurved, the others ascending, $\frac{1}{8}$ in. broad, glaucous-green; spikelets unisexual, the single male terminal, with usually 3 distant females, 1 in each of the upper leaf-bract axils, the lowermost bract sometimes reaching to the top of the male spikelet; male spikelet $\frac{3}{4}$–1 in. long; covered with overlapping brownish obovate glumes (A, $\times$ 2) with thin margins; stamens 3, the anthers exserted on very slender filaments; female spikelets shortly stalked, about 1 in. long; glumes (C, $\times$ 2) obovate, the lower (B, $\times$ 2) with a short hairy tip and green midrib; utricle bottle-shaped; style (D, $\times$ 2) 3-lobed, hairy; nutlet 3-sided, enclosed by the beaked utricle; fruiting spikelet fat, with a short stalk clear of the accompanying leaf-like bract (family *Cyperaceae*).—Male spikelets marked ♂, female marked ♀.

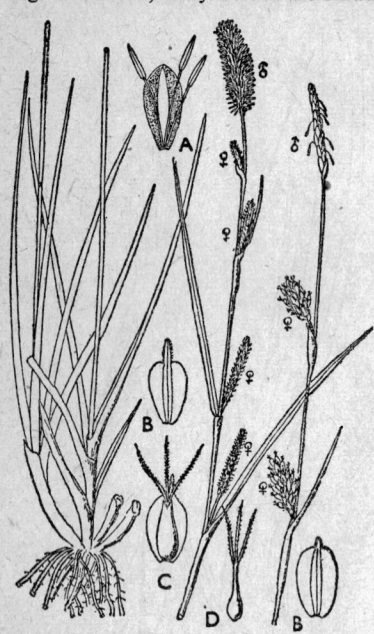

This very distinctive species has no other names to be recorded as synonyms. It is found throughout Europe and the eastern Mediterranean countries, in North Africa, and is also recorded from Madeira and the Azores.

FLABBY SEDGE, *Carex flacca* Schreb.

403. Flabby Sedge, *Carex flacca* Schreb. ($\times \frac{2}{5}$); perennial with creeping runners from the base; leaves flat, with a prominent midrib, slightly rough on the margins, tapered to a sharp point; sheath truncate (abruptly cut off) opposite the base of the blade; flower spikelets of 1 sex (unisexual), the uppermost 2 male (A), the rest (usually about 3) female (B); male spikelets unequal in length, the uppermost longer and about 1 in. long; stamens (C, $\times$ 2) 3, the long yellow anthers long-exserted from the bracts (glumes); bracts (glumes) oblong-oblanceolate, with wide brown margins; female spikelets on slender stalks, $\frac{1}{2}$–1 in. long when in flower; bracts (glumes) (D, $\times$ 2) oblong-lanceolate, with a green midrib and wide brown margins; utricle (E, $\times$ 2) not beaked; ovary (F, $\times$ 1$\frac{1}{2}$) smooth; styles 3; nutlet (G, $\times$ 2) obovoid, 3-angled, pale straw-coloured (family *Cyperaceae*).—Male spikelets marked ♂, female marked ♀.

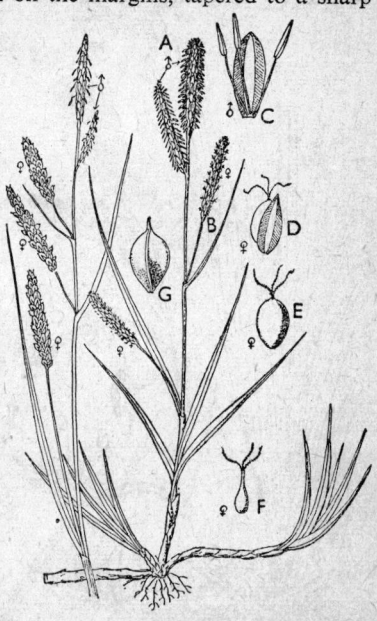

Another name for this species is *C. glauca* Scop. It is widely distributed in Europe and North Africa and in western Asia, and has been introduced into North America and a few other parts of the world.

PENDULOUS SEDGE, *Carex pendula* Huds.

404. Pendulous Sedge, *Carex pendula* Huds. ($\times \frac{2}{5}$); a tall perennial up to 5 ft. high with thick triangular leafy stems; leaves very long and about ¾ in. broad, keeled towards the base, tapered to the apex, margins smooth, with 3 main longitudinal nerves and several close less conspicuous nerves; flowers in at length slender pendulous spikelets, the terminal spikelet (A) entirely male and about 3 in. long, with very conspicuous stamens within broadly oblanceolate acute thin bracts (B, $\times 1\frac{1}{4}$), remainder of spikelets entirely female (C), slender, often nearly 6 in. long, especially in fruit; bracts of female (D, $\times 1\frac{1}{2}$) obovate, acutely pointed, 3-nerved, brown between the nerves and the margin; utricle (E, $\times 2$) enclosing the ovary 3-sided; style (G, $\times 3$) 3-lobed; nutlet (F, $\times 2\frac{1}{2}$) 3-sided, pale, tipped by the persistent style (family *Cyperaceae*).—Male spikelets marked ♂, female marked ♀.

This species is easily spotted because of the long slender pendulous spikelets. It is not quite so widely distributed as most of the other species described in this book, being found in Europe, Asia Minor and North Africa.

SAND CAREX, *Carex arenaria* L.

405. Sand Carex, *Carex arenaria* L. ($\times \frac{2}{5}$); perennial herb with a root-stock creeping for several feet in maritime sands; stems arising singly here and there along the root-stock, from a few inches up to $1\frac{1}{2}$ ft. high; root-stock covered with overlapping sheaths which soon split into threads, rooting at the joints, the roots covered with very fine much-branched rootlets; lowermost leaves reduced to sheaths, the few upper leaves linear and falling short of the spike; spikelets (A, $\times$ 0) unisexual, arranged in a dense spike which becomes laxer in fruit, 3 or 4 of the lower spikelets entirely female, the remainder above male, all rather short and narrowly ovoid, about $\frac{1}{2}$ in. long; bract subtending the lowermost female spikelet (B, $\times 1\frac{1}{2}$) much longer than the latter, ovate at the base and 3-ribbed outside, shortly barbellate on the margins; bracts (glumes) of the male (E, $\times 1\frac{1}{2}$) broadly lanceolate, acute, very thin; stamens (C, $\times$ 2) 3; lowermost bract (D, $\times 1\frac{1}{2}$) of the female spikelet lanceolate and long-acuminate; remainder ovate-lanceolate, shortly pointed: utricle (G, $\times 1\frac{1}{2}$) flattened, ovate, barbellate on the margin; style branches (F, $\times 1\frac{1}{2}$) 2 (family *Cyperaceae*).—Male spikelets marked ♂, female marked ♀.

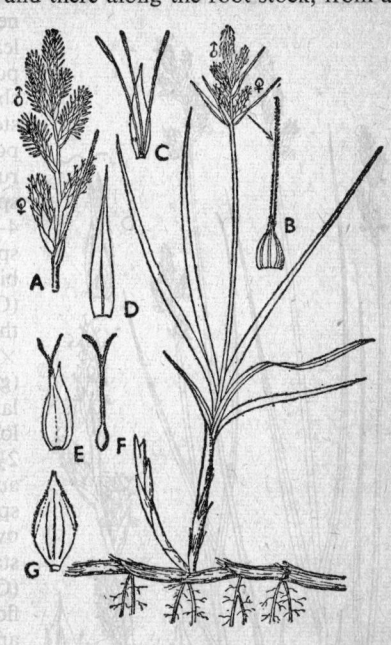

This species is widely distributed around Britain, growing in sandy places near the sea; common also inland in Breckland. It is useful as a sand-binder. As a native plant it is confined to Europe, but has been introduced into Atlantic North America.

OVAL SEDGE, *Carex ovalis* Gooden.

406. Oval Sedge, *Carex ovalis* Gooden. ($\times \frac{1}{2}$); perennial growing in tufts, covered at the base with thread-like fibres of remains of leaf-bases; roots fairly stout; flowering stems up to nearly 2 ft. high; lower leaves quite short and sharp-pointed, upper leaves shorter than the flowering stems, ending in very fine points, microscopically serrulate on the margins; spikelets (A, $\times 1\frac{1}{2}$) about 4–7 and arranged in a close spike, each spikelet sessile, bisexual, a few male flowers (C, $\times 2$) at the base of each, the rest above female (D, $\times 2$), lowermost bract (glume) broadly elliptic-lanceolate, ending in a fairly long serrulate awn (B, $\times 2\frac{1}{2}$), but sometimes leaf-like and half as long as the spike; remainder of bracts ovate-lanceolate, acute; stamens of male flowers (C, $\times 2$) 3; utricle of female flowers (E, $\times 2$) flattened and lanceolate, shortly bristly on the wing-like margins; style divided into 2 branches (family *Cyperaceae*).—Male portions of spikelets marked ♂, female marked ♀.

In most Floras and lists of British plants this is called *C. leporina*, but the name used above takes precedence. The species is found in Europe, from northern Asia to Kamchatka, and in Atlantic North America.

REMOTE SEDGE, *Carex remota* L.

407. Remote Sedge, *Carex remota* L. ($\times \frac{2}{5}$); a tufted perennial up to $1\frac{1}{2}$ ft. high; stems very slender, bearing spikelets widely separated from one another and sessile; leaves very narrow, ending in fine thread-like points, minutely rough on the margins; spikelets (A, $\times 2$) nearly as broad as long, about $\frac{1}{4}$ in., the lower half of each with male flowers, the upper half with female flowers; bracts pale and ovate-lanceolate, 1-nerved; utricle (C, $\times 2$) longer than the bract, tapered to a point: style with 2 branches; nut (D, $\times 2$) ellipsoid, slightly flattened; the terminal spikelet often has more male flowers than the others, and the lowest placed spikelet is sometimes completely female (family *Cyperaceae*).—Male portions of spikelets marked ♂, females marked ♀ (B, stamen $\times 3$).

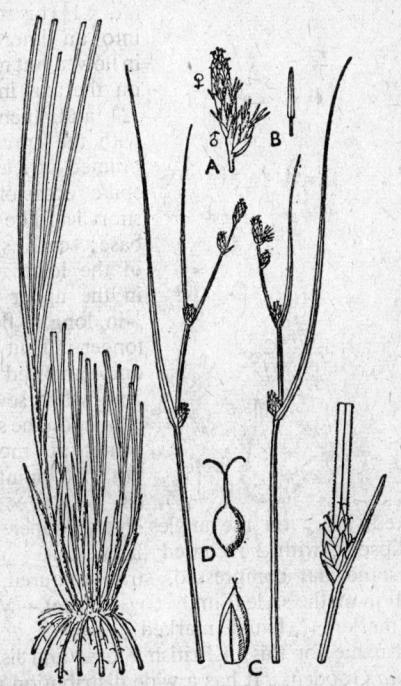

Grows in woods and moist shady places and widely spread in Europe, North Africa and western Asia, flowering in early summer.

PRICKLY SEDGE, *Carex echinata* Murr.

408. Prickly Sedge, *Carex echinata* Murr. ($\times \frac{2}{5}$); a tufted perennial up to about 9 in. high; leaves shorter than the flowering stems or sometimes about as long, very narrow and rather rough on the edges, sheaths with membranous margins and a ligule-like top; spikelets (A, $\times 1\frac{1}{4}$) bisexual, collected into an interrupted spike in flower, but more crowded on the axis in fruit (D, $\times 1\frac{1}{4}$) and then "prickly" with the spreading sharp-pointed utricles, the whole spike occasionally with a short leaf-like bract at the base; each spikelet male in the lower part, female in the upper part, ovoid, $\frac{1}{4}$-in. long in flower, a little longer in fruit, the terminal one narrowed to the base and with several barren glumes on the stalk; glumes ovate, at most subacute but not pointed; utricles (B, $\times 1\frac{1}{4}$, E, $\times 2\frac{1}{2}$) narrowly ovoid, beaked, hairy on the angles in the upper part; ovary (C, $\times 2$) ellipsoid, with 2 recurved hairy styles; nut (F, $\times 2$) ovoid and somewhat compressed, straw-coloured, beaked by a short portion of the style (family *Cyperaceae*).—Male portions of spikelets marked ♂, female marked ♀.

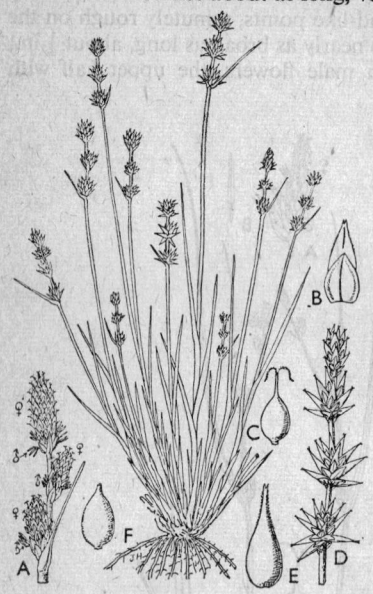

The usual name for this in British Floras and lists of species is *C. stellulata* Gooden. It has a wide distribution right around the north temperate zone, and, curiously enough, is also found in the mountains of South-east Australia and New Zealand, though not anywhere between these widely separated regions.

GLOSSARY OF BOTANICAL TERMS

Achene: a small, dry seed-like fruit.
acuminate: gradually pointed.
adnate: attached the whole length to another structure.
alternate: not opposite to something else.
annual: lasting only one year or season.
anther: portion of stamen bearing the pollen.
apiculate: with a little point.
aquatic: living in water.
aril: outgrowth from seed-stalk (common in Euphorbia family).
astringent: contracting or binding.
axil: the angle between leaf and branch or stem.
axillary: in the axil.

berry: succulent fruit with seeds immersed in the pulp.
biennial: lasting two years.
bisexual: having two sexes (i.e., stamens and pistil in the same flower).
bract: modified leaf at base of flower-stalk, or leaves around a flower-head.
bracteole: small bract on the flower-stalk.
bullate: blistered or puckered.

calcareous: chalky or limy.
calyx: outermost, usually green, floral envelope.
capitate: arranged in a head, or head-like.
capsule: dry fruit which opens.
carpel: one or more divisions of ovary or fruit.
caruncle: wart or protuberance near stalk of seed.
catkin: slender, often pendulous spike of flowers.
compound: formed of many similar parts.

concave: scooped out.
connate: united similar parts.
connective: portion of filament connecting lobes of the anther.
convex: humped.
cordate: heart-shaped.
corolla: collective name for petals.
corymb: more or less flat-topped collection of flowers.
crenate: with blunt, curved teeth.
crenulate: diminutive of crenate.
cross-pollination: transference of pollen from one flower to stigmas of another.
cyme: an inflorescence repeatedly divided with the oldest flower in the middle of each fork.
cystoliths: mineral markings in the leaves as found in the Nettle family.

deciduous: falling off.
decumbent: lying on the ground.
decurrent: running down.
dentate: toothed.
dioecious: male and female flowers on different plants.
disk: a fleshy portion of floral axis, often secreting nectar.
disk-flower: flowers in the middle of a flower-head with rays.
drupe: stone fruit such as a plum.

elliptic: shaped like an ellipse.
endosperm: reserve food material in a seed.
entire: not divided or toothed.
epicalyx: collection of bracteoles like an extra calyx.

falcate: sickle-shaped.
female: the fruiting part of the flower (ovary or carpels).
filament: stalk of stamen.

255

GLOSSARY OF BOTANICAL TERMS

fruit : the fertilized and mature ovary or carpel.

glabrous : not hairy.
glaucous : with a whitish-blue lustre like the "bloom" of a grape.
globose : round like a globe.

hastate : like an arrow, but with the barbs turned outwards.

imbricate : overlapping with one part wholly outside.
inferior : below.
inflexed : turned inwards.
inflorescence : collection of flowers on the shoot.
introrse : facing inwards.
involucre : a number of bracts surrounding one or more flowers.
irregular : applied to a flower (like that of pea) which cannot be divided into equal halves in more than one direction.

lanceolate : lance-shaped.
leaflet : unit of a compound leaf.
lenticels : corky spots on bark.
lobulate : divided into small lobes.
locular : divided into chambers.
loculus : a chamber or cavity of an ovary, fruit, or anther.
longitudinal : lengthwise.

male : a plant or flower which bears stamens.
monoecious : male and female flowers on the same plant.
mucronate : bearing a little tip.

nectary : organ in which nectar is secreted.
node : point of insertion of a leaf or leaves.
nutlet : little nut.

oblanceolate : reverse of lanceolate.
obovate : reverse of ovate.
opposite : inserted at same level, as leaves on a shoot.
orbicular : circular.

ovary : the female part of the flowers, represented by the carpels.
ovate : egg-shaped.
ovoid : ovate in outline.
ovule : the organ which after fertilisation develops into a seed.

panicle : a branched raceme.
papillous : clothed with short, knob-like hairs.
pappus : modified calyx of the Compositae.
pectinate : divided like a comb.
pedicel : the ultimate flower-stalk.
peduncle : common stalk of several flowers.
peltate : attached in the middle (like the stalk of a mushroom).
pendulous : hanging down.
perennial : lasting more than two years.
perianth : the collective outer covering of the flower.
persistent : not falling off.
petal : the usually coloured inner part of the floral leaves.
petiolate : stalked leaves.
petiole : leaf-stalk.
pinnate : divided like a feather.
placenta : the part of the ovary or carpel which bears the ovules.
plumose : feather-like.
pollen : the fertilising, dust-like powder in the anthers.
procumbent : lying down.
pubescent : hairy.
pustulate : covered with little warts.

raceme : unbranched inflorescence with individual flowers stalked.
radical : from the root.
ray-flower : marginal flower of the Compositae.
receptacle : floral axis.
reflexed : bent back.
regular : symmetrical.
reticulate : like a net.

GLOSSARY OF BOTANICAL TERMS

root-stock: underground stem.
scabrid: rough.
segment: division of an organ.
self-pollination: pollen from the same flower.
serrate: with saw-like teeth.
serrulate: diminutive of serrate.
sessile: without a stalk.
spadix: spike with a fleshy axis (as in *Arum*).
spathe: envelope around the spadix.
spike: stiff unbranched inflorescence with the flowers not stalked.
stamen: the male organ of the flower.
stigma: tip of the style.
stipule: appendage at base of leaf or leaf-stalk.
stolon: basal branch which roots.
style: narrow portion of pistil between ovary and stigma.
superior: placed above.

tendril: thread-like production.
terminal: at the top or end.
ternate: in threes.
tomentose: densely covered with short hairs.
truncate: cut off abruptly.
tuber: fleshy underground part of the stem.
tuberculate: with small outgrowths like warts.

umbel: inflorescence branched like the ribs of an umbrella.
unisexual: of one sex.

valve: portion into which a fruit or other organ separates or opens.
villous: with long shaggy hairs.
viscid: sticky.
vitta: oil tubes of fruits of Umbelliferae.

whorl: arranged in a circle around an axis.

INDEX TO COMMON NAMES

(The numbers refer to the illustrations.)

ALDER BUCKTHORN, 249
All-seed, 243
Annual Dog's Mercury, 244
Arrowhead, 382
Aspen, 230
Autumn Crocus, 383

Barberry, 269
Basil, 375
Beaked Carex, 398
Bedstraw, 253
Bell-flower, 321
Bird's-Foot, 221
Black Alder, 249
Black Bindweed, 298
Black Bog-rush, 395
Black Horehound, 377
Black Medick, 218
Black Mullein, 350
Black Mustard, 276
Bloody Crane's Bill, 365
Bluebottle, 337
Bog Asphodel, 384
Bog Pimpernel, 304
Brandy Bottle, 267
Bristly Scirpus, 392
Broad-leaved Dock, 300
Brook-lime Speedwell, 349
Brookweed, 306
Buckshorn Plantain, 308
Bugloss, 370
Bulrush, 391
Burdock, 341
Bur Marigold, 324
Burnet Rose, 205
Bur-reed, 385
Bush Vetch, 222
Butterwort, 364

Campion, 289, 290
Cat's Ear, 329
Celery-Leaved Buttercup, 260
Chamomile, 332, 333
Clary, 380
Clustered Bell-flower, 322
Common Mallow, 241
Common Melilot, 217

Common Rush, 387
Common Speedwell, 352
Corn Buttercup, 264
Corn Chamomile, 332
Cornflower, 337
Corn Gromwell, 371
Corn Marigold, 330
Corn Rattle, 362
Corn Sow-thistle, 342
Corydalis, 270
Cotton Grass, 396
Cotton Thistle, 338
Cow-wheat, 361
Crack Willow, 233
Creeping Bell-flower, 321
Creeping Buttercup, 261
Creeping Forget-me-not, 369
Creeping Jenny, 302
Creeping St. John's Wort, 248
Creeping Willow, 236
Crosswort, 252
Cudweed, 326, 328

Dead Nettle, 378
Deer's Grass, 393
Deer's Hair, 393
Distant Sedge, 402
Dog's Mercury, 244
Dropwort, 207
Dwarf Willow, 236

Eared Willow, 234
Erect Potentilla, 209

Fetid Chamomile, 333
Feverfew, 331
Field Cress, 282
Field Madder, 255
Field Myosotis, 368
Field Scabious, 318
Field Speedwell, 355
Figwort, 357
Flea Sedge, 399
Floating Polygonum, 297
Flowering Rush, 381
Fuller's Teasel, 320

INDEX TO COMMON NAMES

Gipsywort, 373
Globe-flower, 257
Goat's Beard Salsify, 347
Goldilocks, 262
Gooseberry, 229
Grass-leaved Pea, 228
Great Hedge Bedstraw, 253
Great Spearwort, 259
Grey Willow, 235

Hairy Bittercress, 271
Hairy Buttercup, 263
Hairy Sedge, 400
Hairy Vetch, 224
Hare's-foot Trefoil, 219
Hawksbit, 345
Heath Cudweed, 327
Heath Rush, 390
Heath Stitchwort, 285
Hedge Mustard, 273
Hedge Vetch, 222
Hemlock-Wort, 316
Hoary Cress, 279
Hoary Willow Herb, 293
Hop, 238
Hop Trefoil, 220
Horse Radish, 277
Hound's Tongue, 372
Hunger-weed, 264

Iceland Watercress, 278
Ivy-leaved Crowfoot, 265
Ivy-leaved Speedwell, 356

Jointed Rush, 388

Kidney Vetch, 216

Lady's Fingers, 216
Lesser Burdock, 340
Lesser-Jointed Rush, 389
Lesser Sium, 315
Lettuce, 343
Long-headed Poppy, 268

Mallow, 241
Marjoram, 374
Marsh Bedstraw, 254
Marsh Bird's Foot Trefoil, 215
Marsh Club Rush, 394
Marsh Cudweed, 325
Marsh Lousewort, 359

Marsh Ragwort, 335
Marsh Sedge, 401
Marsh Speedwell, 351
Marsh Thistle, 341
Marsh Violet, 240
Marsh Willow-Herb, 294
Marsh Wort, 314
Meadow Crowfoot, 258
Meadow Geranium, 367
Meadow Saffron, 383
Melilot, 217
Moneywort, 302
Monkey Flower, 358
Moschatel, 311
Mountain Avens, 211
Mountain Everlasting, 329
Mountain Willow-Herb, 292
Musk Mallow, 242
Musk Thistle, 339

Needle Furze, 213
Nettle, 237
Nonsuch, 218

Osier, 231

Parsley Piert, 212
Peachwort, 295
Pearlwort, 288
Pencilled Geranium, 366
Pendulous Sedge, 404
Pepperwort, 282
Perfoliate Montia, 291
Periwinkle, 251
Petty Whin, 213
Pimpernel, 303
Prickly Sedge, 408
Privet, 250

Raspberry, 204
Rayless Chamomile, 334
Red Bartsia, 360
Red-Shanks, 295
Rough Chervil, 313
Rue-leaved Saxifrage, 310
Rush, 387

St. John's Wort, 247
Sand Carex, 405
Scabious, 318
Scotch Rose, 205
Scotch Thistle, 338

INDEX TO COMMON NAMES

Scurvy Grass, 280
Sea Aster, 326
Sea Campion, 290
Sea Kale, 281
Sea Milkwort, 305
Sea Pea, 225
Sea Plantain, 307
Sea Purslane, 287
Sharp Dock, 299
Sheep's Bit, 323
Shepherd's Cress, 283
Shepherd's Needle, 317
Shoreweed, 309
Skull Cap, 376
Small Wintergreen, 246
Sow-thistle, 342
Spearwort, 259
Speedwell, 352
Spiny Rest-Harrow, 214
Spurry, 284
Stinging Nettle, 237
Strawberry-leaved Potentilla, 210
Sundew, 312
Sun Spurge, 245
Sweet Briar, 206
Sweet Violet, 239

Tea Plant, 346
Teasel, 320
Thistles, 338–340
Three-lobed Bur Marigold, 324
Thyme-Leaved Speedwell, 353
Toad Rush, 386

Toothwort, 363
Tuberous Pea, 226
Tumbling Mustard, 274

Upright St. John's Wort, 247

Valerian, 319
Venus' Comb, 317
Vervain, 256

Wall Cress, 272
Wall Lettuce, 344
Wall Speedwell, 354
Water Avens, 208
Water Drop-Wort, 316
Waterlily, 266
Waterpepper, 296
White Beam, 203
White Campion, 289
White Mustard, 275
White Waterlily, 266
White Willow, 232
Wild Basil, 375
Wintergreen, 246
Wood Cudweed, 327
Wood Pea, 227
Wood Pimpernel, 303
Wood Senecio, 336
Wood Vetch, 223

Yellow Archangel, 379
Yellow Toad Flax, 348
Yellow Waterlily, 267
Yellow-wort, 301

INDEX TO NAMES OF GENERA

(The numbers refer to the illustrations.)

ADOXA, 311
Alchemilla, 212
Anagallis, 304
Antennaria, 329
Anthemis, 332, 333
Anthyllis, 216
Apium, 314
Arabidopsis, 272
Arctium, 341
Arenaria, 287
Armoracia, 277
Aster, 325

Ballota, 377
Bartsia, 360
Berberis, 269
Bidens, 324
Blackstonia, 301
Brassica, 276
Butomus, 381

Calamintha, 375
Campanula, 321, 322
Cardamine, 271
Cardaria, 279
Carduus, 339
Carex, 397–408
Centaurea, 337
Cerastium, 286
Chaerophyllum, 313
Chlora, 301
Chrysanthemum, 330, 331
Cirsium, 341
Claytonia, 291
Clinopodium, 375
Cochlearia, 277, 280
Colchicum, 383
Corydalis, 270
Crambe, 281
Cynoglossum, 372

Dipsacus, 320
Drosera, 312
Dryas, 211

Eleocharis, 394
Epilobium, 292–294

Eriophorum, 396
Euphorbia, 245

Filago, 328
Filipendula, 207
Frangula, 249

Galium, 252–254
Genista, 213
Geranium, 365–367
Geum, 208
Glaux, 305
Gnaphalium, 325, 327

Humulus, 238
Hypericum, 247, 248

Jasione, 323
Juncus, 386–390

Knautia, 318

Lactuca, 343, 344
Lamium, 378, 379
Lathraea, 363
Lathyrus, 225–228
Leontodon, 345
Lepidium, 279, 282
Ligustrum, 250
Linaria, 348
Lithospermum, 371
Littorella, 309
Lotus, 215
Lychnis, 289
Lycium, 346
Lycopsis, 370
Lycopus, 373
Lysimachia, 302, 303

Malva, 241, 242
Matricaria, 334
Medicago, 218
Melampyrum, 361
Melandrium, 289
Melilotus, 217
Mercurialis, 244
Mimulus, 358

INDEX TO NAMES OF GENERA

Montia, 291
Myosotis, 368, 369

Narthecium, 384
Nasturtium, 278
Nuphar, 267
Nymphaea, 266

Oenanthe, 316
Ononis, 214
Onopordon, 338
Origanum, 374
Ornithopus, 221

Papaver, 268
Pedicularis, 359
Pinguicula, 364
Plantago, 307, 308
Polygonum, 295–298
Populus, 230
Potentilla, 209, 210
Pyrola, 246
Pyrus, 203

Radiola, 243
Ranunculus, 258–265
Rhamnus, 249
Rhinanthus, 362
Ribes, 229
Rorippa, 278
Rosa, 205, 206
Rubus, 204
Rumex, 299, 300

Sagina, 288
Sagittaria, 382

Salix, 231–236
Salvia, 380
Samolus, 306
Saxifraga, 310
Scandix, 317
Schoenus, 395
Scirpus, 391–393
Scrophularia, 357
Scutellaria, 376
Senecio, 335, 336
Sherardia, 255
Silene, 290
Sinapis, 275
Sisymbrium, 272, 273, 274
Sium, 315
Sonchus, 342
Sorbus, 203
Sparganium, 385
Spergula, 284
Spiraea, 207
Stellaria, 285

Teesdalia, 283
Tragopogon, 347
Trifolium, 219–220
Trollius, 257

Ulmaria, 207
Urtica, 237

Valeriana, 319
Verbascum, 350
Verbena, 256
Veronica, 349, 351, 356
Vicia, 222–224
Vinca, 251
Viola, 239, 240

APPRECIATIONS OF "COMMON WILD FLOWERS"

From a Schoolmaster in Oxfordshire:—

"During the past week I have spent many happy hours browsing through your recent 'Pelican,' *Common Wild Flowers*. There is scarcely a page which does not contain something new to me, as a life-long lover of wild flowers—I will not say botanist, being indeed a chemist. . . . The drawings are marvels of accuracy and helpfulness, and I am proposing to try out the key on boys here during the summer. . . . Please accept my grateful thanks for so great a treasure."

From an Artist:—

"I have already been right through the book quickly, and find it altogether admirable. It is just what was wanted, and I don't think it will be long before they need a reprint. I shall, of course, recommend it most warmly whenever I have the opportunity to do so. And what a bountiful and gifted illustrator you are! My very sincere congratulations and thanks."

From another Publisher:—

"I had a dozen of your *British Flora* and everyone is delighted with the little book."

From Books Across the Sea Circle in England:—

"We have much pleasure in informing you that your book *Common Wild Flowers* has been chosen as an ambassador book for July by our selection committee."

From Salop:—

"I am on holiday in Church Stretton. To-day my husband and I have had a long walk, and found on the hills and in the lanes 35 specimens of wild flowers. The enclosed specimen is the only one to which we cannot give a name."

From a Judge? or Lawyer?:—

The Court House, ——. "I bought your *Common Wild Flowers* here yesterday, and on going immediately with it into a

APPRECIATIONS

restaurant, found there a lovely bunch of berried twigs of the Spindle tree. I thought I will just look that up, and turning to your little book found 'The Spindle tree is poisonous in all its parts. The wood is . . . used for making butchers' skewers.' Ought an Undertaker or a Doctor to be retained as waiter at dinner?"

Jovially yours,
———.

From a German Prisoner of War at Shap, Penrith, Cumberland:—

"May I take the liberty of thanking you ever so much for the high pleasure that your little book *Common Wild Flowers* gave me during the desolate period of my captivity. . . . I wonder what to admire more in your little guide, the skilful selection or the vivid description in connection with the exact drawings warranting not only a precise identification of the species but also providing the non-professional with a deeper insight into the wonders of nature. In the very limited exercise area of Shap Wells I succeeded in identifying 144 among the 202 numbers. . . . Please, Sir, accept these lines in the sense I wrote them, i.e. an amateur botanist's grateful acknowledgment of an excellent achievement."

From a Professor of Botany (Wales):—

"—— has been fortunate enough to have a consignment of your delightful new Pelican book. I can say with sincerity: A wonderful bird is the Pelican! We think it is an absolutely first-rate beakful and we congratulate you most warmly. It is wonderful to be able to put all that information and the charming plates and drawings into the hands of the public for a few pence. Thank you so much for it—we shall use it a great deal for students."

From a Lecturer at Oxford:—

"Thank you for sending me *Common Wild Flowers*, which really seems an extraordinary good piece of work. It has gone through this department like Fire-Weed and is now sold out locally. We all think it a most timely and admirable production which will do much to bolster further the evident return to popularity of our dear subject in this country."

APPRECIATIONS

From a critic in Cambridgeshire:—

"Having an amateur interest in flowers I eagerly bought your book (*Common Wild Flowers*) on sight. I must confess that my enthusiasm was almost shattered on further investigation. Up to now I have come across 46 words that bar the way to edification and enjoyment. Some of these words are even excluded by the *Oxford Dictionary* (*Concise*). . . . Words such as corymb, stipules, scabrid, etc. are completely hostile to my enjoyment. . . . I beg you to insert a glossary."

From a Sheffield steelworker:—

"I feel I must write to let you know (if it's not already history) how well your Pelican book has been received. Getting to know quite early of its publication, I put myself to some trouble and in three weeks had purchased 14 copies. All but two have been given to friends and nothing but praise and pleasure for your work. . . . What a wonderful 9*d.*; and what a delight to read the life histories. —— joins with me in sending many thanks from Yorkshire. That means a lot, coming from *God's own country*."

From nearby Richmond (Surrey):—

"We want to thank you for your wonderful little book, which meets a need at small expense of just ordinary people who work in offices and who crave to know more of the lovely things of wild nature."

From Bexley Heath, Kent:—

"I have just purchased a copy of your little book and am writing to let you know how much I enjoy it. I have been interested in wild flowers from a child and this is the best I have so far come across. I trust you will be able to issue volumes 2 and 3 in due course."

From the Secretary, Authors' Club, London:—

"Congratulations upon the delightful Penguin. It is one of the very best I have seen in the Series and your illustrations are delightful."

SOME PUBLICATIONS
OF
PENGUIN BOOKS

KING PENGUIN BOOKS

British Birds: *Phyllis Barclay-Smith*	K1
Fishes of Britain's Rivers and Lakes: *J. R. Norman*	K11
Edible Fungi: *J. Ramsbottom*	K13
A Book of Lilies: *Fred Stoker*	K14
Seashore Life and Pattern: *T. A. Stephenson*	K15
Some British Moths: *N. Riley*	K18
Garden Birds: *Phyllis Barclay-Smith*	K19
Poisonous Fungi: *J. Ramsbottom*	K23
Birds of the Sea: *R. M. Lockley*	K24
Flowers of the Marsh and Stream: *Iolo A. Williams*	K27
Flowers of the Woods: *Sir E. J. Salisbury*	K29
A Book of Spiders: *W. S. Bristowe*	K35
Wild Flowers of the Chalk: *John Gilmour*	K37

Two shillings and sixpence each

PUFFIN PICTURE BOOKS

This series of children's books contains a number of titles on Natural History. Among them are the following:

*Butterflies in Britain: *Richard Chopping*	PP29
Our Horses: *Lionel Edwards*	PP43
Animals of Australia: *Sheila Hawkins*	PP45
*Wonders of Sea Life: *E. C. Boulenger and Peggy Jeremy*	PP51
Paper Birds: *R. B. Talbot Kelly* (Purchase tax 7½d. extra)	PP52
Fish and Fishing: *Bernard Venables*	PP53
*Extinct Animals: *Hilary Stebbing*	PP55
Our Dogs: *Maurice Wilson*	PP56
The Story of Plant Life: *Isobel Alexander*	PP58
Mountain and Moorland Birds: *R. B. Talbot Kelly*	PP65
Zoo Animals: *E. C. Boulenger and Maurice Wilson*	PP73
Our Cattle: *Illustrated by Lionel Edwards*	PP90
Insect Life: *Arthur Smith*	PP92

One shilling and sixpence each
★ Boards only, 2s. 6d.

PENGUIN HANDBOOKS

This is a series compiled for the practical man. Each book is lucid, and comprehensive, and written by an authority on the subject. Some of the recent titles are shown here.

Soft Fruit Growing: *Raymond Bush* — PH1

Tree Fruit Growing: *Raymond Bush*

   Vol. I Apples — PH2

   Vol. II Pears, Quinces and Stone Fruits — PH3

Rabbit Farming: *Claude H. Goodchild* — PH4

Poultry Farming: *Edited by Alan Thompson* — PH5

Trees, Shrubs, and How to Grow Them:

   W. H. Rowe — PH6

The Vegetable Growers' Handbook:

   A. J. Simons — PH7

The Penguin Handyman: *Foster Wiseman* — PH9

The Breeding of Farm Animals:

   Chapman Pincher — PH10

Common Sense in the Nursery:

   Mrs Sydney Frankenburg — PH11

Preserves for all Occasions: *Alice Crang* — PH12

Your Smallholding: *Edited by Alan Thompson* — PH13

One shilling and sixpence each

BIRD RECOGNITION

JAMES FISHER

Bird books are usually expensive, bulky, and, to the novice, bewildering. James Fisher, the famous ornithologist and author of BIRD WATCHING (Pelican Books A71) has now written, specially for the Pelican series, a cheap and lucid manual of British birds. Each volume (there are three) is specially designed to assist the ignorant to identify the birds they see. All you need to know before using it is:—
  a. where you are when you see any particular bird,
  b. what time of year it is.
Beyond this all that is necessary is a pair of eyes and, less important, ears.

When you have seen an unknown bird and noticed its size and distinctive characteristics you can start your treasure-hunt with the aid of the Field Character Key. First you decide what *sort* of bird it is. The place you saw it, and what it was doing, will help you to guess if it is a sea-bird, a perching bird, a wader, etc. Some of them overlap, of course; the Key is no more infallible than the clues in any other treasure-hunt, because birds are live things that sometimes crop up at times and in places where the naturalist does not expect them. But usually this part will not be difficult and a glance at the picture will tell you whereabouts to begin looking. After that, if you keep your memory clear and your wits about you, you will soon be able to name the bird you saw.

Identification is the first step to the whole world of delight that birds in all their variety and beauty can afford to the man with no pretensions as a naturalist. This book can give the entry to that world to everyone who is able to spend a few shillings on the book and an occasional day in the country.

Volume   I, A175, Sea Birds and Waders
Volume II, A176, Game Birds, Water-fowl and Birds of Prey
Volume III, A177, Perching and Singing Birds

At present only volume I is published